Cooking Light

COOKBOOK 1990

Cooking Light

COOKBOOK 1990

Oxmoor House

Library of Congress Catalog Number: 87-61020
ISBN: 0-8487-0795-8
ISSN: 1043-7061

Manufactured in the United States of America
First Printing 1989

Executive Editor: Ann H. Harvey
Production Manager: Jerry Higdon
Associate Production Manager: Rick Litton
Art Director: Bob Nance

Cooking Light® Cookbook 1990

Editor: Cathy A. Wesler, R.D.
Menu Editor: Janice L. Krahn
Copy Editor: Melinda E. West
Editorial Assistants: Kelly E. Hooper, Pam Beasley Bullock
Production Assistant: Theresa L. Beste
Test Kitchen Directors: Julie Fisher, Vanessa Taylor Johnson
Test Kitchen Home Economists: Angie Neskaug, Christina A. Pieroni, Kathleen Royal, Gayle Hays Sadler, Paula N. Saunders, Jill Wills
Senior Photographer: Jim Bathie. Additional photography by: Colleen Duffley, pages 20, 21, 26; Sylvia Martin, 17, 25, 182, 184, 203, 204, 209
Photo Stylist: Kay E. Clarke. Additional styling by: Monica Lassiter Ard, pages 31, 32, 34, 36, 38, 40, 42, 46, 50; Leslie Byars, 24; Susan Spain Merrill, 90, 123, 157, 231, 234, 237, 246
Designer: Design for Publishing
Recipe and Menu Developers: Marilyn Wyrick Ingram, OTT Communications, Inc., Jane Ingrassia Reinsel, Lisa Weiss
Exercise Model: Karen M. Anderson

Consultants: Maureen Callahan, M.S., R.D.; University of Alabama School of Medicine in Birmingham: Julius Linn, M.D.; Susan Brown, Assistant Editor; Charlotte Bragg, M.S., R.D.; Heidi Hataway, M.S., R.D.; Laura Dunnam, Exercise Physiologist.

Cover: *Beef Roast with Wild Mushroom Sauce* (page 155).
Back cover: *Pear and Arugula Salad* (page 180).
Page 2: *Raspberry Chiffon Pie* (page 64).

To subscribe to *Cooking Light* magazine, write to *Cooking Light*, P.O. Box C-549 Birmingham, Alabama 35283.

Contents

Living Well Is The Best Reward

Welcome to *Cooking Light Cookbook 1990*. And welcome to a new decade in which research continues on the relationship between nutrition, fitness, and good health.

Gradually Americans are adopting healthier eating habits. The American Heart Association says Americans are indeed eating less fat, but fatty foods still make up too much of our everyday meals. The Surgeon General's report in 1988 singled out fat as the chief health problem in American diets, but a recent Gallup poll revealed that not even one in five people realized that fat was the culprit.

Research continues to show that variety, balance, and moderation are important in meal planning. To help you achieve these, try following *Cooking Light*'s "Menu Plans" or "Healthy American Meals" for low-fat, high-flavor fare.

To achieve taut muscles as well as cardiovascular fitness follow the suggested exercise guidelines. The U.S. Public Health Service had set fitness objectives for Americans to achieve by 1990. The year has arrived, but most Americans have not met the objectives. Although the agency is revising the guidelines for the year 2000, now's the time to get started if you aren't already physically active.

Living well with *Cooking Light* means healthy living. So relax and enjoy this all-new volume, and reap the benefits that good health and fitness bring to you and your family.

There is no better time to enjoy life than right now. And as you do so, enjoy a relaxing brunch consisting of Ambrosia Cup Coolers (page 103), Vegetable Omelet (page 144), Pumpkin Muffins (page 44), and an assortment of fresh fruit.

Update '90

If you're like most Americans, you're more interested than ever in what's being said about health and fitness. And indeed much is being said. But despite the deluge of information, the old verity still stands—moderation remains the key both to good living and to good health.

In 1989, the National Research Council summed up what's known about nutrition and recommended that long-term eating plans reflect these goals: to eat less fat and fewer cholesterol-rich foods but more vegetables, fruits, and whole grains. In addition, the guidelines recommend drinking more low-fat or skim milk for calcium, limiting sodium intake, and using alcohol in moderation, if at all—no more than two drinks a day.

Five Fruits and Vegetables

To help people get away from fatty foods, the California Health Department has started a "Five-a-Day" campaign to encourage people to eat five servings of fruits and vegetables each day. Fully one-fourth of Americans have a steady diet of fat-rich fast foods, and the aim of the program is to change that.

California is also working to develop disclosure laws to help consumers make more informed food choices. One proposal is that all packaged foods be required to list levels of cholesterol and saturated fat, and similar initiatives are being pursued in New York and Rhode Island. However, food industry lobbyists have hampered passage of such bills, saying that labeling laws should be legislated by the Federal Government rather than by the state.

The Nation's Exercise Pulse

In the fitness realm we may be doing a bit better. Fitness centers are booming social hubs for people in many communities. In fact, Americans spent $5 billion on health club memberships last year. Schools and hospitals are offering specialized exercise classes that are tailored for senior citizens, pregnant women, and overweight people. And sales of exercise items continue to climb. People spent $6 billion last year on running shoes alone.

However, getting hard facts on who's really exercising and how much has been difficult. The government is trying—its national objectives for physical education (P.E.) and exercise set definite goals for the nation to achieve by 1990. But a recent interim report showed that many goals aren't likely to be met. Perhaps the least progress has been made in getting school children in daily P.E. programs—only one-half of all children in grades 5 through 8 had classes daily, and only one-half of 12th graders were enrolled in P.E. classes.

Are these children exercising in their free time to build workout habits to last a lifetime? The national goal is that 90 percent will exercise for 20 minutes three times a week at aerobic levels, but the statistics show that only 66 percent of 10- to 17-year-olds actually do.

What about adults? The goal is the same—20 minutes of aerobic activity three times a week—and the government hoped 60 percent of American adults would meet this goal by 1990. Unfortunately, we're far short of that goal; surveys show only 8 percent of people age 18 to 65 are exercising vigorously enough to qualify for aerobic benefits. This is true of the over-65 group as well. Almost half of this group reported walking for exercise, but less than 10 percent exercised often or long enough to reach aerobic levels.

Because research has shown that less intense activity such as gardening and fairly leisurely walking is beneficial, the government is expected to devise new goals soon that will encourage less intense exercise as well.

On the plus side, the goal of getting doctors to talk to patients about exercise is being realized. Half of all physicians surveyed include an exercise history in their initial evaluations. And 25 percent of corporations employing more than 500 people now sponsor employee fitness programs. Also, the government has met its goal of devising methods to better test the physical fitness of the nation's youth. The experts are ready to keep a finger on the nation's pulse by monitoring physical activity as we slowly respond to the need for regular exercise.

Fine-tuning Cholesterol

A recent Gallup poll showed that 37 percent of Americans now know their cholesterol levels. It's no longer news that high levels of cholesterol in the blood increase the risk of heart disease and lowering those levels lowers the risk.

Researchers are now studying how the body produces, transports, and disposes of cholesterol. Last year, research focused on substances called lipoproteins that carry cholesterol through the bloodstream to its destination. As the name implies, these substances are made of fats (lipids) and proteins. The protein components called apoproteins can be measured and eventually may prove a more accurate and reliable measure of heart disease risk than measurements of either total cholesterol or lipoproteins. But for now, lipoproteins best tell the story.

Low-density lipoproteins (LDLs) carry cholesterol to cells for manufacture of cell walls, hormones, and other essential substances. They dump any excess cholesterol that the cells don't need into artery walls, where it gradually builds up, narrowing the blood vessels. Consequently, too many LDLs increase the risk of developing heart disease, and lowering LDLs decreases the risk. But that's not the whole picture. A high LDL and total cholesterol identifies only one-third of people with coronary heart disease. Another type of lipoprotein, the high-density variety (HDL), also plays an important role in determining risks of heart disease.

Highlighting HDLs

HDLs grabbed the research spotlight in 1989 and made the cover of *Time* magazine. Acting like biological vacuum cleaners, HDLs whisk cholesterol away from blood vessel walls, carrying it to the liver for disposal. In 1988, reports from the U.S., Finland, Canada, and Israel confirmed that low levels of HDLs contribute to heart disease risk, even when total cholesterol is normal.

Other reports noted that high levels of HDLs appear to protect people from the ill effects of too much cholesterol. And according to the Helsinki Heart Study, which involved more than 4,000 men, increasing the amount of HDLs appears to decrease the risks of developing heart disease.

Now scientists are searching for ways to raise HDL levels. Stopping smoking and losing excess weight help do it. Stanford researchers

looked at how both exercise and dieting affect HDL levels. Dieters and exercisers who lost weight increased their HDL levels, so weight loss may be the factor that proves to be the benefit. On the other hand, a Brown University study showed that aerobic exercise involving stationary cycling for one hour five times a week raised HDL levels by an average of 13 percent even when participants did not lose weight.

Reversing Damage

If your doctor says cholesterol buildup has narrowed your blood vessels, don't despair. There's encouraging evidence that the right lifestyle changes can help reverse this damage. One study found that when blood cholesterol levels are drastically reduced, coronary arteries begin to clear in as little as a year. For the study, a group of men were placed on a very low-fat vegetarian diet containing less than 10 percent of the calories from fat. The study also included regular exercise and yoga to control stress.

In another study, a group of people with an inherited condition that strikingly elevates cholesterol took cholesterol-lowering drugs and followed special diets. Their cholesterol levels dropped from 400 to 200. The result: Coronary artery blockage decreased by an average of 30 to 40 percent. If cholesterol deposits in arteries can be reversed, they can be prevented.

Other Players in the Game

While new research on cholesterol's effect on atherosclerosis is exciting, don't overlook the other risk factors for heart and blood vessel disease—obesity, sedentary lifestyle, cigarette smoking, and high blood pressure. Cigarette smoking and

high blood pressure each contribute to as many deaths from heart attacks and strokes as do high cholesterol levels.

If you smoke and use the fear of weight gain as a reason not to quit, consider this: Although smokers do tend to be 5 to 10 pounds lighter than nonsmokers, they have more fat around their waists than nonsmokers, according to a study from the National Institute of Aging. Fat located at the waist increases the risks of heart disease, diabetes, and stroke more than fat located elsewhere. The study also showed that although you may gain a few pounds when you stop smoking, it will be deposited in safer areas.

Brans in Perspective

If you're trying to find a way to lower your cholesterol level, you may be relying on the soluble fiber in oat bran muffins and cereals to do the trick. A recent study did show that people who ate 1 to 1½ cups of oat bran a day lowered cholesterol levels by 13 to 19 percent, which was a better bargain cost-wise than purchasing cholesterol-lowering drugs. But that much oat bran amounts to 1 bowl of oat bran cereal and 4 oat bran muffins a day. Although there's no doubt that the soluble fiber in oat bran, beans, peas, and legumes will lower cholesterol, bear in mind that no one food can substitute for a low-saturated fat, low-cholesterol diet.

Finding Fish Oils

Fish oil supplements have been much publicized as a quick route to heart health, but scientists continue to caution that until more is learned about the long-term effects, fish oil should come from eating cold-water fish, not from taking supplements.

Research has shown that fish oils can lower blood pressure, keep arteries open after coronary artery surgery, and perhaps interfere with the process of inflammation that leads to arthritis and psoriasis.

Eating fish may not be the only way to get the benefit of omega-3 fatty acids. U.S. Department of Agriculture scientists have found that the body can convert linolenic acid from soybean oil into the same omega-3s that are found in fish oils. This evidence, though preliminary, may have far-reaching implications because many margarines, crackers, bread products, and a wide array of vegetable cooking oils are made with soybean oil.

Preventing Cancer

Cutting back on fats may benefit more than your heart. Previous studies have linked excess fat intake to cancer of the colon and prostate gland.

An Italian study also linked breast cancer and fat intake, a finding that other researchers have long suspected but have been unable to confirm. When the scientists analyzed the diets of 750 women in an area of Italy known for its high rates of breast cancer, they found that women who ate an abundance of fat were three times more likely to develop breast cancer than those who ate less fat. The women with a low incidence of breast cancer consumed only 28 percent of their daily calories as fat—they ate fewer meats, whole-milk dairy products, and cheeses.

This information may explain why a recent Harvard study failed to find a link between a high-fat diet and breast cancer. That study found no difference in breast cancer rates between women whose caloric intake was 44 percent fat and those whose intake was 32 percent fat. To achieve cancer-related benefits, the

diet may need to contain less than 32 percent of total calories as fat.

Fake Fats

Soon you may be eating foods made with oils that don't count as much toward your daily fat allotment as do today's fats. One of these is olestra, a no-calorie fat substitute made from sugars and fats that the body cannot absorb. This product tastes like fat and can replace much of the fat in shortenings used for cooking, according to its producer, Procter & Gamble. The company says an all-purpose shortening that is about 35 percent olestra would cut by half the amount of saturated fat in foods fried in the proposed product.

Because of concern about a slight increase in cancer rates among rats fed the substance, Procter & Gamble is conducting studies on mice to be sure there's no cancer risk. In earlier versions, the fat substitute interfered with the digestion of vitamin E, but this and other problems have been corrected. Spokespersons for the product expect it to be on the market soon.

Another fat substitute, Simplesse®, may soon be available. Made from micro particles of egg whites and milk, Simplesse will be confined for use in mayonnaise, salad dressings, and frozen desserts such as ice cream because Simplesse breaks down when heated for cooking or frying.

Its manufacturer, The NutraSweet Company, has filed for Food and Drug Administration (FDA) approval for use in frozen desserts, and hopes its product will be on the shelves shortly. Spokespersons say products made with Simplesse will be 100 percent fat-free.

Nutrition experts stress, however, that even when these products become available, eating a varied, balanced diet is still a must.

Changing Images

Egg yolks are a source of cholesterol, but they have about 22 percent less than once thought. The U.S. Department of Agriculture recently used new, more accurate methods to measure cholesterol in eggs and found that an average large egg has only 213 milligrams of cholesterol instead of 274, the previous figure. As a result, the American Heart Association upped its recommended weekly egg allowance from 3 eggs per week to 4.

If you want to start a family soon, you may want to cut back on caffeine consumption. Caffeine decreases a woman's fertility, according to a preliminary study from the National Institute of Environmental Health Sciences. Researchers found that healthy women who consumed more than the amount of caffeine in one cup of coffee or three carbonated beverages were only half as likely to conceive during a given menstrual cycle as women who drank less.

Vitamin and Mineral News

If you eat vitamin E-rich foods, the harmful plaque that clogs blood vessels may be reduced, according to a New York Academy of Sciences conference on vitamin E. The fat-soluble vitamin may help lower harmful levels of LDLs. In studies of elderly people, the U.S. Department of Agriculture and the University of Western Ontario have found that adequate vitamin E intake helps protect against cataracts and may improve immune system function.

Should you take vitamin E supplements? The consensus of nutritionists is that these supplements aren't needed. They believe the average American obtains plenty of vitamin E from food sources.

If cold weather bothers you more

than it does most people, you may not be getting enough iron. A study from the Human Nutrition Research Center showed that the ability to maintain body temperature in a cold climate depends in part on daily intake of iron. Meats and legumes are good sources.

Aluminum and Alzheimer's

Aluminum has made the headlines as a possible cause of Alzheimer's disease in areas where the water has a high aluminum content, according to a study of drinking water in Wales and England. But many scientists question the methods used in the study and point out that researchers didn't actually measure aluminum content but relied on reports from the water boards. In addition, aluminum in water contributes only a small amount of the aluminum everyone is exposed to each day. For now, most scientists have concluded that there's no evidence that aluminum in water, cookware, or other sources causes Alzheimer's. The presence of aluminum in the brain of people with Alzheimer's may be an effect of the disease rather than a cause.

Exercise, Exercise

You're probably aware that exercise slows loss of bone substance during and after menopause, which reduces the chances of developing osteoporosis. Evidence now shows that exercise not only prevents bone loss but can increase the amount of bone substance as well.

In a study at Washington University in St. Louis, a group of sedentary postmenopausal women began an exercise program of walking, jogging, or climbing steps 50 to 60 minutes three times a week. After 9 months, their bone mass had increased 5 percent.

In contrast, another group of women of similar ages and characteristics who didn't exercise lost more than 1 percent of bone mass during the same period. The gains made by the exercise group disappeared when they quit, emphasizing the importance of maintaining a regular exercise program.

If you're a woman who's kept up your exercise in the years since your school days, you may have less risk of developing certain cancers than less physically active women. A study of more than 5,000 women revealed that half had engaged regularly in athletics and exercise in the years since school days. The exercising group was slimmer and had less risk of developing cancer of the breast and reproductive system than the non-athletic group. Researchers believe leanness, which is the direct result of a life of regular exercise, is the reason.

Staying Alive

A 10-year follow-up of participants in the MR FIT study (Multiple Risk Factor Intervention Trial) confirmed that physically active men were less likely to die from coronary heart disease than those who weren't active. Men who spent an average of 45 minutes a day in leisure-time physical activity had a 35 percent lower death rate from heart disease than those who engaged in only about 15 minutes of activity a day.

In a similar study of 3,000 railroad workers, those who burned less than 250 calories a week in leisure-time physical activities had a 30 to 40 percent greater risk of dying from heart disease than those who burned between 1,000 and 2,000 calories a week.

The researchers estimated that it would take about 30 minutes of moderate physical activity such as softball, gardening, golfing, ballroom dancing, strolling, or bowling each

day to burn 1,000 calories a week.

As this and other studies have shown, you don't have to sweat and strain in order for the activity to qualify as exercise. Australian researchers found than an evening of ballroom dancing can be strenuous enough to improve the heart's strength and endurance.

At the same time, you'll be relieving stress, according to Arizona State University researchers. Physically fit bodies can deal with mental stress in a healthier way than sedentary ones. Authorities agree that to get out of the sedentary category you must exercise at least 20 minutes, and preferably 30 minutes, three times a week.

A Rational Plan

Does your head spin when you read all of the research and recommendations about food and exercise? Just remember that no food is entirely good or bad in and of itself. Instead, your total diet and your lifestyle are what contribute to health or disease. Rather than thinking of specific foods as good or bad, plan meals with the idea that eliminating one food or relying too much on another will neither protect against disease nor confer good health.

When the National Research Council members announced their nutrition guidelines of less fat, cholesterol, sodium, and protein, they also urged that people eat more fruits, whole grains, and vegetables. They noted that anyone can live this way without sacrifice. You can eat well by including a variety of foods, and the council's guidelines don't prohibit occasional sweets nor a glass of wine with a relaxing dinner.

Recently, two leading scientists urged people to seek pleasure in their lives rather than focusing on health hazards. They reminded us that people who enjoy life tend to have long, vital lives and that good health is often a by-product.

The Food & Fitness Connection

Research is taking a closer look at the health benefits of leisure-time activities such as golfing, leisurely walking, and gardening. As you finish your round of golf, enjoy Cobb Sandwiches (page 196), Moroccan Carrot Salad (page 181), and Mixed Greens, Mushroom, and Hazelnut Salad (page 183).

Scientific studies prove that lifestyle—how we live and what we eat—clearly affects our risk for developing certain diseases: high blood pressure, obesity, heart disease, osteoporosis, and cancer. The problem lies in two areas—overeating and lack of exercise. Simply put, many Americans eat too much, particularly fat. But that's not all. As the National Research Council spelled out in a recent *Diet and Health* report, Americans should be eating more foods that sport a lean but nutrient-dense profile. Whole grains, fresh fruits, and vegetables topped the council's list. Yet, while most of us are trying to make some headway toward attaining these goals, figuring out how to make the changes palatable often proves frustrating.

Sprinkled throughout the pages of *Cooking Light* are meal-planning specifics that simplify the problem. What seems like a "tall" diet order is broken down into just a few easily managed parts. Instead of a parade of different recommendations, we have condensed the bulk of diet information into seven key components. Take a look at page 15 for the specifics.

As you conquer the "how-to's" of good eating, you can move into the action part of a healthy lifestyle—exercise. Studies show that people who keep active—walking, jogging, swimming, and cycling—reap psychological rewards as well as physical benefits. Studies are now being done to include the benefits of aerobic activity along with the benefits of moderate activity such as golfing, gardening, and leisurely walking. *Cooking Light*'s concise but comprehensive exercise guidelines will help you build a fitness program that best suits your body type and your time schedule. The prescription for good health starts by combining a healthy dose of activity with a balanced approach to good eating.

Turn to the *Cooking Light* Kitchen for ways to trim fat and calories from recipes while still attaining great-tasting results. And if you feel stressed, read *Cooking Light*'s suggestions for remaining calm.

Put *Cooking Light* into action. And as you incorporate the nutrition and fitness guidelines into your lifestyle, be sure to read the food and fitness facts placed throughout the book. Share these with your family, and you will encourage even the heartiest eater to be more health-conscious. You'll find these facts flagged with the following symbols:

NUTRITION   FITNESS

Nutrition Basics for *Cooking Light*

As more is learned about nutrition, recommendations about what constitutes a healthful diet sometimes change. Yet, in the overall scheme of things, the underlying message is still quite simple: Healthful eating revolves around three key concepts—variety, balance, and moderation. Choosing a broad selection of fruits, vegetables, grains, lean meats, and low-fat dairy products easily fulfills the variety component and ensures a rich assortment of the nutrients needed for good health. The challenge comes with balance and moderation.

Many Americans are overeating because of changes in lifestyles, hectic schedules, and time shortages. And the biggest problem, says the Surgeon General, is that Americans are eating too much fat. But the solution is well within reach. By focusing on complex carbohydrate foods such as pasta, whole grains, and fresh vegetables, we are shifting the emphasis away from fat.

In the new recommendations, meat portions shrink but the plate fills up with an assortment of tasty vegetables and grains. The key to this healthful style of eating is an understanding of the nutrients that foods provide. Nutrients are the underlying components of a healthful diet. Mix them up well, add a proven health-enhancer such as fiber, and it's easy to make good health a matter of good taste.

KEY COMPONENTS TO A HEALTHFUL DIET

Carbohydrates. Specifically, carbohydrates provide the major source of fuel that keeps the body going. And they do it with fewer calories than other nutrients. Each gram of carbohydrate has only 4 calories, which is less than half of the calories provided by a gram of fat. Health experts urge people to aim for a diet that derives half or more of its calories from this nutrient. As such, carbohydrates become the cornerstone of healthful eating.

There are two types of carbohydrates: simple carbohydrates and complex carbohydrates.

Nutritionists continue to favor the complex variety. Simple carbohydrates such as sugar and honey offer little more than energy, while the complex variety supplies many other nutrients. Apples, whole grain breads, and pasta are all examples of complex carbohydrates. In addition to providing energy, these foods contain rich amounts of fiber, vitamins, and minerals. Contrary to popular belief, complex carbohydrate foods are not fattening. The margarine or sour cream that is slathered on a baked potato is the real calorie-adding culprit.

Fat. A certain amount of fat is essential in the diet, particularly for growing children. Unfortunately, however, too many Americans have an unhealthy preoccupation with high-fat foods. Croissants, premium ice creams, and cookies aren't necessarily taboo, but these high-fat foods should have a minor place in the diet. Consider them the rare indulgence and not the routine choice if you want to start skimming the fat from your diet.

Incidentally, you need less than 1 tablespoon of fat per day, but it has been found that many Americans take in eight times that much, which totals a full ½ cup each day. Much of that fat comes from meats and cheeses, but the fat hidden in convenience foods, snacks, and desserts makes a generous contribution.

What happens to all this extra fat? It's stored as body fat, and it complicates our health. Fat, particularly the saturated fat found in animal foods such as butter, heavily marbled meats, and whole milk, increases the risk for coronary heart disease. Too much fat also puts people at risk for high blood pressure and certain types of cancer.

There are three types of fat found in food: saturated, polyunsaturated, and monounsaturated. Saturated fat is the most harmful because it raises levels of cholesterol in the blood. Polyunsaturated fat from vegetable sources such as corn and sunflower oil, on the other hand, lowers blood cholesterol. Monounsaturated fat like that found in olive oil also appears to be helpful in lowering cholesterol. But no matter what type you consume, remember that fat is a concentrated source of energy, carrying 9 calories in each gram. The cautionary word for this nutrient is this: use with discretion.

Protein. The upkeep and maintenance of every tissue in the body depend on protein. Protein builds muscles and is a necessary component of hair, enzymes, certain key hormones, hemoglobin, and insulin, the compound that regulates blood sugar. Different foods carry different types of protein. Some protein, like that found in meat, milk, cheese, and other animal foods, is of high quality. Protein from vegetables, legumes, nuts, and seeds makes a valuable contribution, but is of a lower quality and needs to be consumed in conjunction with other vegetable proteins.

On the average, men need about 60 grams of protein each day, women about 45. To put those numbers into perspective, 1 ounce of meat or cheese has about 7 grams of protein. If you eat a generous-size steak, say 8 or 9 ounces, it's possible to fulfill your daily protein needs in just one sitting. Needless to say, Americans rarely fall short of this nutrient.

Vitamins and Minerals. Of the long list of vitamins and minerals scientists have discovered over the years, no one stands out as the most important. All are critical to good health. The B vitamins, for instance, help convert food into energy. Minerals such as calcium and iron keep bones and blood strong.

Routinely, the Food and Nutrition Board of the National Academy of Science reviews the research and sets recommended dietary allowances (RDA) for most vitamins and minerals. But there is really no need to count numbers. In an exhaustive report entitled *Diet and Health*, the National Research Council urged Americans to fulfill nutrient needs by including 5 servings from the fruit and vegetable group each day and 6 servings from the grain and cereal group. Following their advice not only boosts fiber and complex carbohydrate intake, but it also ensures that you'll get the whole spectrum of vitamins and minerals needed for optimal health.

While food is the best source of vitamins and minerals, some people have difficulty meeting requirements. Pregnant women, people who eat

erratically, and those with certain illnesses sometimes require vitamin/mineral supplements to meet nutrient demands. But supplements are not recommended for the population at large. What's more, health organizations urge people not to take more than 100 percent of the RDA for any one nutrient because large doses of certain nutrients can be toxic.

Water. Often taken for granted, water is one of the most essential nutrients. No one survives without water. It's necessary for all chemical reactions in the body ranging from digestion to absorption. Water prevents dehydration, aids in maintaining the body's internal thermostat, and bathes body tissues. Roughly one-half to two-thirds of the body is water.

To keep your body hydrated, you need at least 2 to 3 quarts of water each day. Adults need about eight glasses of water per day as part of this requirement. The rest of the supply comes from foods, all of which contain some water. Fruits and vegetables are good sources. They often contain as much as 97 percent water. Even breads and meats are about 36 to 37 percent water.

Fiber. Although it is not really a nutrient, fiber is crucial. It is found in plant foods such as the skins of fruits and vegetables and in the outer coating or the "bran" of grains. Fiber can't be digested, but that is part of its benefit. The National Cancer Institute recommends that people aim for 20 to 35 grams of fiber per day and that it come from several sources.

Oat bran is the current fiber favorite, but experts say no one fiber fills all our needs. There are two types of fiber: water-soluble and insoluble. The water-soluble fiber found in oats, apples, and dried peas and beans is helpful for lowering blood cholesterol. Insoluble fiber such as wheat bran works to prevent constipation. This type of fiber also may help to decrease the risk of colon cancer.

When you begin to boost your fiber intake, it's a good idea to add high-fiber foods gradually to the diet. Make a sandwich with whole grain bread for a change. Switch to a higher fiber cereal at breakfast on occasion. And, as the National Research Council encourages, eat more fruits and vegetables.

Computing Nutrition

Your Daily Needs

To estimate your calorie requirement, multiply your current weight by 15 to get your estimated need. Remember that this is only a rough guide because calorie requirements vary according to age, body size, and level of activity. If a change of weight is desired, either add or subtract 500 calories per day to allow for weight gain or loss of 1 pound a week. However, a diet of less than 1,200 calories a day is not recommended unless medically supervised. For more information concerning your individual requirements, consult a registered dietitian (R.D.).

Implement the *Cooking Light* 50-20-30 guidelines (page 24) by calculating the amount of carbohydrate, protein, and fat for optimal health. Multiply your calorie requirement by the percentages 50, 20, and 30 to give the calories from each nutrient. Divide the carbohydrate and protein calories by 4 (4 calories per gram) and the fat by 9 (9 calories per gram) to determine how many grams of each nutrient you need.

For example, here's how to calculate the distribution of a 2,000-calorie diet:

50% carbohydrate = 1,000 calories ÷ 4 = 250 grams carbohydrate

20% protein = 400 calories ÷ 4 = 100 grams protein

30% fat = 600 calories ÷ 9 = 67 grams fat

Therefore, for a person eating 2,000 calories a day, 1,000 calories would meet the 50% carbohydrate guideline, while no more than 400 calories and 600 calories would be from protein and fat, respectively.

When planning your meals, refer to the daily amounts to help you make the most of the nutrient values that follow *Cooking Light* recipes. Although there is no RDA for sodium or cholesterol, suggested intake is listed below along with the RDA for iron and calcium.

Iron	15 mg
Calcium	800 mg
Sodium	1,100 to 3,300 mg
Cholesterol	less than 300 mg

Every Recipe Analyzed

Calories per serving and a nutrient breakdown accompany every recipe. The nutrients listed include grams of carbohydrate, protein, and fat along with milligrams of cholesterol, calcium, iron, and sodium.

Determining Calorie Percentages

Use *Cooking Light* nutrient breakdowns to calculate the percentage of calories contributed by carbohydrate, protein, and fat. Let's say you are looking at the recipe for Mixed Grains-Buttermilk Bread (complete recipe on page 116), and you want to determine the percentage of fat in a serving (one ½-inch slice).

First, find the number of grams of fat per serving. This is calculated in the analysis to be 1.2 grams. To find the percentage of calories from fat, multiply grams of fat by 9 (the number of calories per gram of fat) to get fat calories per serving. Then divide this quantity by the total calories. You'll find that fat contributes 10 percent of the calories in one slice of Mixed Grains-Buttermilk Bread.

MIXED GRAINS-BUTTERMILK BREAD

PROTEIN 3.7 / FAT 1.2 / CARBOHYDRATE 20.6 / CHOLESTEROL 0 / IRON 0.9 / SODIUM 72 / CALCIUM 10

To calculate the calories contributed by carbohydrate and protein, multiply grams of carbohydrate or protein per serving by 4 (the number of calories per gram of carbohydrate or protein). Divide the quantity by total calories.

Menus and Menu Plans Meet 50-20-30 Guidelines

Each slice of Mixed Grains-Buttermilk Bread meets the recommended percentages: more than 50 percent carbohydrate and no more than 20 percent protein or 30 percent fat. All recipes will not fall so neatly within the guidelines. The goal is to achieve the recommended balance of nutrients on a daily basis, taking into consideration three meals and a snack. Use "Light Recipes" (page 95) and "*Cooking Light* Menu Plans" (pages 248–249) to create meals that meet the 50-20-30 guidelines.

How the Recipes Are Analyzed

The recipes are developed for people who are interested in lowering their intake of calories, sodium, fat, and/or cholesterol to maintain healthy eating patterns. If you are following a medically prescribed diet, consult a registered dietitian to see how *Cooking Light* recipes can fit into your specific meal plan.

The calorie and nutrient breakdown of each of these recipes is derived from computer analysis, based primarily on information from the U.S. Department of Agriculture. The values are as accurate as possible and are based on these assumptions:
- All nutrient breakdowns are listed per serving.
- All meats are trimmed of fat and skin before cooking.
- When a range is given for an ingredient (for example, 3 to 3½ cups flour), the lesser amount is calculated.
- Alcohol calories evaporate when heated, and this reduction is reflected in the calculations.
- When a marinade is used, only the amount of marinade used (not discarded) is calculated.
- Garnishes and other optional ingredients are not calculated.
- Fruits and vegetables listed in the ingredients are not peeled unless otherwise specified.

Exercise—The Perfect Partner

Eating right is only half of the fitness picture, of course. The flip side is exercise. Simply put, exercise promotes good health. Medical reports clearly indicate that a regular exercise program may help to ward off certain lifestyle illnesses including high blood pressure and heart disease. Sedentary living, on the other hand, has been shown to increase health risks.

When people don't exercise, the risk of developing heart disease increases greatly. At least that's the conclusion of one group of researchers who found that active men are 30 percent less likely to die from heart attacks than their less active counterparts. In addition, exercise plays an indirect role in reducing heart attack risk by reducing other risk factors for heart disease: high blood pressure, obesity, and stress.

Physically active people also tend to live longer. One Harvard University study revealed that sedentary men are twice as likely to die from heart attacks as those who swim, jog, walk, or keep otherwise vigorously active. What these studies all show is that the exercise-health link is no longer just theory. It's a scientifically proven fact.

LIFETIME FITNESS BENEFITS

Although "for the health of it" is reason enough to get fit, reviewing the specific benefits of exercising often pays. The list is a long one. Exercise can help prevent or improve a myriad of health problems including heart disease, high blood pressure, high blood cholesterol levels, obesity, diabetes, stroke, varicose veins, back pain, constipation, arthritis, osteoporosis, and depression.

Physical benefits aside, exercise is worth the effort for the way it makes you look and feel. Not everyone can be an Olympic athlete, but a lifetime commitment to exercise will put you in the best shape you can be. Not only does that help boost self-esteem but it also improves the quality of life. Active people get the full enjoyment out of life, no matter what their age.

FINDING A PERFECT MATCH

When choosing the exercise program that best meets your needs, select one you are likely to stick with. Consider your physical needs, fitness goals, lifestyle, and what you excel at to gain the greatest health benefits.

Matching an exercise program to your interests is paramount to the success of your fitness routine. Even the most dedicated exercisers get bored when their workout schedule doesn't suit their physical needs, fitness goals, or lifestyle. Check the chart below to decide which aerobic activities to put on your "A" list. Then slip into the habit of exercising; it only takes a few minutes a day!

CHOOSING A LIFETIME SPORT

SPORT	PHYSICAL REQUIREMENTS	FITNESS BENEFITS	RISK OF INJURY
WALKING	Suitable for most anyone, especially beginners and older people	Cardiovascular conditioning, strengthens and tones legs	Little or none
JOGGING	For the well-conditioned without back, knee, or foot problems; not for the seriously overweight	Excellent cardiovascular conditioning, strengthens and tones calves, thighs, and buttocks	Stress injuries of feet, knees, and back
CYCLING Stationary or Outdoor	Good choice for anyone especially those with joint problems	Cardiovascular conditioning and tones thighs	Little or none
AEROBIC DANCE	Classes available for all fitness levels	Cardiovascular conditioning, flexibility, coordination, and tones muscles of upper and lower body	High impact aerobics can cause stress injuries; low impact reduces risk of injuries
SWIMMING	Good choice for most everyone, especially good for injury rehabilitation and overweight people	Cardiovascular conditioning, strength, flexibility, and total body training	Little or none

GLOWING WITH GOOD HEALTH

Taut muscles, a trim waist, and a springy step are sure signs that a person works at keeping in shape. But have you ever spotted men or women who positively glow with good health? The physically fit just seem to have an aura about them. Perhaps it's because they feel good about themselves. It's certainly true that exercise revitalizes a person mentally as well as physically. In fact, if you were to delve deeper into the habits of these "in-shape" people, you would probably find that exercise is just one part of a healthy attention to lifestyle. Good food and balanced meals, as well as a sound fitness program, are also part of their secret.

Most of us probably already know this secret, and now we want to attain that same glow. Leafing through the pages of *Cooking Light* is a good way to get started. With the right attitude and a little bit of information, anyone—no matter what age, shape, height, or weight—can build a more active and healthy lifestyle. And that's the key to a lifetime of both physical and mental fitness.

TOTAL BODY FITNESS

Building a better physique with exercise involves three basic components: cardiovascular endurance, muscle strength and endurance, and flexibility. Of these three factors, the most important one for good health is cardiovascular endurance. Aerobic exercises such as running, brisk walking, and swimming work to strengthen the heart and circulatory system. And don't forget that an aerobic workout burns fat.

Aerobic exercise provides increased oxygen supplies to body tissues, making it possible for the body to use energy more efficiently. Simply put, aerobic exercise involves the use of large muscle groups, such as those in the legs, to keep the heart rate elevated. When the heart rate is elevated for 20 to 30 minutes, the heart's strength is improved. The heart becomes more efficient at pumping blood. It pumps more blood with each beat and consequently has to beat fewer times to deliver the appropriate amount of blood. In addition, the body's tissues become more efficient at extracting oxygen from blood.

But aerobic exercise is only one part of the fitness equation. To complement aerobic workouts, add weight training to your exercise schedule. Weight training builds individual muscle strength and endurance. This type of training firms and shapes muscles, giving them a toned, sleek look. Strong, firm muscles are what allow you to sprint up a flight of stairs with ease or grab a bag of heavy groceries with little effort.

Another key to total body fitness is flexibility. Some people are just naturally more flexible than others, but everyone can benefit from stretching the muscles, tendons, and joints. Stretching helps to prevent injuries and release tension.

HIGH-LEVEL FITNESS MAINTENANCE

Nothing lasts forever, particularly fitness. That is, unless you work at it. Keeping active and maintaining health and fitness at optimal levels takes commitment. While different people enjoy different fitness activities, the amount of time devoted to exercise should be about the same. Fitness experts recommend at least three exercise sessions a week to get you fit and to help you stay fit. Specifically, the aerobic portion of each work-out must last 20 to 30 minutes. That's not counting the time spent to warm up or cool down.

In any fitness routine, the level of intensity is of prime importance. To get maximum cardiovascular benefits from aerobic exercises such as swimming, jogging, brisk walking, cycling, or low-impact aerobics, check periodically to see that your heart rate is falling in the healthy training zone. The goal is to exercise at a level at which your heart rate is 70 to 85 percent of your maximum heart rate. To learn how to calculate your maximum and healthy training heart rate, turn to page 163. If your heart rate falls below the proper training limits, your workout is not improving cardiovascular fitness. If it stays above 85 percent of your maximum heart rate, it may in fact be harmful.

Pay careful attention to the non-aerobic part of exercise class, too. Stretching and weight-training exercises complement any aerobic routine. On the following pages are a few key exercises to help you get started.

Muscle Toning and Stretching

Complement the aerobic phase of your exercise session with muscle toning and stretching. Build muscle strength and endurance by using weight-resistance equipment, free weights, or calisthenics. Below are exercises using hand and ankle weights. Start with 1- to 2-pound weights. Do one set of 10 to 15 repetitions; as your strength improves, increase to 2 to 3 sets. Using heavier weights will increase the intensity of the workout. Concentrate on proper form and controlling the movement. Stretch muscles before working out to prepare them for activity and afterwards to prevent tightness. Hold each stretch for 30 seconds, without bouncing. The secret of safe stretching is to keep it gentle, smooth, and rhythmical.

Arms, shoulder, and chest— Clasp hands behind back. Gently raise arms without leaning forward. Hold for 30 seconds and repeat stretch.

Quadriceps—Lie on stomach with head resting on arm. Pull leg back with matching arm until a gentle stretch is felt. Hold for 30 seconds. Repeat with other leg.

Buttocks—Begin without weights and add them only when comfortable with the routine. Position body on elbows and one knee. Hold other leg up, with knee at a 90-degree angle. Keep spine and neck in line, and tightly pull in abdominal muscles. With a slow, controlled movement, raise working leg just above hip level and lower to starting position without arching your back. Continue 10 to 15 times and repeat with other leg.

Abdominals—Lie on floor with lower back pressed to floor. Extend legs in air with knees slightly bent; place arms across chest. Use abdominal muscles to lift shoulder blades off floor. Slowly lower upper body to starting position. Repeat 10 to 15 times.

Outer thigh—Lie on side with knees slightly bent and head relaxed on arm. Using ankle weights, slowly raise bent top leg to shoulder height. Slowly lower top leg without resting it on bottom leg. Repeat 10 to 15 times; then do inner thigh exercise. Repeat sequence on other side.

Inner thigh—Lie on side, with bottom leg slightly bent and top leg crossed over in front of other knee. Relax head on arm to keep spine straight. Without allowing hips to roll forward, raise bottom leg off floor. Lower leg slowly, not allowing it to rest on floor. Repeat 10 to 15 times; then switch to other leg.

Upper back and shoulders—Stand with feet shoulder-width apart and knees slightly bent. Extend arms downward in front of body. Raise arms to just below shoulder height, keeping elbows slightly bent and forearms pointing down. Return to starting position and repeat 10 to 15 times.

Set Yourself Up for Success

Getting in good shape and staying that way isn't always easy. Achieving total fitness calls for a life-long commitment to good eating and healthy activity. And even then all sorts of obstacles can get in the way. Time, of course, is a major stumbling block. Most of us don't seem to have enough time in the day to keep pace with job and family responsibilities. Fixing a balanced meal or working out at the gym may be the last thing on our minds. But with a little discipline, most of us can manage to put forth the effort necessary to maintain health and fitness.

In addition to discipline, our attitude is an all-important ingredient in maintaining a healthier lifestyle. How we deal with life's trials and tribulations may have more to do with the quality of our health than any other single item. Being successful at maintaining lifelong fitness means learning to deal with the curve balls that life throws, particularly the stressful ones.

SHORT-CIRCUITING STRESS

Not all forms of pressure are bad. A certain amount of stress, in fact, can be beneficial. Small doses of stress actually motivate many people to finish tasks and projects. Stress can also heighten creativity. In a positive sense, stress acts as a mechanism of protection for the body. When we perceive stress, our heart rate and blood pressure rise dramatically in preparation for "fight or flight." Muscles tense up for action. In effect, the body is ready to do battle or to make a quick escape. However, if the body is still in high gear once the stress has passed, damage can result.

People who can't diffuse everyday strains and pressures risk damaging their health. If you find yourself becoming hostile in the face of stress, chances are that you will suffer distinct physical consequences. Studies show that of the three major traits of a type A personality—time urgency, competitiveness, and hostility—hostility can do the most damage. High hostility levels can boost blood pressure, heart rate, and cholesterol levels into an "unhealthy" zone. When you let hostility, impatience, or anxiety become the "norm" in your life, you can expect your health to deteriorate.

Too much stress causes the body to overproduce adrenaline and other stress-fighting hormones. Eventually, these high hormone levels can cause damage to artery walls and lead to atherosclerosis. Left untreated, atherosclerosis sets the body up for a heart attack or stroke.

POINTERS ON COPING

Keeping your feelings to yourself is a sure way to create internal stress. The strong silent type is more movie hero than fitness model. In fact, people who express emotions—anger, fear, sadness, elation—generally fare better healthwise. If you find yourself covering up feelings, break out of the pattern. This will offer two positive effects. First, by sharing emotions, you open yourself up to others and thus avoid the hostility that comes with being preoccupied with yourself. Second, by expressing your feelings, you invite others to share their emotions with you. Becoming aware of another person's problems often makes your own problems seem small, and it tends to build self-esteem as well.

In order to deal with the problems and stresses of life, implement the three Cs—stay **calm**, **communicate**, and have **control**. They can do wonders for diffusing life's stresses.

CALM DOWN WITH EXERCISE

Exercise is the single best strategy for coping with and getting rid of stress. One study found that walking is actually more effective for relieving stress than a tranquilizer. Numerous other studies have found that people who exercise are more capable of dealing with stress than their sedentary counterparts. Researchers speculate that regular aerobic exercise conditions the body to handle stress. Stress can raise the heart rate and blood pressure, but physically-fit people start from a lower resting heart rate and blood pressure than sedentary people. In addition, their hearts don't have to work as hard to deliver the same amount of blood.

Several factors may be at work to bring this about. Exercise raises the body temperature and thus automatically increases production of the brain-calming chemical serotonin. Other soothing chemicals released during exercise, called endorphins, also contribute to an upbeat attitude. Exercise controls the body's fluid balance, too, which may be related to the ability to handle stress. And finally, vigorous activity helps keep body systems— blood pressure, circulation, blood sugar, and breathing—on an even keel.

To be sure, exercise seems to be a way of completing the adaptive response to stress. Scientists now realize that activity helps burn off excess levels of the hormones that stress generates. Most of us have felt pressure, anxiety, and tension slip away when we walk, jog, swim, or cycle for moderate distances.

ON CONTINUOUS COMMUNICATION

If stress is caused in part by bottling up feelings, talking may help to circumvent a blow-up. Talking with friends or family about the frustrations of everyday life can help put those problems into perspective. Talking about a problem can often be one of the best ways to solve it, too. If something is bothering you, discuss the situation with a trusted family member, co-worker, or friend. Getting an outside opinion sometimes helps. If you have a legitimate gripe with someone, tell that person. Not many people are mind readers, which is why communication is so important in all parts of your life.

If being overweight is the reason for your anxiety, set a realistic time schedule for shedding excess pounds. Then tell someone about it. The simple act of talking to someone about your plan helps to strengthen resolve. Moreover, talking about your weight loss strategy puts you more in control of the outcome.

PUSHING THE CONTROL BUTTON

Everyone, even the youngest of children, needs to feel some control over his life. Loss of control often leads to anxiety and stress. Passive people who don't take charge of their lives often are more likely to feel the ill effects of stress. Studies show that stress can impair the body's immune system and hence diminish its ability to ward off infection. Letting others make decisions that you want to make yourself is a sure way to build up stress. Actively working to control the events in life that are important to you, on the other hand, can help to reduce harmful stress.

CONJURE UP SOME CALM

Everyone succumbs to anxiety now and then. Maybe you have the jitters prior to making a speech or an important presentation. Or perhaps you can't get your check book to balance. But don't let stress get to you, the experts caution.

Sometimes just "thinking" yourself away from the frustrating situation helps. Call it a "stress-relief break." All you need to do is take a few seconds to mentally escape to a calm environment. For example, visualize watching a beautiful sunset or snorkeling in clear blue water just off a tropical island. Or perhaps your idea of paradise is skiing down the slopes somewhere in the Rockies. Whatever boosts your spirits and takes you away from the everyday grind, try envisioning it.

If daydreaming away stress doesn't work for you, try muscle relaxation techniques. Alternately tense and relax your muscles, starting from the tip of your toes and ending with your neck and face. When you concentrate on working muscles, you are taking the focus off the stressful situation and placing it elsewhere.

Deep breathing seems to have the same relaxing effect. Relaxing away the stress, however, is more than just catching your breath. True deep breathing requires special attention to the "how" of inhaling air. To start, inhale very deeply through your nose; you'll feel a filling sensation all the way to your abdomen. Hold that breath; then exhale, first from the abdomen and then up through the chest. Repeat for 5 to 10 times for the full effect.

Setting yourself up for good health and fitness requires employing whatever methods are necessary to combat life's stresses and strains.

The *Cooking Light* Kitchen

In *Cooking Light*'s Oriental Pork Quiche (complete recipe on page 165), a few changes in ingredients allows almost 350 calories to be shaved from each serving. This recipe is a perfect example of how to prepare flavorful foods without being guilt-ridden about the calories, fat, and cholesterol. Each serving of the quiche contains 72 percent fewer calories, 82 percent less fat, and 90 percent less cholesterol than the traditional version.

The commercial egg substitute used in this recipe can also be used for baked items such as cakes, pies, and other desserts. This, along with the omission of a crust, allows for a major reduction of saturated fat and cholesterol from the traditional version. Lean cooked pork replaces bacon for a substantial savings of fat, and the pork contributes a source of good-quality protein to the recipe. Skim milk is used to save additional calories and fat without affecting the flavor.

Cooking Light encourages the use of fresh vegetables and herbs for flavor that is superb, and this recipe is no exception. Snow pea pods, mushrooms, water chestnuts, onion, and sweet red pepper add both flavor and texture to the quiche.

ORIENTAL PORK QUICHE

Cooking Light

1 (6-ounce) package frozen snow pea pods, thawed and drained
½ cup sliced fresh mushrooms
½ cup sliced water chestnuts
¼ cup chopped onion
¼ cup chopped sweet red pepper
¼ cup water
¾ cup diced lean cooked pork
1 (8-ounce) carton frozen egg substitute, thawed
½ cup (2 ounces) shredded Monterey Jack cheese
½ cup skim milk
2 tablespoons chopped fresh parsley
½ teaspoon salt
⅛ teaspoon ground red pepper
Vegetable cooking spray
Sliced fresh mushrooms (optional)

Yield: 6 servings
Calories: 137 per serving

PROTEIN 12.8 / FAT 5.9 / CARBOHYDRATE 7.5 / CHOLESTEROL 26 / IRON 1.9 / SODIUM 331 / CALCIUM 128

Traditional

1 cup flour
½ teaspoon salt
⅓ cup lard
3 tablespoons cold water
8 slices bacon
2 cups (8 ounces) shredded Swiss cheese
6 eggs, beaten
1 cup milk
⅓ cup chopped green onion
¼ cup sliced fresh mushrooms
½ teaspoon salt
¼ teaspoon pepper

Yield: 6 servings
Calories: 483 per serving

PROTEIN 23.9 / FAT 33.2 / CARBOHYDRATE 21.6 / CHOLESTEROL 259 / IRON 1.9 / SODIUM 733 / CALCIUM 447

TESTED FOR ASSURANCE

Feel confident as you prepare *Cooking Light* recipes and menus. Each recipe and menu has been developed and tested by a staff of home economists to meet strict standards for sound nutrition, excellent flavor, and visual appeal. And to add to the visual appeal, garnishing and serving suggestions have been provided to help you create great-looking, good-tasting meals. As you prepare *Cooking Light* recipes and menus for family and friends, feel good knowing that you are making nutritious meals an enjoyable, pleasant experience.

KEEP IT LIGHT AND KEEP THE FLAVOR

PERFECT PORTIONS
Use a pasta portioner to help ensure the correct yield for pasta recipes. Place the pasta in the desired measuring opening, and fill until full.

GRATING FOR FRESH FLAVOR
Add flavor by grating fresh gingerroot or horseradish with a porcelain grater. This type of grater is easy to use and clean.

FLAVOR WITH ZEST
Use a zester on oranges, lemons, and limes for an easy but flavorful garnish. To use, place zester on fruit and pull towards you, using pressure.

HERBS ADD FLAVOR
After carefully rinsing fresh herbs, spin herbs dry in a small salad or herb spinner. Ready to be used are (clockwise from top) mint, oregano, dillweed, rosemary. In spinner, basil.

PIPING ON CONTRAST
Pipe nonfat yogurt or low-fat sour cream on soups for an easy, attractive garnish. Pipe it in a pattern or circle; then pull through the mixture with a wooden pick, if desired.

SHAPES ADD INTEREST
Add interest to fruit dishes with various shaped melon ballers. Round, oval, or scalloped melon balls are appealing to the eye and to the palate.

What's New in the Marketplace?

As you walk down the aisles in the supermarket today, you're likely to be more aware of the information that food labels contain than you were five years ago. According to a recent FDA survey, consumers can now more readily identify sources of saturated fat in foods. In response, manufacturers not only are changing ingredients in their products, but also are making their labels easier to read and understand.

BETTER SNACKS

Perhaps the most widely publicized change in the marketplace is in the replacement of tropical oils with vegetable oils in snack products. One consumer group, the National Heart Savers Association, launched a full-scale campaign to make the public more aware of the use of highly saturated tropical oils—palm, palm kernel, or coconut oil—in snack products. Many of the major manufacturers responded by switching to healthier vegetable oils in many of their products.

But one of the most healthful steps that manufacturers can take is to properly label the fat in products—to state plainly the amount of fat in the product, what kind of oil it contains, and whether it is hydrogenated. It would greatly assist consumers if manufacturers could avoid using some of today's misleading labeling practices. For example, stating that a vegetable oil product contains no cholesterol can be misleading. Vegetable oils do not contain cholesterol, but they may contain hydrogenated fats that act like saturated fats and raise blood cholesterol levels.

HIGH-TECH FITNESS

The fitness marketplace offers highly specialized gear. Recent innovation is diagnostic screening of the feet to help provide better fitting shoes. Molds are made of the feet to form individually tailored inserts to make these shoes fit feet of all shapes.

Sports fabrics especially made for exercise allow proper air ventilation and ease of movement during workouts. And a wide range of specially insulated gear is designed for cold-weather sports. Today's models of everything from rowing machines to treadmills offer computerized displays that can give you such instant readouts as heart rate, time elapsed, and your personal fitness profile.

STEP UP ON THE STAIRS

A new workout now being seen in fitness centers is called stairing—you step up on a machine that works like a set of stairs for a vigorous cardiovascular workout. Called the StairMaster™, it works the entire lower body including calves, quadriceps,

hamstrings, and buttocks. It is designed for all fitness levels. However, beginners should build aerobic fitness through activities such as walking or jogging before beginning to use the stairclimber.

These machines feature settings that allow you to choose between 10 intensity levels, according to your level of fitness. Ask the instructor at your fitness center for a demonstration and a personalized stairing workout schedule.

ENDLESS MUSHROOM VARIETIES

Gone are the days when a mushroom was simply a mushroom—a button-shaped entity to be sliced up for salads, casseroles, or pizza. Suddenly turning up in supermarkets are several types of wild and cultivated mushrooms in a variety of shapes, colors, and textures. Mushrooms lend themselves to *Cooking Light* fare because they are low in calories, a fair source of fiber, and contain the B vitamins thiamine, niacin, and riboflavin.

When foraging in the grocery store for your next mushroom selection, look for fresh mushrooms that are free of excess moisture. Store your selections in the refrigerator in either a paper bag or kitchen towel. If the mushrooms are packaged in plastic, remove them from the container because plastic will trap moisture and hasten spoilage. Fresh mushrooms usually last an average of two to four days when properly refrigerated.

Store dried mushrooms in an airtight container in a dark, dry place. When you are ready to prepare dried mushrooms, simply rehydrate them. Hot liquids tend to be best at bringing out the flavor. Fresh mushrooms need to be cleaned gently with a soft brush or cloth. Because fresh mushrooms are quite porous, they should never be soaked in water to clean. However, several gentle rinsings may be necessary for some wild varieties. Once cleaned and prepared, both dried and fresh mushrooms offer distinct flavor and texture. Why not become more familiar with what's available by taking a look at the list below.

● Enoki—The flavor and crisp texture of enoki mushrooms make them a perfect addition to salads or stir-fry dishes. They can be identified by their tiny button tops and long, thin stems.

A variety of fresh wild and cultivated mushrooms are readily available: (clockwise from top) enoki, shiitake, oyster, and wood ear.

● Oyster—Oyster mushrooms vary in color from pearly gray to creamy beige. They can be identified by their ruffled caps, which are fan-shaped and clustered together, attached by short stems. They can be eaten either raw or cooked. Their mild flavor is at its best when the mushrooms are simply prepared. Toss them into a salad or cook them briefly to retain the delicate texture and flavor.

● Shiitake—Long a staple in the Far East, this woodsy-flavored mushroom is now common in U.S. supermarkets in both dried and fresh varieties. Sauté them lightly with seasonings or garlic for outstanding results. The stems of these mushrooms are tougher than those of other varieties, but can be used to flavor soups or stocks.

● Wood ears—These mild-flavored Oriental mushrooms are a staple in popular Chinese dishes. They should be cleaned by rinsing vigorously under running water to eliminate their musty odor. Use them to add texture and a mild flavor to stir-fried dishes, soups, or stews.

Healthy American Meals

Burgundy Beef with Parslied Fettuccine is the star of the Elegant Autumn Dinner Party menu. The rich-tasting stew is brimming with chunks of tender beef and a variety of vegetables: carrots, onions, artichoke hearts, and snow pea pods. The hearty mixture is blanketed in a flavorful Burgundy wine-based broth, then served on a bed of parslied fettuccine. (Menu begins on page 74.)

Each of our creative menus has been developed to follow the nutrition guidelines for a healthy heart and body. At least 50 percent of the total calories of each menu are derived from carbohydrate, no more than 20 percent from protein, and less than 30 percent from fat. Remember this healthy 50-20-30 ratio and use it as a guide when planning your own menus, whatever the occasion.

The four chapters of menus include something for everyone! Whether you are skiing down the slopes and want a hearty breakfast or are entertaining friends with an elegant Victorian tea party, you are sure to find the answer to your menu needs.

Breakfast and Brunch. Eating a nutritious breakfast or brunch will give you and your family the energy needed to meet the physical and mental demands of the day. Try tempting your children with our Off-To-School breakfast featuring treats such as Chocolate Milk Shakes, Breakfast Cookies, and Kinda Crazy Cupcakes. Bring warmth and cheer to a Christmas Morning Brunch with Pumpkin Muffins and glistening Cranberry-Lime Jam, and enjoy the good feeling that comes from knowing you are eating the right foods.

Quick and Easy. Preparing balanced meals while living with a hectic schedule can be a real challenge. Take advantage of our menu ideas created with the thought that time is of the essence. Stop at the grocery store and pick up ingredients at the salad bar to prepare our Speedy Salad Bar Supper starring Gazpacho Pasta.

Microwave It Light. The microwave oven has probably become the most used timesaver in America. Use it to create the Country Chicken with Creamy Gravy featured in our hearty menu entitled The Heartland Table. Big game being televised? Make the TV Tailgate Party menu and settle back to cheer the team. In the mood for something more exotic for dinner? Use the microwave to create Curried Lamb and Vegetable Medley and Savory Rice.

That's Entertaining. Invite friends over to herald the beginning of autumn with our Elegant Autumn Dinner Party. Begin with a Wild Mushroom Consomme, and serve a hearty but elegant entrée of Burgundy Beef with Parslied Fettuccine. Enjoy a Chinese New Year Celebration including all your favorites—Hot and Sour Soup, Beef with Broccoli, Chinese "Not Fried" Rice, and a fortune cookie!

Crab Papaya Vera-Cruz (page 39) makes a refreshing main-course for a leisurely brunch.

Off-To-School Breakfast

Breakfast Cookies
Orange-Carrot Cookies
No-Bake Peanut
Butter Balls
Kinda Crazy Cupcakes
Chocolate Milk Shake

Serves 3
Total calories per serving: 404

Eating a nutritious breakfast gives your children the energy they need to be mentally and physically alert to meet the demands of the day. If your children balk when it comes to breakfast, try tempting them with breakfast treats like a low-fat Chocolate Milk Shake and Breakfast Cookies filled with oats, cheese, and lean ham. Surprise them with No-Bake Peanut Butter Balls and wholesome Orange-Carrot Cookies. You are sure to create an interest in eating fruit

Chocolate Milk Shake, Breakfast Cookies, Orange-Carrot Cookies, No-Bake Peanut Butter Balls, and Kinda Crazy Cupcakes.

when you serve Kinda Crazy Cupcakes. One per person of each of these fun-to-eat breakfast treats adds up to good nutrition.

BREAKFAST COOKIES

½ cup reduced-calorie margarine
¼ cup sugar
1 egg
½ teaspoon vanilla extract
1¼ cups all-purpose flour
¼ teaspoon baking soda
¾ cup quick-cooking oats, uncooked
½ cup (2 ounces) shredded 40% less-fat Cheddar cheese
½ cup minced lean cooked ham
Vegetable cooking spray

Cream reduced-calorie margarine; gradually add sugar, beating well at medium speed of an electric mixer. (Reduced-calorie margarine will separate while beating.) Add egg and vanilla; beat well.

Combine flour and soda; add to margarine mixture, stirring well. Stir in oats, cheese, and ham. Drop dough by 2 level teaspoonfuls per cookie 2 inches apart onto cookie sheets that have been coated with cooking spray; flatten slightly. Bake at 375° for 10 minutes or until lightly browned. Cool on wire racks. Yield: 2½ dozen (72 calories each).

PROTEIN 2.3 / FAT 2.9 / CARBOHYDRATE 9.5 / CHOLESTEROL 8 / IRON 0.4 / SODIUM 77 / CALCIUM 19

ORANGE-CARROT COOKIES

½ cup water
¾ pound carrots, scraped and sliced
½ cup reduced-calorie margarine
⅓ cup firmly packed brown sugar
½ cup unsweetened orange juice
1 egg
1 teaspoon vanilla extract
¼ teaspoon orange extract
1 cup all-purpose flour
1 cup whole wheat flour
3 tablespoons wheat germ
1 teaspoon baking powder
½ teaspoon baking soda
Vegetable cooking spray

Place water in a medium saucepan; bring to a boil. Add carrots; return to a boil. Cover, reduce heat, and simmer 20 minutes or until carrots are very tender. Drain well. Mash carrots with a potato masher until smooth; set aside.

Cream margarine; gradually add brown sugar, beating well at medium speed of an electric mixer. (Reduced-calorie margarine will separate while beating.) Add mashed carrot, orange juice, egg, and flavorings; beat well.

Combine flours, wheat germ, baking powder, and soda; add flour mixture to creamed mixture, beating until well blended.

Drop dough by level tablespoonfuls 2 inches apart onto cookie sheets that have been coated with cooking spray. Bake at 350° for 12 minutes or until lightly browned. Cool on wire racks. Yield: 4 dozen (58 calories each).

PROTEIN 1.0 / FAT 1.5 / CARBOHYDRATE 10.7 / CHOLESTEROL 4 / IRON 0.4 / SODIUM 38 / CALCIUM 15

NO-BAKE PEANUT BUTTER BALLS

½ cup skim milk
⅓ cup honey
⅓ cup creamy peanut butter
2 tablespoons instant nonfat dry milk powder
¾ teaspoon vanilla extract
3 cups oat bran flakes cereal
1 cup crisp rice cereal

Combine milk, honey, peanut butter, and milk powder in a medium saucepan; stir well.

Cook over medium heat until thoroughly heated, stirring occasionally. Remove from heat; stir in vanilla.

Combine cereals in a large bowl. Pour peanut butter mixture over cereal mixture, stirring gently to combine. Shape cereal mixture into 1½-inch balls. Place balls on a flat surface. Cover and chill thoroughly. Yield: 16 balls (108 calories each).

PROTEIN 4.3 / FAT 3.8 / CARBOHYDRATE 15.0 / CHOLESTEROL 0 / IRON 0.7 / SODIUM 52 / CALCIUM 31

KINDA CRAZY CUPCAKES

2 envelopes unflavored gelatin
2 cups cranberry juice cocktail
12 foil muffin liners
Vegetable cooking spray
24 seedless green grapes, halved
1 medium banana, thinly sliced

Sprinkle gelatin over cranberry juice in a small saucepan; let stand 5 minutes. Cook over low heat, stirring constantly, until gelatin dissolves. Remove from heat, and let cool slightly.

Place muffin liners in muffin pan; coat liners with cooking spray. Divide grape halves and banana slices evenly among liners. Pour gelatin mixture evenly over fruit. Chill until firm. Carefully remove liners before serving. Yield: 1 dozen (47 calories each).

PROTEIN 1.2 / FAT 0.3 / CARBOHYDRATE 10.3 / CHOLESTEROL 0 / IRON 0.1 / SODIUM 3 / CALCIUM 3

CHOCOLATE MILK SHAKE

1 cup 1% low-fat chocolate milk
1 (8-ounce) carton vanilla low-fat yogurt
¼ teaspoon ground cinnamon
¼ teaspoon vanilla extract
3 ice cubes

Place all ingredients except ice cubes in container of an electric blender; top with cover, and process until smooth. Add ice cubes; process until smooth. Serve immediately. Yield: 2¼ cups (119 calories per ¾-cup serving).

PROTEIN 6.4 / FAT 1.8 / CARBOHYDRATE 19.4 / CHOLESTEROL 6 / IRON 0.3 / SODIUM 101 / CALCIUM 227

Down-home breakfast fare features creamy Oat Bran Custard, Peppered Pork Links, and refreshing Citrus Mixer.

Down-Home Delicious

Fond memories from child-hood are often filled with favorite family foods. For example, many family breakfasts consisted of freshly squeezed orange juice, eggs fried in the drippings from bacon or sausage, and bowls of oatmeal topped with pools of butter and rivers of cream.

Breakfast in the 1990s has changed, however. Now we are more aware of the critical importance of limiting the amount of fat in our diets in the fight against heart disease. But we can still keep those warm memories of favorite childhood foods intact by substituting foods that

Oat Bran Custard
Peppered Pork Links
Citrus Mixer

Serves 4
Total calories per serving: 374

we know are more nutritious.

In that spirit, we offer Peppered Pork Links. Flecks of crushed red pepper and rubbed sage give a flavor very reminiscent of its high-fat counterpart.

Colorful Citrus Mixer is a refreshing twist to orange juice. Just combine freshly squeezed orange, grapefruit juice, and lime-

flavored sparkling mineral water. Grenadine adds color and a little zing to the beverage.

Hot oat cereal has always been considered stick-to-your-ribs "comfort food." Oat Bran Custard, made with egg substitute, takes the old standby to new heights. The raisin-studded custard is flavored with a pleasing combination of vanilla, cinnamon, and nutmeg. Make the custard mixture the night before and chill. The next morning, pop the custard into the oven, and prepare a breakfast that your children are sure to remember fondly in years to come.

OAT BRAN CUSTARD

2 cups skim milk
¼ cup plus 2 tablespoons frozen egg substitute, thawed
3 tablespoons sugar
⅔ cup oat bran
2 tablespoons raisins
1 teaspoon vanilla extract
¼ teaspoon ground cinnamon
⅛ teaspoon ground nutmeg
Vegetable cooking spray
½ cup warm skim milk

Combine 2 cups milk, egg substitute, and sugar in a large bowl; stir well. Add oat bran and next 4 ingredients, stirring well to combine. Pour mixture into a shallow 1-quart casserole that has been coated with cooking spray. Place casserole in a 13- x 9- x 2-inch baking dish; pour hot water into baking dish to a depth of 1 inch. Bake at 350° for 40 minutes or until custard is set, stirring halfway through cooking time.

To serve, divide custard evenly among 4 serving bowls. Spoon 2 tablespoons warm milk over each serving. Serve immediately. Yield: 4 servings (189 calories per serving).

PROTEIN 11.3 / FAT 1.7 / CARBOHYDRATE 31.9 / CHOLESTEROL 3 / IRON 1.8 / SODIUM 115 / CALCIUM 214

PEPPERED PORK LINKS

¼ teaspoon beef-flavored bouillon granules
¼ cup hot water
½ pound lean ground pork
2 tablespoons fine, dry breadcrumbs
¼ teaspoon crushed red pepper
¼ teaspoon rubbed sage
⅛ teaspoon salt
⅛ teaspoon ground red pepper
Vegetable cooking spray

Combine bouillon granules and hot water in a medium bowl, stirring until granules dissolve. Add pork and next 5 ingredients, stirring well to combine. Cover and chill 15 minutes. Shape mixture into 8 links. Cover links and chill at least 2 hours.

Coat a medium skillet with cooking spray; place over medium heat until hot. Place links in skillet, and cook 9 to 10 minutes or until lightly browned, turning frequently. Drain links well on paper towels. Serve warm. Yield: 4 servings (124 calories per serving).

PROTEIN 12.3 / FAT 6.8 / CARBOHYDRATE 2.4 / CHOLESTEROL 41 / IRON 0.5 / SODIUM 188 / CALCIUM 8

CITRUS MIXER

1 cup freshly squeezed orange juice
1 cup freshly squeezed grapefruit juice
2 teaspoons grenadine syrup
2 cups lime-flavored sparkling mineral water, chilled
Lime slices (optional)

Combine orange juice, grapefruit juice, and grenadine syrup in a pitcher; mix well. Gently stir in mineral water just before serving. Serve over cracked ice. Garnish each serving with a lime slice, if desired. Yield: 4 cups (61 calories per 1-cup serving).

PROTEIN 0.7 / FAT 0.1 / CARBOHYDRATE 14.7 / CHOLESTEROL 0 / IRON 1.3 / SODIUM 30 / CALCIUM 10

WARMING UP FOR MUSCLE SAFETY

Researchers emphasize that warming up before exercise is absolutely essential in order to prevent injury to muscles. Researchers at Duke University examined muscle fibers under the microscope and confirmed that warmed-up muscles are much less likely to be injured than cold ones. So to prevent injury, take the time to warm up at the start of your exercise routine.

Skier's Breakfast

Whole Wheat Pancakes
Maple-Cinnamon Syrup
or
Warm Peach Sauce
Baked Canadian Bacon
Hot Malted Nog

Serves 4
Total calories per serving: 381

A day of skiing down challenging slopes demands a large dose of energy, and pancakes are a favorite breakfast choice. Adding sparkling water to the batter makes these whole wheat pancakes extra light. You have a choice of toppings—Warm Peach Sauce or Maple-Cinnamon Syrup. (Menu calories are based on a 3-tablespoon serving of Maple-Cinnamon Syrup.) A mixture of apple juice, mustard, and raspberry vinegar gives Baked Canadian Bacon extra flavor. Serve Hot Malted Nog for a feeling of warmth that will linger after you've hit the slopes.

Baked Canadian Bacon and Whole Wheat Pancakes topped with Warm Peach Sauce are an energizing way to start an active day.

WHOLE WHEAT PANCAKES

½ cup whole wheat flour
¼ cup all-purpose flour
2 teaspoons baking powder
2 teaspoons sugar
1 egg, beaten
½ cup plain nonfat yogurt
¼ cup sparkling mineral water
1 tablespoon reduced-calorie margarine, melted
Vegetable cooking spray

Combine flours, baking powder, and sugar in a large bowl; make a well in center of mixture.

Combine egg, yogurt, water, and margarine; add to dry ingredients, stirring just until dry ingredients are moistened.

For each pancake, pour 3 tablespoons batter onto a hot griddle or nonstick skillet that has been coated with cooking spray. Turn pancakes when tops are covered with bubbles and edges look cooked. Yield: 8 (4-inch) pancakes (140 calories each).

PROTEIN 6.1 / FAT 3.6 / CARBOHYDRATE 21.9 / CHOLESTEROL 50 / IRON 1.0 / SODIUM 219 / CALCIUM 165

MAPLE-CINNAMON SYRUP

¼ cup firmly packed brown sugar
1 teaspoon cornstarch
¼ teaspoon ground cinnamon
½ cup plus 2 tablespoons skim milk
1 tablespoon reduced-calorie margarine
¼ teaspoon maple flavoring

Combine sugar, cornstarch, and cinnamon in a small saucepan, stirring well. Gradually stir in milk. Bring to a boil; reduce heat, and simmer until slightly thickened, stirring constantly. Remove from heat; add margarine and maple flavoring, stirring until margarine melts. Serve syrup warm over pancakes. Yield: ¾ cup (27 calories per tablespoon).

PROTEIN 0.4 / FAT 0.6 / CARBOHYDRATE 5.3 / CHOLESTEROL 0 / IRON 0.2 / SODIUM 17 / CALCIUM 20

WARM PEACH SAUCE

¾ cup fresh or frozen sliced peaches, thawed
¼ cup unsweetened orange juice
⅛ teaspoon ground nutmeg
2 teaspoons brown sugar
¼ teaspoon almond extract

Combine peaches, orange juice, and nutmeg in a small saucepan; bring to a boil. Cover, reduce heat, and simmer 5 minutes or until peaches are tender. Remove from heat; mash peaches with a potato masher until almost smooth. Add brown sugar and almond extract, stirring until sugar dissolves. Serve sauce warm over pancakes. Yield: ½ cup (13 calories per tablespoon).

PROTEIN 0.2 / FAT 0.1 / CARBOHYDRATE 3.3 / CHOLESTEROL 0 / IRON 0.1 / SODIUM 0 / CALCIUM 2

BAKED CANADIAN BACON

8 (½-ounce) slices Canadian bacon
Vegetable cooking spray
2 tablespoons unsweetened apple juice
1 tablespoon water
2 teaspoons raspberry vinegar
½ teaspoon sugar
⅛ teaspoon dry mustard
Dash of ground cloves

Arrange bacon slices in a 10- x 6- x 2-inch baking dish that has been coated with cooking spray. Combine apple juice and remaining ingredients, stirring well. Pour apple juice mixture over bacon slices. Cover and bake at 375° for 10 to 12 minutes or until bacon is thoroughly heated. Serve warm. Yield: 4 servings (57 calories per serving).

PROTEIN 6.6 / FAT 2.4 / CARBOHYDRATE 2.1 / CHOLESTEROL 16 / IRON 0.2 / SODIUM 450 / CALCIUM 4

HOT MALTED NOG

3 cups skim milk
2 tablespoons malted milk powder
1 egg, beaten
1 teaspoon vanilla extract
Ground cinnamon (optional)

Combine milk, malted milk powder, and egg in a saucepan, stirring well. Cook mixture over low heat until thoroughly heated, stirring constantly with a wire whisk (do not boil). Remove from heat; stir in vanilla. Beat milk mixture at medium speed of an electric mixer until frothy. To serve, pour nog into mugs. Sprinkle with cinnamon, if desired. Serve immediately. Yield: 3 cups (103 calories per ¾-cup serving).

PROTEIN 8.3 / FAT 1.9 / CARBOHYDRATE 12.5 / CHOLESTEROL 54 / IRON 0.3 / SODIUM 133 / CALCIUM 245

Brandied Peach Ice Milk brings a lovely brunch to a sweet conclusion.

Take-A-Break Brunch

Once in a while, everyone needs a break from busy morning routines. So put aside thoughts of car pools, endless errands, and commitments to clubs and committees. It's time to invite a few close friends to put a stop to their hurried pace, and lavish themselves with some lovely leisure time.

Set the table with your prettiest dishes and the most fragrant fresh flowers you can find. This brunch menu is simple to prepare but elegant in its presentation. Crab-Papaya Veracruz is a mixture of sweet red and green

Crab-Papaya Veracruz
Poppy Seed Bowknots
Brandied Peach Ice Milk
Hot Tea

Serves 6
Total calories per serving: 445

peppers, green onions, tomato, and cilantro blended with fresh lump crabmeat. Serve the stuffed papaya halves on beds of colorful salad greens.

Poppy Seed Bowknots are made from an easily prepared biscuit dough enhanced with the

flavors of poppy seeds and lemon. Save the bowknot centers for a snack for the children.

The brunch comes to a close on a slightly indulgent note—Brandied Peach Ice Milk. Vanilla ice milk becomes a sophisticated dessert when peach brandy is added and the mixture is frozen to a satiny-smooth consistency. Top the delicately peach-colored scoops of ice milk with slices of fresh peaches that have been flavored with more peach brandy. A cup of hot brewed tea makes a rejuvenating meal accompaniment.

CRAB-PAPAYA VERACRUZ

3 ripe papayas
Curly leaf lettuce leaves
Vegetable cooking spray
1 teaspoon unsalted margarine
¼ cup chopped green onions
¼ cup chopped green pepper
¼ cup chopped sweet red pepper
2 medium tomatoes, seeded and chopped
¼ cup tomato and green chile cocktail
1 tablespoon lime juice
1 tablespoon chopped fresh cilantro
½ teaspoon dried whole oregano
¾ pound fresh lump crabmeat, drained and flaked
Fresh cilantro sprigs (optional)

Cut papayas in half lengthwise; scoop out and discard seeds. (Cut a thin slice from bottom of each papaya half, allowing it to sit flat, if necessary.) Place papaya halves, cut side up, on a lettuce-lined platter; set aside.

Coat a large nonstick skillet with cooking spray; add margarine. Place over medium heat until hot. Add green onions, green pepper, and red pepper; sauté until tender. Add tomato and next 4 ingredients; cook 2 minutes, stirring occasionally. Add crabmeat, stirring well; cook 2 minutes or until thoroughly heated. Mound ½ cup crab mixture into each papaya half using a slotted spoon. If desired, garnish each serving with fresh cilantro sprigs. Yield: 6 servings (149 calories per serving).

PROTEIN 13.0 / FAT 2.1 / CARBOHYDRATE 21.3 / CHOLESTEROL 30 / IRON 1.2 / SODIUM 620 / CALCIUM 88

POPPY SEED BOWKNOTS

1 cup all-purpose flour
2 teaspoons baking powder
2 teaspoons sugar
2 teaspoons poppy seeds
1 teaspoon grated lemon rind
¼ teaspoon salt
2 tablespoons unsalted margarine
¼ cup plus 2 tablespoons skim milk
¼ teaspoon lemon extract
2 teaspoons all-purpose flour
Vegetable cooking spray

Combine flour, baking powder, sugar, poppy seeds, grated lemon rind, and salt in a medium bowl; cut in margarine with a pastry blender until mixture resembles coarse meal. Add milk and lemon extract, stirring just until dry ingredients are moistened.

Sprinkle 2 teaspoons flour evenly over work surface. Turn dough out onto floured surface and knead 4 to 5 times. Roll dough to ½-inch thickness; cut with a 2½-inch doughnut cutter. Set centers aside. Twist each dough ring to form a figure 8.

Place bowknots and centers on a baking sheet that has been coated with cooking spray. Bake at 425° for 8 minutes or until golden brown. Let bowknots and centers cool slightly on wire racks. Serve warm. Yield: 6 bowknots and 6 centers (123 calories per bowknot and 18 calories per center).

PROTEIN 2.8 / FAT 4.1 / CARBOHYDRATE 18.3 / CHOLESTEROL 0 / IRON 0.7 / SODIUM 182 / CALCIUM 90

BRANDIED PEACH ICE MILK

3 cups vanilla ice milk, softened
2 tablespoons peach brandy
¼ teaspoon almond extract
1 tablespoon margarine
1 tablespoon sugar
2 tablespoons peach brandy
1½ cups frozen sliced peaches, thawed
¼ teaspoon almond extract

Combine ice milk, 2 tablespoons brandy, and ¼ teaspoon almond extract in a medium bowl, stirring until smooth. Spoon mixture into a freezer container; cover and freeze until firm.

Melt margarine in a medium skillet; add sugar, and cook over medium heat until mixture is bubbly. Add 2 tablespoons brandy and sliced peaches; cook 3 minutes or until peaches are tender, stirring occasionally. Remove mixture from heat; stir in ¼ teaspoon almond extract. Cover and chill.

To serve, scoop ½ cup ice milk mixture into individual dessert dishes. Top each serving with ¼ cup peach sauce. Yield: 6 servings (173 calories per serving).

PROTEIN 3.0 / FAT 4.8 / CARBOHYDRATE 25.6 / CHOLESTEROL 9 / IRON 0.2 / SODIUM 75 / CALCIUM 91

Blintzes For Brunch

Lasagna Blintzes
Fruited Ham Kabobs
Almond Crisps
Morning Milk Punch

Serves 6
Total calories per serving: 545

When your brunch seems to be more tired than traditional, try something new. Create blintzes by marrying two compatible foods—pasta and cheese. Top Lasagna Blintzes with a sweet cherry sauce. Skewer marinated ham, baby prunes, mandarin oranges, and green pepper to create an easy and attractive addition to the brunch scene. Almond Crisps (two per serving) are a cross between a cracker and a bread, and are unbeatable alongside a cup of brandy-flavored Morning Milk Punch.

Lasagna Blintzes and Fruited Ham Kabobs lend a creative touch to the brunch scene.

LASAGNA BLINTZES

6 lasagna noodles, uncooked
1½ cups part-skim ricotta cheese
2 tablespoons sugar
1 teaspoon grated orange rind
¼ teaspoon orange extract
¼ teaspoon vanilla extract
Vegetable cooking spray
2 tablespoons sugar
2½ teaspoons cornstarch
1½ cups frozen sweet cherries, thawed
1 cup water
1 teaspoon vanilla extract

Cook noodles according to package directions, omitting salt and fat. Drain and set aside.
Combine cheese and next 4 ingredients in a small bowl, stirring well. Spread cheese mixture evenly on one side of lasagna noodles. Roll lasagna noodles up jellyroll fashion, beginning at narrow end. Arrange rolls, seam side down, in a 10- x 6- x 2-inch baking dish that has been coated with cooking spray. Cover and bake at 350° for 15 minutes or until thoroughly heated.
Combine 2 tablespoons sugar and cornstarch in a saucepan. Add cherries and water, stirring gently to combine. Cook over medium heat until mixture is thickened, stirring constantly. Remove from heat; stir in 1 teaspoon vanilla. Spoon sauce evenly over blintzes. Serve immediately. Yield: 6 servings (237 calories per serving).

PROTEIN 10.4 / FAT 5.5 / CARBOHYDRATE 36.0 / CHOLESTEROL 19 / IRON 1.1 / SODIUM 77 / CALCIUM 179

FRUITED HAM KABOBS

1 small green pepper, cut into 1-inch pieces
1 (¾-pound) slice lean cooked ham, cut into
   1-inch cubes
1 (10¼-ounce) can unsweetened mandarin
   oranges, drained
12 dried pitted baby prunes
¼ cup unsweetened orange juice
1 teaspoon reduced-sodium soy sauce
⅛ teaspoon ground cinnamon
Dash of garlic powder

Parboil green pepper pieces 3 to 5 minutes; drain and let cool.

Alternately thread green pepper pieces, ham cubes, orange segments, and prunes on 6 (12-inch) wooden skewers. Place kabobs in a 13- x 9- x 2-inch baking dish. Combine orange juice and remaining ingredients, stirring well. Pour marinade mixture over kabobs. Cover and marinate in refrigerator 2 hours.

Bake, uncovered, at 350° for 15 minutes or until thoroughly heated. Yield: 6 servings (109 calories per serving).

PROTEIN 11.2 / FAT 3.2 / CARBOHYDRATE 9.7 / CHOLESTEROL 35 / IRON 0.9 / SODIUM 836 / CALCIUM 10

ALMOND CRISPS

3 cups sifted cake flour, divided
1 tablespoon baking powder
½ cup plain nonfat yogurt
2 eggs
¼ cup sugar
¼ cup firmly packed brown sugar
3 tablespoons vegetable oil
2 teaspoons almond extract
1 teaspoon vanilla extract
1 teaspoon lemon juice
½ cup sliced blanched almonds
Vegetable cooking spray

Combine 2¾ cups flour and baking powder in a small bowl; set aside. Combine yogurt and next 7 ingredients in a large bowl; beat well at medium speed of an electric mixer. Add dry ingredients to yogurt mixture, mixing well. Dredge almonds in remaining ¼ cup flour. Add almonds to dough, stirring well.

Shape dough into three 8-inch rolls. Place rolls 4 inches apart on a baking sheet that has been coated with cooking spray. Flatten rolls to ½-inch thickness. Bake at 350° for 15 minutes. Remove from oven; let cool slightly on baking sheet. Cut rolls into ¾-inch slices; arrange slices, cut side down, on baking sheets that have been coated with cooking spray. Bake at 350° for an additional 12 minutes or until slices are lightly browned, turning slices halfway through baking time. Cool on wire racks. Yield: 3 dozen (66 calories each).

PROTEIN 1.4 / FAT 2.3 / CARBOHYDRATE 9.9 / CHOLESTEROL 11 / IRON 0.2 / SODIUM 32 / CALCIUM 30

MORNING MILK PUNCH

3 cups strong, hot coffee
1 tablespoon plus 1½ teaspoons sugar
3 cups skim milk
1 tablespoon brandy extract

Combine coffee and sugar, stirring until sugar dissolves. Let cool. Stir in milk and brandy extract. Chill thoroughly. Serve over ice. Yield: 6 servings (67 calories per 1-cup serving).

PROTEIN 4.3 / FAT 0.2 / CARBOHYDRATE 9.5 / CHOLESTEROL 2 / IRON 0.5 / SODIUM 66 / CALCIUM 153

 FOOD SAFETY TIP FOR HAM

Fully cooked hams, now a staple in supermarket refrigerator cases, are a boon to the busy cook. In seconds, they transfer right from package to serving plate, all with a minimum of fuss. But if you decide to heat a precooked ham before serving, do so with caution, say food experts. Bacteria from your hands can easily be transmitted to the ham during unwrapping. Warming the meat just a little bit does nothing to kill these bacteria. In fact, lukewarm temperatures create a perfect environment for bacteria to grow and multiply. In other words, the risk for food poisoning increases when a precooked ham isn't heated thoroughly. To play it safe, either serve precooked ham cold right from the refrigerator or heat it to an internal temperature of 170° before serving. That way you'll be sure it's safe.

Christmas Morning Brunch

The allure of Christmas lies in its magical blend of family, food, and unexpected surprises. Begin the day with a delightful brunch featuring Clam Bisque Florentine. It has the rich flavor of a traditional bisque, but the fat content is greatly reduced. Ribbons of fresh spinach are stirred into the bisque during the last few minutes of cooking time, giving a flavorful and festive touch.

You will have to look twice at the Artichoke-Mushroom Quiche to discover the secret to its crisp brown crust—minced fresh mushrooms mixed with breadcrumbs and spices. The filling is flavored with a combination of three low-fat cheeses. Each serving of Christmas Aspic is topped with a dollop of creamy Avocado Dressing. Pumpkin Muffins (one per serving) and Cranberry-Lime Jam use traditional holiday ingredients to produce a high-fiber, low-fat muffin and low-sugar jam. Top each muffin with 1 tablespoon of glistening jam, thick with cranberries and tartly flavored with fresh lime. Save any remaining muffins and jam for a breakfast treat the next day.

Clam Bisque Florentine
Artichoke-Mushroom Quiche
Christmas Aspic with Avocado Dressing
Cranberry-Lime Jam
Pumpkin Muffins

Serves 6
Total calories per serving: 423

(Clockwise from bottom): Artichoke-Mushroom Quiche, Cranberry-Lime Jam, Pumpkin Muffins, and Christmas Aspic.

CLAM BISQUE FLORENTINE

2 (6½-ounce) cans minced clams, undrained
2½ cups water
1 tablespoon chicken-flavored bouillon granules
1 bay leaf
⅛ teaspoon garlic powder
1 (12-ounce) can evaporated skimmed milk
½ cup sliced fresh spinach leaves

Drain clams, reserving ½ cup liquid. Set clams and ½ cup liquid aside.

Combine remaining clam liquid, water, and next 3 ingredients in a medium saucepan; bring to a boil. Cover, reduce heat, and simmer 15 minutes. Remove and discard bay leaf. Stir in clams, milk, and spinach. Simmer, uncovered, 5 minutes or until spinach wilts. Yield: 4½ cups (82 calories per ¾-cup serving).

PROTEIN 10.1 / FAT 1.1 / CARBOHYDRATE 7.9 / CHOLESTEROL 17 / IRON 6.2 / SODIUM 543 / CALCIUM 189

KUDOS FOR COPPER

While there is no RDA for copper, there probably should be. According to research, this trace mineral is critical to health for two distinctly different reasons. First, copper is a key element in heart health. Several of the enzymes needed to keep the heart functioning properly contain copper as one of their main ingredients. Second, studies show that a deficiency of copper in the diet can lead to a rise in blood cholesterol levels.

Although the research is preliminary, scientists have found a connection between diets low in copper and poor sleep quality. Health experts estimate that between 2 to 3 milligrams of this mineral are needed every day. Most Americans, however, fall quite short of these minimal needs.

Still, that's no reason to panic. A wide assortment of foods contain copper: shellfish, nuts, dried beans, and organ meats such as liver. What's more, food is a safe copper source while supplements can be risky, especially since scientists have not established a safe requirement. If taken in too large a dose, copper can be toxic. Moreover, extra-large doses of the nutrient tend to upset the balance of other trace minerals. For example, excess copper interferes with the absorption of both iron and zinc. This is all the more reason why scientists recommend that food be your copper connection.

ARTICHOKE-MUSHROOM QUICHE

1 (9-ounce) package frozen artichoke hearts
2 tablespoons commercial reduced-calorie Italian dressing
½ pound fresh mushrooms
Vegetable cooking spray
½ cup fine, dry breadcrumbs
½ teaspoon paprika
⅛ teaspoon garlic powder
⅛ teaspoon salt
¼ cup (1 ounce) shredded 40% less-fat Cheddar cheese
¼ cup (1 ounce) shredded part-skim mozzarella cheese
1 cup skim milk
2 eggs, beaten
⅛ teaspoon ground white pepper
2 tablespoons grated Parmesan cheese
Dash of ground red pepper

Cook artichoke hearts according to package directions, omitting salt. Drain well; press artichoke hearts between paper towels to remove excess moisture. Postion knife blade in food processor bowl; add artichoke hearts. Top with cover, and process until finely chopped. Combine artichoke hearts and dressing in a bowl, stirring well. Cover and chill at least 3 hours.

Position knife blade in food processor bowl; add mushrooms. Top with cover, and process until minced. Coat a nonstick skillet with cooking spray; place over medium heat until hot. Add mushrooms; sauté 15 minutes or until liquid evaporates, stirring frequently. Remove from heat; stir in breadcrumbs and next 3 ingredients. Firmly press mushroom mixture evenly over bottom and up sides of a 9-inch pieplate that has been coated with cooking spray. Bake at 350° for 8 to 10 minutes or until dry.

Spoon artichoke mixture into mushroom shell; spread evenly. Sprinkle shredded cheeses evenly over artichoke mixture. Combine milk, eggs, and white pepper. Pour milk mixture over artichoke-cheese mixture. Sprinkle Parmesan cheese and red pepper evenly over milk mixture. Bake at 350° for 35 minutes or until set. Let stand 10 minutes before serving. Yield: 6 servings (137 calories per serving).

PROTEIN 9.8 / FAT 4.8 / CARBOHYDRATE 15.0 / CHOLESTEROL 72 / IRON 1.4 / SODIUM 300 / CALCIUM 171

CHRISTMAS ASPIC WITH AVOCADO DRESSING

1 envelope unflavored gelatin
1 cup no-salt-added tomato juice
1 cup tomato and green chile cocktail
¼ cup peeled, seeded, and chopped tomato
3 tablespoons seeded and finely chopped cucumber
3 tablespoons finely chopped celery
Vegetable cooking spray
Lettuce leaves (optional)
Avocado Dressing

Sprinkle gelatin over tomato juice and tomato and green chile cocktail in a nonaluminum saucepan; let stand 1 minute. Cook over low heat, stirring until gelatin dissolves. Chill until the consistency of unbeaten egg white.

Add tomato, cucumber, and celery to gelatin mixture, stirring gently to combine. Spoon mixture into a 2-cup mold that has been coated with cooking spray. Cover and chill until firm. Unmold aspic onto lettuce leaves, if desired. Top each serving with 1 tablespoon plus 1 teaspoon Avocado Dressing. Yield: 6 servings (62 calories per serving).

Avocado Dressing:

½ medium avocado, peeled and coarsely chopped
2 tablespoons plain nonfat yogurt
2 tablespoons low-fat sour cream
2 teaspoons lime juice
¼ teaspoon ground red pepper
⅛ teaspoon garlic powder

Combine all ingredients in container of an electric blender or food processor; top with cover, and process until smooth. Cover and chill thoroughly. Yield: ½ cup.

PROTEIN 2.6 / FAT 3.3 / CARBOHYDRATE 6.5 / CHOLESTEROL 2 / IRON 0.4 / SODIUM 154 / CALCIUM 20

CRANBERRY-LIME JAM

1 cup fresh or frozen cranberries, thawed
¼ cup plus 2 tablespoons sugar
¼ cup cranberry juice cocktail
2 tablespoons lime juice
1 teaspoon grated lime rind

Combine all ingredients in a medium saucepan; bring to a boil over medium heat. Cover, reduce heat, and simmer 15 minutes or until cranberry skins pop and mixture thickens. Chill thoroughly. Stir before serving. Yield: ¾ cup (32 calories per tablespoon).

PROTEIN 0.0 / FAT 0.0 / CARBOHYDRATE 8.3 / CHOLESTEROL 0 / IRON 0.0 / SODIUM 0 / CALCIUM 1

PUMPKIN MUFFINS

1 cup all-purpose flour
1 cup whole wheat flour
2 teaspoons baking powder
½ teaspoon baking soda
¼ teaspoon salt
3 tablespoons brown sugar
¾ teaspoon ground cinnamon
¼ teaspoon ground nutmeg
Dash of ground mace
1 cup cooked, mashed pumpkin
½ cup skim milk
¼ cup vegetable oil
2 tablespoons reduced-calorie maple syrup
1 egg, beaten
¾ teaspoon maple flavoring
¼ cup chopped pecans, toasted
Vegetable cooking spray

Combine first 9 ingredients in a large bowl, stirring well. Make a well in center of mixture. Combine pumpkin, milk, oil, syrup, egg, and flavoring, stirring well. Add liquid ingredients to dry ingredients, stirring just until dry ingredients are moistened. Gently fold in pecans.

Spoon batter into muffin pans that have been coated with cooking spray, filling two-thirds full. Bake at 400° for 20 minutes or until lightly browned. Remove from pans immediately. Yield: 1½ dozen (110 calories each).

PROTEIN 2.5 / FAT 4.9 / CARBOHYDRATE 14.7 / CHOLESTEROL 11 / IRON 0.8 / SODIUM 102 / CALCIUM 46

Oriental Grilled Flank Steak (page 48) is a simple yet festive entrée when garnished with carrot and green onion bundles.

Speedy Salad Bar Supper

Gazpacho Pasta
Ginger-Berry Spinach Salad
Tangy French Bread
Sparkling Cantaloupe
Sherbet

Serves 6
Total calories per serving: 444

Try Gazpacho Pasta, Tangy French Bread, and Ginger-Berry Spinach Salad for a supper from the salad bar.

Stopping by the salad bar of the local grocery store has become a popular and convenient way to pick up a quick meal while out on the run. The preparation has been done for you, saving time that would normally be spent cutting and chopping vegetables and greens.

But why limit yourself to an ordinary salad? For a change of pace, use the variety of salad fixings from the supermarket to create a satisfying pasta supper. Gazpacho Pasta is a lively pasta dish made by sautéing vegetables that are commonly featured in salad bars. The mixture is spiked with a splash of dry vermouth for flavor. There are few calories contributed to the dish by the vermouth because its alcohol content is burned off during cooking. Toss the vegetable mixture with spaghetti and you have a speedy, main-dish meal.

For a different side salad combination, toss fresh spinach leaves with a creamy dressing made with fresh strawberries, low-fat cottage cheese, and ground ginger. Top the salad with a sprinkling of sunflower kernels just before serving.

To balance the meal, serve a slice of French bread topped with herbs and melted mozarella cheese. Conclude with a simple, refreshing dessert made with juicy chunks of cantaloupe, a scoop of lime sherbet, and sparkling mineral water.

GAZPACHO PASTA

6 ounces spaghetti, uncooked
Vegetable cooking spray
1 cup broccoli flowerets
1 cup thinly sliced carrots
1 cup sliced zucchini
¼ cup sliced onion
1 small sweet yellow pepper, cut into julienne strips
½ cup sliced cucumber
½ cup sliced fresh mushrooms
1 small tomato, cut into 8 wedges
2 tablespoons dry vermouth
¼ cup plus 2 tablespoons grated Parmesan cheese
1 tablespoon minced fresh parsley
¼ teaspoon sweet red pepper flakes

Cook pasta according to package directions, omitting salt and fat. Drain and set aside.

Coat a large nonstick skillet with cooking spray; place over medium heat until hot. Add broccoli and next 3 ingredients; sauté 4 minutes. Add pepper strips, cucumber, and mushrooms; sauté 4 minutes. Add pasta, tomato, and vermouth; toss gently. Cook until thoroughly heated. Sprinkle with cheese, parsley, and pepper flakes; toss gently. Serve immediately. Yield: 6 servings (159 calories per 1-cup serving).

PROTEIN 7.2 / FAT 2.3 / CARBOHYDRATE 28.0 / CHOLESTEROL 4 / IRON 1.7 / SODIUM 109 / CALCIUM 100

GINGER-BERRY SPINACH SALAD

1 cup sliced fresh strawberries
½ cup low-fat cottage cheese
½ teaspoon ground ginger
3 cups torn fresh spinach
3 cups torn iceberg lettuce
½ cup sliced celery
¼ cup unsalted sunflower kernels

Combine first 3 ingredients in container of an electric blender or food processor; top with cover, and process until smooth. Chill.

Place torn spinach, lettuce, and celery in a large bowl, tossing gently to combine. Pour dressing mixture over spinach mixture; sprinkle with sunflower kernels. Yield: 6 servings (65 calories per serving).

PROTEIN 4.7 / FAT 3.4 / CARBOHYDRATE 5.1 / CHOLESTEROL 1 / IRON 1.2 / SODIUM 102 / CALCIUM 49

TANGY FRENCH BREAD

6 (1-ounce) slices French bread, toasted
2 tablespoons commercial reduced-calorie Italian dressing
½ cup (2 ounces) shredded part-skim mozzarella cheese
1 tablespoon minced fresh parsley
2 teaspoons minced fresh basil

Place bread slices on a broiler rack. Brush top side of each bread slice lightly with salad dressing. Sprinkle cheese, parsley, and basil evenly over bread slices. Broil 6 inches from heat until cheese melts. Serve immediately. Yield: 6 servings (122 calories per serving).

PROTEIN 5.3 / FAT 2.5 / CARBOHYDRATE 19.1 / CHOLESTEROL 7 / IRON 0.8 / SODIUM 281 / CALCIUM 77

 ## IT'S NOT WHEN YOU EAT THAT MATTERS

Contrary to popular belief, food eaten late at night is not more fattening than food eaten earlier. A piece of chocolate cake has the same number of calories whether you eat it at lunch or during the late night news. In fact, when you eat probably has little bearing on whether your body converts food to fat. How much you eat is what really counts. If you eat more calories than you expend in one day, the extra energy will be stored as fat. That you can count on.

SPARKLING CANTALOUPE SHERBET

3 cups cubed cantaloupe
1 (10-ounce) bottle lemon-lime flavored sparkling mineral water, chilled
2 cups lime sherbet
Fresh mint sprigs (optional)

Combine cantaloupe and water in a bowl; toss gently. Spoon ½ cup cantaloupe into individual dessert dishes using a slotted spoon; reserve water. Top each serving with ⅓ cup of sherbet. Spoon remaining mineral water evenly over sherbet. Garnish with fresh mint sprigs, if desired. Serve immediately. Yield: 6 servings (98 calories per serving).

PROTEIN 1.3 / FAT 0.8 / CARBOHYDRATE 22.7 / CHOLESTEROL 0 / IRON 0.2 / SODIUM 62 / CALCIUM 35

Clock-Watcher's Cuisine

After coming home from a hard day at work, preparing dinner is probably the last thing you want to think about. The question "What's for dinner?" ceases to be a problem with this menu because almost everything can be assembled ahead of time.

For a refreshingly different dessert idea, cut 1½-pound slices of watermelon, wrap them in plastic wrap, and pop them into the freezer when you get home

Crispy Wonton Skins
Oriental Grilled Flank Steak
Spinach-Rice Salad
Frozen Watermelon Slices
Peachy Tea

Serves 4
Total calories per serving: 615

from work. By the time you finish dinner, the watermelon will be icy and ready to enjoy.

While you make dinner, relax with a glass of the Peachy Tea and munch on Crispy Wonton Skins (six per person). The wonton skins have been prepared in advance and stored in an airtight container. Spinach-Rice Salad requires advance preparation so that it has time to chill. The flank steak that has been marinating overnight simply needs to be grilled before you can enjoy your Clock-Watcher's Cuisine.

CRISPY WONTON SKINS

1 teaspoon ground ginger
½ teaspoon onion powder
1 tablespoon water
2 teaspoons dark sesame oil
12 frozen wonton skins, thawed

Combine first 4 ingredients in a small bowl, stirring well; set aside.

Cut each wonton skin in half crosswise. Place wonton skins in an ungreased 15- x 10- x 1-inch jellyroll pan. Brush oil mixture evenly over wonton skins. Bake at 375° for 6 to 8 minutes or until crisp and lightly browned. Remove from jellyroll pan, and let cool completely on wire racks. Store in an airtight container. Yield: 2 dozen (8 calories each).

PROTEIN 0.2 / FAT 0.5 / CARBOHYDRATE 0.7 / CHOLESTEROL 4.0 / IRON 0.0 / SODIUM 9 / CALCIUM 1

ORIENTAL GRILLED FLANK STEAK

1 (1-pound) lean flank steak
⅓ cup dry sherry
3 tablespoons reduced-sodium soy sauce
1 teaspoon dark sesame oil
1 teaspoon dry mustard
½ teaspoon garlic powder
½ cup water
Vegetable cooking spray
2 medium zucchini (1 pound)

Trim fat from steak. Place steak in a large shallow dish. Combine sherry and next 4 ingredients; pour marinade mixture over steak. Cover and marinate in refrigerator 24 hours, turning occasionally. Remove steak from marinade, reserving marinade. Place marinade and water in a saucepan; bring to a boil. Reduce heat, and

cook 1 minute. Coat grill rack with cooking spray; place on grill over medium-hot coals. Place steak on rack, and cook 6 to 7 minutes on each side or to desired degree of doneness, basting frequently with marinade. Set aside; keep warm.

Slice zucchini lengthwise into ⅛-inch slices. Brush slices with marinade; grill over medium-hot coals 2 minutes on each side or until tender.

To serve, slice steak diagonally across grain into ¼-inch-thick slices. Arrange steak slices in center of serving platter. Arrange zucchini slices around steak. Serve immediately. Yield: 4 servings (241 calories per serving).

PROTEIN 23.7 / FAT 13.7 / CARBOHYDRATE 3.7 / CHOLESTEROL 61 / IRON 2.8 / SODIUM 189 / CALCIUM 24

A refreshing glass of Peachy Tea and Crispy Wonton Skins kick off the Clock-Watcher's Cuisine menu.

SPINACH-RICE SALAD

1¼ cups water
½ cup uncooked long-grain rice
2 tablespoons reduced-sodium soy sauce
1 tablespoon honey
1 tablespoon rice wine vinegar
½ teaspoon sweet red pepper flakes
1½ cups fresh spinach leaves, cut into thin strips
1½ cups thinly sliced fresh mushrooms
¼ cup thinly sliced celery
¼ cup thinly sliced green onions

Bring water to a boil in a small saucepan over medium heat; add rice. Cover, reduce heat, and simmer 20 minutes or until rice is tender and liquid is absorbed. Transfer rice to a large bowl, and let cool slightly.

Combine soy sauce, honey, vinegar, and red pepper flakes in a jar; cover tightly and shake vigorously. Pour soy sauce mixture over rice. Add spinach and remaining ingredients, tossing gently to combine. Cover and chill 8 hours. Yield: 4 servings (119 calories per 1-cup serving).

PROTEIN 3.3 / FAT 0.3 / CARBOHYDRATE 26.5 / CHOLESTEROL 0 / IRON 1.9 / SODIUM 324 / CALCIUM 34

PEACHY TEA

2½ cups peach nectar
2 cinnamon herb tea bags
2 (6½-ounce) bottles sparkling mineral water, chilled
Lemon wedges (optional)
Ground cinnamon (optional)

Combine peach nectar and herb tea bags in a glass jar; cover tightly and shake vigorously. Chill at least 8 hours.

Remove and discard tea bags. Gently stir mineral water into nectar mixture. Serve over ice. If desired, dip edges of lemon wedges into cinnamon, and place on rims of serving glasses. Yield: 4 cups (85 calories per 1-cup serving).

PROTEIN 0.4 / FAT 0.3 / CARBOHYDRATE 22.0 / CHOLESTEROL 0 / IRON 0.4 / SODIUM 32 / CALCIUM 13

Fresh cilantro and three colors of sweet pepper rings add a lively spark to a spicy Mexican Pizza.

Mexican Madness

This Mexican menu highlights south-of-the-border flavors without the usual calories from the traditionally, fat-laden fare. Now you can dance to the music of a mariachi band without feeling weighted down by dinner!

Begin by focusing your attention on a pizza with distinctive Mexican flair. The crispy pizza crust is enriched with yellow cornmeal and flavored with garlic and pepper. A rich tomato

**Mexican Pizza
Easy Ensalada
Angel Food Cake with
Caramel-Coffee Sauce**

Serves 6
Total calories per serving: 632

sauce is spread over the crust. The pizza is topped with a spicy ground beef mixture, sweet pepper rings, sliced olives, and a generous amount of shredded

Monterey Jack cheese.

As the pizza bakes, toss together the Easy Ensalada, a simple tossed salad dressed in a lively combination of reduced-calorie creamy cucumber dressing and picante sauce.

Rather than make a more time-consuming, traditional caramel flan for dessert, prepare a simple caramel-coffee sauce to drizzle over slices of angel food cake. Olé! Dinner is served!

MEXICAN PIZZA

¾ cup warm water (105° to 115°), divided
1 package dry yeast
1 teaspoon sugar
1½ cups all-purpose flour
½ cup yellow cornmeal
¼ teaspoon garlic powder
¼ teaspoon freshly ground pepper
Vegetable cooking spray
¾ pound lean ground beef
¼ cup chopped onion
1 jalapeño pepper, seeded and minced
½ teaspoon salt
¼ teaspoon ground cumin
1 cup no-salt-added tomato sauce
¾ cup seeded, chopped tomato
3 tablespoons minced fresh cilantro
1 medium-size sweet red, yellow, or green pepper, sliced into rings
3 tablespoons sliced ripe olives
1 cup (4 ounces) shredded Monterey Jack cheese

Combine ¼ cup water, yeast, and sugar in a small bowl; let stand 5 minutes.

Position knife blade in food processor bowl. Add flour, cornmeal, garlic powder, and freshly ground pepper; top with cover, and process 10 seconds. Add yeast mixture, and process until blended. With processor running, slowly add enough of remaining ½ cup water to form a ball that leaves sides of bowl; continue processing 15 to 20 seconds after dough forms a ball. Let stand 2 minutes. With processor running, add enough remaining water to make a soft, smooth dough; process 10 to 15 seconds.

Turn dough out onto a 15-inch pizza pan that has been coated with cooking spray. Shape dough into a ball; cover and let stand 10 minutes. Pat dough evenly into pan. Bake at 425° for 5 minutes; set aside.

Coat a large nonstick skillet with cooking spray; place over medium heat until hot. Add ground beef and next 4 ingredients; cook until meat is browned, stirring to crumble meat. Drain and pat dry with paper towels; set aside.

Combine tomato sauce, chopped tomato, and cilantro. Spread mixture over crust, leaving a ½-inch border around edges. Top with ground beef mixture, pepper rings, and olives. Sprinkle cheese evenly over pizza. Bake at 425° for 15 to 20 minutes or until crust is lightly browned and cheese melts. Yield: 6 servings (388 calories per serving).

PROTEIN 20.7 / FAT 15.0 / CARBOHYDRATE 41.6 / CHOLESTEROL 48 / IRON 3.3 / SODIUM 396 / CALCIUM 167

EASY ENSALADA

5 cups torn salad greens
½ cup chopped zucchini
½ cup frozen whole kernel corn, thawed and drained
½ cup diced sweet red pepper
¼ cup sliced green onions
½ cup commercial reduced-calorie creamy cucumber dressing
¼ cup commercial picante sauce

Combine first 5 ingredients in a large bowl, tossing gently; chill.

Combine dressing and picante sauce, stirring well. Cover dressing mixture and chill. To serve, pour dressing over salad mixture; toss gently to combine. Yield: 6 servings (60 calories per ½-cup serving).

PROTEIN 1.3 / FAT 3.0 / CARBOHYDRATE 7.0 / CHOLESTEROL 0 / IRON 0.8 / SODIUM 369 / CALCIUM 24

ANGEL FOOD CAKE WITH CARAMEL-COFFEE SAUCE

3 tablespoons brown sugar
1 tablespoon cornstarch
½ teaspoon instant espresso powder
1 cup skim milk
½ teaspoon vanilla extract
6 (2-ounce) slices commercial angel food cake

Combine brown sugar, cornstarch, and espresso powder in a small saucepan, stirring well. Gradually stir in milk; bring to a boil, stirring constantly. Remove from heat; stir in vanilla. Place cake slices on individual dessert plates. Top each serving with 2 tablespoons sauce. Serve immediately. Yield: 6 servings (184 calories per serving).

PROTEIN 4.6 / FAT 0.2 / CARBOHYDRATE 41.3 / CHOLESTEROL 1 / IRON 0.3 / SODIUM 105 / CALCIUM 108

Enjoy Easy Tomato-Bean Soup, Hot Turkey Sandwiches, Raspberry Fudge Brownies, and Kahlúa Cider fireside.

Fireside Fare

When it's cold and frosty outdoors, who can resist the lure of a crackling fire? When you feel the pull to escape the kitchen and settle in front of the fire's warm glow, don't hesitate for a moment. But before you leave the kitchen, make our quick and easy supper to take with you. Start preparations with hearty mugfuls of Easy Tomato-Bean Soup. The aromatic combination of pinto beans and tomatoes is

**Easy Tomato-Bean Soup
Hot Turkey Sandwiches
Raspberry Fudge Brownies
Kahlúa Cider**

Serves 4
Total calories per serving: 648

perfect for a cold-weather supper, and is simple to prepare. Team the soup with tangy, open-faced Hot Turkey Sandwiches—a

great way to combine leftover turkey breast with a favorite winter fruit, the apple. A generous slice of fontina cheese is melted over each chewy, bagel-based sandwich. Complete the chill-chasing supper with decadent Raspberry Fudge Brownies (two per person). If you can't decide between cider or coffee to go with your dessert, try Kahlúa Cider—a beverage combining the best of both.

EASY TOMATO-BEAN SOUP

Vegetable cooking spray
½ cup chopped onion
1 tablespoon seeded, finely chopped jalapeño
    pepper
1 clove garlic, minced
1 (14½-ounce) can no-salt-added stewed tomatoes,
    undrained
1¼ cups water
1 (15-ounce) can pinto beans, drained
¼ teaspoon ground white pepper
1 tablespoon plus 1 teaspoon minced fresh parsley

Coat a nonstick skillet with cooking spray; place over medium-high heat until hot. Add onion, jalapeño pepper, and garlic; sauté until tender. Add tomatoes and next 3 ingredients; bring to a boil, stirring occasionally. Cover, reduce heat, and simmer 15 minutes. To serve, ladle into individual serving bowls. Sprinkle 1 teaspoon parsley over each serving. Yield: 4 cups (102 calories per 1-cup serving).

PROTEIN 4.6 / FAT 0.8 / CARBOHYDRATE 20.0 / CHOLESTEROL 0 /
IRON 1.6 / SODIUM 19 / CALCIUM 64

HOT TURKEY SANDWICHES

2 bagels, split crosswise
2 tablespoons plain low-fat yogurt
1 tablespoon minced fresh parsley
2 teaspoons Dijon mustard
½ teaspoon prepared horseradish
1 apple, cored and thinly sliced into 12 rings
4 (2-ounce) slices cooked turkey breast (skinned
    before cooking and cooked without salt)
4 (1-ounce) slices fontina cheese

Place bagels, cut side up, on an ungreased baking sheet. Broil 6 inches from heat 1 minute or until golden brown. Set aside.
Combine yogurt and next 3 ingredients in a small bowl. Spread yogurt mixture evenly over each bagel half. Place 3 apple rings and 1 slice of turkey over each bagel half. Top each slice of turkey with 1 slice of cheese. Broil 6 inches from heat 5 minutes or until cheese melts. Yield: 4 servings (314 calories per serving).

PROTEIN 28.2 / FAT 10.6 / CARBOHYDRATE 25.4 / CHOLESTEROL 80 /
IRON 1.9 / SODIUM 231 / CALCIUM 194

RASPBERRY FUDGE BROWNIES

1 (10-ounce) package frozen raspberries in light
    syrup, thawed and undrained
¼ cup plus 2 tablespoons unsalted margarine
¼ cup plus 2 tablespoons unsweetened cocoa
⅔ cup sugar
2 eggs, beaten
½ teaspoon vanilla extract
½ cup all-purpose flour
⅛ teaspoon salt
Vegetable cooking spray

Drain raspberries, reserving 3 tablespoons juice. Set raspberries and juice aside.
Combine margarine and cocoa in a large saucepan. Cook over low heat, stirring constantly, until margarine melts and mixture becomes smooth. Remove from heat; let cool slightly. Add sugar, eggs, and vanilla to cocoa mixture, stirring well to combine. Stir in 3 tablespoons reserved raspberry juice. Combine flour and salt; add flour mixture to cocoa mixture, stirring well to combine. Gently fold raspberries into cocoa mixture.
Spoon batter into an 8-inch square baking pan that has been coated with cooking spray. Bake at 350° for 20 minutes or until a wooden pick inserted in center comes out clean. Let brownies cool completely; cut into 2-inch squares. Cut squares in half to form triangles. Yield: 32 brownies (61 calories each).

PROTEIN 1.0 / FAT 2.6 / CARBOHYDRATE 8.2 / CHOLESTEROL 13 /
IRON 0.4 / SODIUM 14 / CALCIUM 6

KAHLÚA CIDER

3 cups unsweetened apple cider
2 tablespoons Kahlúa or other coffee-flavored
    liqueur
4 (3-inch) sticks cinnamon

Place apple cider in a large saucepan; bring to a boil over medium heat. Remove from heat, and stir in Kahlúa. Pour cider into mugs; stir each serving with a cinnamon stick. Serve immediately. Yield: 3 cups (110 calories per ¾-cup serving).

PROTEIN 0.1 / FAT 0.2 / CARBOHYDRATE 23.8 / CHOLESTEROL 0 /
IRON 0.7 / SODIUM 6 / CALCIUM 13

Sunset Supper

When the sun hangs low in the western sky, don't let the thought of tackling dinner preparation destroy the peaceful feeling that such a beautiful view can inspire. Plan your time in the kitchen in advance, and these dishes will come together with relative ease within an hour.

Prepare the Fresh Fruit Medley as early as possible so that the fresh orange, pear, apple, grape, and strawberry mixture can fully absorb the flavor of the brandy while chilling.

Broiled Lamb Chops with Rosemary Sauce
Zucchini Toss
Mushroom Rice
Commercial Hard Roll
Fresh Fruit Medley

Serves 6
Total calories per serving: 601

Closer to mealtime, start cooking the rice, prepare the lamb chops for broiling, and make the colorful Zucchini Toss.

While the lamb chops are cooking, complete the Mushroom Rice, and pull together a simple Rosemary Sauce to complement the lamb entrée. Accompany each satisfying serving with a crusty hard roll spread with 1 teaspoon margarine.

For an appetizing presentation, place the lamb chops on beds of rice and drizzle with Rosemary Sauce. Then, if desired, garnish each serving with a fresh sprig of rosemary or thyme.

BROILED LAMB CHOPS WITH ROSEMARY SAUCE

Vegetable cooking spray
1 tablespoon minced green onions
2 teaspoons minced fresh rosemary
3 tablespoons dry vermouth
¾ cup water
½ teaspoon beef-flavored bouillon granules
¾ cup evaporated skimmed milk
2 teaspoons cornstarch
6 (6-ounce) lean lamb loin chops (1-inch thick)
½ teaspoon cracked pepper
Fresh rosemary sprigs (optional)

Coat a small nonstick skillet with cooking spray; place over medium heat until hot. Add onions and rosemary, and sauté 3 minutes. Stir in vermouth, and continue cooking until liquid evaporates. Add water and bouillon granules; bring mixture to a boil over medium heat, and cook 4 minutes, stirring occasionally. Combine milk and cornstarch, stirring well. Gradually add milk mixture to bouillon mixture, stirring well; cook until slightly thickened. Reduce heat, and keep warm.

Sprinkle lamb chops evenly with cracked pepper. Place chops on rack of a broiler pan that has been coated with cooking spray. Broil chops 4 inches from heat 5 to 6 minutes on each side or to desired degree of doneness. To serve, spoon 2 tablespoons sauce over each lamb chop. Garnish each serving with fresh rosemary sprigs, if desired. Yield: 6 servings (189 calories per serving).

PROTEIN 26.5 / FAT 6.3 / CARBOHYDRATE 4.9 / CHOLESTEROL 86 / IRON 1.9 / SODIUM 176 / CALCIUM 106

ZUCCHINI TOSS

Vegetable cooking spray
2 medium zucchini, cut into julienne strips
2 medium tomatoes, seeded and coarsely chopped
½ teaspoon minced fresh thyme
¼ teaspoon salt

Coat a large nonstick skillet with cooking spray; place over medium-high heat until hot. Add zucchini, and sauté 3 minutes or until crisp-tender. Add tomato, thyme, and salt, and sauté 1 minute or until thoroughly heated. Yield: 6 servings (19 calories per ½-cup serving).

PROTEIN 1.1 / FAT 0.3 / CARBOHYDRATE 4.0 / CHOLESTEROL 0 / IRON 0.5 / SODIUM 104 / CALCIUM 13

Try Broiled Lamb Chops with Rosemary Sauce, Zucchini Toss, and Mushroom Rice for a satisfying Sunset Supper.

MUSHROOM RICE

1½ cups water
½ teaspoon salt
½ teaspoon garlic powder
¾ cup uncooked long-grain rice
Vegetable cooking spray
1 (4-ounce) can mushroom stems and pieces, drained
½ cup finely chopped celery
1 tablespoon minced fresh parsley

Combine water, salt, and garlic powder in a heavy saucepan; bring to a boil, and add rice. Cover, reduce heat, and simmer 20 minutes or until rice is tender and liquid is absorbed.

Coat a nonstick skillet with cooking spray; place over medium-high heat until hot. Add mushrooms and celery; sauté 5 minutes. Stir in parsley. Add to rice mixture, tossing gently to combine. Serve immediately. Yield: 6 servings (90 calories per ½-cup serving).

PROTEIN 1.7 / FAT 0.2 / CARBOHYDRATE 19.8 / CHOLESTEROL 0 /
IRON 0.8 / SODIUM 206 / CALCIUM 12

FRESH FRUIT MEDLEY

3 medium navel oranges, peeled and sectioned
1 medium pear, cored and diced
1 medium-size Red Delicious apple, cored and diced
1 cup seedless green grapes, halved
1 cup sliced fresh strawberries
¼ cup unsweetened apple juice
2 tablespoons brandy
¼ cup honey toasted wheat germ

Place orange sections, pear, apple, grapes, strawberries, apple juice, and brandy in a large bowl, tossing gently to combine. Cover and chill thoroughly.

To serve, spoon 1 cup fruit mixture into individual dessert cups. Sprinkle 2 teaspoons honey toasted wheat germ over each serving. Yield: 6 servings (112 calories per serving)

PROTEIN 2.4 / FAT 1.1 / CARBOHYDRATE 23.7 / CHOLESTEROL 0 /
IRON 0.7 / SODIUM 2 / CALCIUM 34

Oven-Fried Fish, Apple-Orange Slaw, Easy Hush Puppies, and rainbow sherbet with Giant Gingersnaps.

Oven Fish Fry

The old-fashioned, calorie-laden fish fry need not become a thing of the past in today's nutrition-conscious world. By using the oven instead of the frying pan to prepare the fish, you'll be able to indulge in this family favorite without feeling guilty.

For crisp and delicious fish, simply dredge the fillets in a combination of unsalted soda cracker crumbs, Parmesan cheese, and lightly toasted sesame seeds. Drizzle the fillets with margarine, and bake at a high temperature for a short time. This method not

Oven-Fried Fish
Apple-Orange Slaw
Easy Hush Puppies
Commercial Rainbow Sherbet
Giant Gingersnaps

Serves 4
Total calories per serving: 581

only saves calories and time, but also cuts out the messy clean-up that follows deep-fat frying.

You won't hush after tasting our streamlined hush puppies!

Again, the oven is used in place of the deep-fat fryer to create Easy Hush Puppies (two per person). And no old-fashioned fish fry would be complete without coleslaw. Our version, Apple-Orange Slaw, is a tangy combination of cabbage, orange segments, and apple tossed with a yogurt-based dressing.

If desired, make the Giant Gingersnaps for dessert ahead of time, and freeze the extras. Serve the jumbo cookies (two per person) with a half-cup scoop of rainbow sherbet.

OVEN-FRIED FISH

1 egg white, lightly beaten
3 tablespoons frozen unsweetened grapefruit juice concentrate, thawed
¼ teaspoon hot sauce
10 soda crackers with unsalted tops
2 tablespoons grated Parmesan cheese
2 tablespoons sesame seeds, lightly toasted
4 grouper fillets (1 pound)
Vegetable cooking spray
1 tablespoon unsalted margarine, melted

Combine egg white, grapefruit juice concentrate, and hot sauce in a small bowl, stirring well. Set aside.

Crush crackers to make ⅓ cup crumbs. Combine crumbs, cheese, and sesame seeds in a small bowl, stirring well.

Dip fillets in egg white mixture; dredge in crumb mixture. Arrange fillets in an 8-inch square baking dish that has been coated with cooking spray.

Drizzle margarine evenly over fillets. Bake at 400° for 20 to 30 minutes or until fish flakes easily when tested with a fork. Yield: 4 servings (201 calories per serving).

PROTEIN 25.1 / FAT 7.7 / CARBOHYDRATE 6.8 / CHOLESTEROL 44 / IRON 1.9 / SODIUM 148 / CALCIUM 115

APPLE-ORANGE SLAW

1½ cups finely shredded cabbage
1 (10¼-ounce) can unsweetened mandarin oranges, drained
1 medium-size Red Delicious apple, cored and diced
½ cup vanilla low-fat yogurt
1 tablespoon brown sugar

Place first 3 ingredients in a medium bowl,

tossing gently to combine. Set aside.

Combine yogurt and brown sugar in a small bowl, stirring well. Add yogurt mixture to cabbage mixture, tossing gently to combine. Cover and chill 1 hour. Yield: 4 servings (76 calories per 1-cup serving).

PROTEIN 1.8 / FAT 0.5 / CARBOHYDRATE 16.7 / CHOLESTEROL 1 / IRON 0.4 / SODIUM 28 / CALCIUM 66

EASY HUSH PUPPIES

¼ cup yellow cornmeal
¼ cup all-purpose flour
¾ teaspoon baking powder
¼ teaspoon salt
¼ teaspoon sugar
¼ teaspoon garlic powder
¼ teaspoon celery flakes
⅛ teaspoon dried whole dillweed
⅛ teaspoon ground red pepper
1 egg white, beaten
2 tablespoons skim milk
2 teaspoons vegetable oil
2 tablespoons minced green onions
1 tablespoon minced fresh parsley
Vegetable cooking spray

Place first 9 ingredients in a large bowl, stirring well to combine. Combine beaten egg white, milk, and oil in a small bowl, stirring well. Add liquid ingredients to dry ingredients, stirring just until blended. Gently stir in green onions and parsley.

Spoon 1 tablespoon batter into each of eight miniature (1¾-inch) muffin pans that have been coated with cooking spray. Bake at 425° for 15 to 20 minutes or until hush puppies are golden brown. Immediately remove hush puppies from muffin pans, and serve warm. Yield: 8 hush puppies (43 calories each).

PROTEIN 1.4 / FAT 1.5 / CARBOHYDRATE 6.2 / CHOLESTEROL 0 / IRON 0.3 / SODIUM 110 / CALCIUM 27

GIANT GINGERSNAPS

3 tablespoons unsalted margarine, softened
⅓ cup sugar
1 egg white
2 tablespoons molasses
1 tablespoon unsweetened orange juice
1¾ cups plus 2 tablespoons all-purpose flour
½ teaspoon baking soda
⅛ teaspoon salt
¾ teaspoon ground ginger
½ teaspoon ground cinnamon
⅛ teaspoon ground cloves
2 teaspoons sugar
Vegetable cooking spray

Cream margarine; gradually add ⅓ cup sugar, beating well at medium speed of an electric mixer. Add egg white, mixing well. Add molasses and orange juice, mixing well. Combine flour and next 5 ingredients. Gradually add flour mixture to molasses mixture, mixing well.

Shape dough into 1-inch balls; roll balls in 2 teaspoons sugar. Place balls 4 inches apart on cookie sheets that have been coated with cooking spray. Flatten balls into 3-inch circles with the bottom of a glass. Bake at 350° for 6 to 8 minutes or until browned. Let cool slightly on cookie sheets. Gently remove cookies from cookie sheets, and cool completely on wire racks. Yield: 34 cookies (49 calories each).

PROTEIN 0.9 / FAT 1.1 / CARBOHYDRATE 8.6 / CHOLESTEROL 0 / IRON 0.3 / SODIUM 23 / CALCIUM 7

A Last-Minute Company Supper featuring (clockwise from bottom): Herbed Tomato Bouillon, Green Salad with Warm Brie Dressing, Lemony Baby Carrots, and Prize Chicken Cutlets (menu begins on page 69).

Microwave It Light

Race-Day Brunch

Frosty Mint Juleps
Ham and Grits Pie
Asparagus Salad with
Watercress Dressing
Double Strawberry Delight

Serves 6
Total calories per serving: 361

The Kentucky Derby is held the first Saturday of May each year. Fans of this spectacular racing event celebrate across the nation with their own version of Derby parties. This brunch menu gives you all of the traditional flavor of the hoopla as well as a feel for the stately grace of this American tradition.

Certain foods are closely associated with the Derby, but none more so than Frosty Mint Juleps. Country Ham and Grits Pie contains two favorite Kentucky foods. Ham gives zesty flavor to this quiche-like dish, and the grits, long a Southern favorite, provide a very mild flavor.

Springtime in Kentucky means fresh asparagus. The asparagus is chilled and arranged over tender Bibb lettuce, which is traditional

Frosty Mint Juleps, made in an electric blender, get a Race-Day Brunch off to a good start.

Kentucky fare. It was first grown in 1870 by Major Jack Bibb of Frankfort, Kentucky. Fresh strawberries are a Derby must. Double

Strawberry Delight features a strawberry sauce poured over succulent whole berries, then topped with toasted almonds.

FROSTY MINT JULEPS

3¼ cups water
1½ cups loosely packed fresh mint sprigs
¾ cup bourbon
¼ cup sifted powdered sugar
Fresh mint sprigs (optional)

Combine first 4 ingredients in container of an electric blender; top with cover, and process until smooth. Cover and chill at least 8 hours. Strain mixture into a large pitcher, discarding mint sprigs. To serve, fill glasses with crushed ice; add bourbon mixture. Garnish each serving with fresh mint sprigs, if desired. Yield: 4 cups (90 calories per ⅔-cup serving).

PROTEIN 0.2 / FAT 0.0 / CARBOHYDRATE 5.5 / CHOLESTEROL 0 / IRON 0.4 / SODIUM 3 / CALCIUM 9

HAM AND GRITS PIE

⅓ cup quick-cooking grits, uncooked
1 cup hot water
1 cup minced lean cooked ham
¾ cup evaporated skimmed milk
½ cup (2 ounces) shredded 40% less-fat Cheddar
  cheese
3 eggs, beaten
3 tablespoons chopped fresh chives
¼ teaspoon garlic powder
¼ teaspoon dry mustard
¼ teaspoon hot sauce
Vegetable cooking spray
½ cup whole wheat flakes cereal, crushed
½ teaspoon paprika

Combine grits and water in a 2-quart casserole. Microwave, uncovered, at HIGH for 5 minutes, stirring after 3½ minutes. Combine grits, ham, and next 7 ingredients in a bowl. Pour mixture into a 9-inch glass pieplate that has been coated with cooking spray. Sprinkle cereal and paprika over top of mixture. Place pieplate in microwave oven on an inverted saucer. Microwave, uncovered, at MEDIUM HIGH (70% power) for 13 to 15 minutes or just until center is set, giving dish a quarter-turn after every 4 minutes. Let stand 10 minutes. Yield: 6 servings (173 calories per serving).

PROTEIN 13.6 / FAT 5.4 / CARBOHYDRATE 18.8 / CHOLESTEROL 117 / IRON 1.2 / SODIUM 533 / CALCIUM 175

ASPARAGUS SALAD WITH WATERCRESS DRESSING

1½ pounds fresh asparagus spears
¼ cup water
6 Bibb lettuce leaves
Watercress Dressing
1 (4-ounce) jar chopped pimiento, drained

Snap off tough ends of asparagus. Remove scales from spears with a knife or vegetable peeler, if desired. Cut asparagus into 1½-inch pieces. Place in an 11- x 7- x 2-inch baking dish; add water. Cover with heavy-duty plastic wrap, and microwave at HIGH for 6 to 7 minutes or until crisp-tender; drain. Cover and chill.
Spoon ½ cup chilled asparagus onto each of 6 lettuce-lined salad plates. Spoon 2 tablespoons Watercress Dressing over each salad, reserving remaining dressing for other uses. Top each salad evenly with chopped pimiento. Yield: 6 servings (33 calories per serving).

Watercress Dressing:

½ cup plain nonfat yogurt
½ cup torn watercress
2 green onions, sliced
1 tablespoon chopped fresh parsley
1 tablespoon lemon juice
2 teaspoons Dijon mustard
¼ teaspoon salt
¼ teaspoon dried whole tarragon
⅛ teaspoon pepper

Combine all ingredients in container of an electric blender; top with cover, and process until smooth. Cover and chill. Yield: 1 cup.

PROTEIN 3.4 / FAT 0.3 / CARBOHYDRATE 5.4 / CHOLESTEROL 0 / IRON 0.9 / SODIUM 128 / CALCIUM 56

DOUBLE STRAWBERRY DELIGHT

4 cups fresh strawberries, hulled and divided
½ cup low-sugar strawberry spread
2 teaspoons cornstarch
2 tablespoons unsweetened orange juice
1 tablespoon grated orange rind
2 tablespoons sliced natural almonds, toasted

Place 1 cup strawberries in container of an electric blender; top with cover, and process until smooth. Combine puree and strawberry spread in a 1-quart baking dish. Microwave, uncovered, at HIGH for 2 to 3 minutes or until mixture begins to boil. Combine cornstarch and orange juice, stirring until smooth. Stir orange juice mixture into strawberry mixture. Microwave, uncovered, at HIGH for 2 minutes or until thickened; stir in orange rind. Cover and chill.
Place remaining 3 cups strawberries in a large bowl. Pour strawberry sauce over berries, tossing gently. To serve, spoon mixture evenly into individual dessert dishes. Sprinkle toasted almonds evenly over each serving. Serve immediately. Yield: 6 servings (65 calories per serving).

PROTEIN 1.1 / FAT 1.6 / CARBOHYDRATE 13.0 / CHOLESTEROL 0 / IRON 0.5 / SODIUM 1 / CALCIUM 22

Country Chicken with Creamy Gravy, Corn and Celery Mingle, Harvest Fruit Salad, and Raspberry Chiffon Pie.

The Heartland Table

Although American lifestyles have become busier than ever, we still enjoy sitting down to a home-cooked meal. This hunger for home cooking is bringing Midwestern cuisine center stage. Basic, wholesome menus featuring the flavors and foods grown and harvested in middle America are gaining in popularity.

This heartland menu uses typical Midwestern foods such as chicken, fresh corn, and ripe raspberries. Country Chicken with Creamy Gravy features skinned and boned chicken breast halves that have been dredged in a crispy cornflake crumb mixture

Country Chicken with
Creamy Gravy
Corn and Celery Mingle
Harvest Fruit Salad
Commercial Whole Wheat
Roll
Raspberry Chiffon Pie

Serves 6
Total calories per serving: 599

seasoned with thyme and poultry seasoning. The Creamy Gravy is made from no-salt-added chicken broth, evaporated skimmed milk, and a roux of flour and melted margarine, and is flavored with

dry sherry and chopped fresh chives. The sherry lends a mellow flavor to the gravy.

Corn and Celery Mingle is a medley of corn, celery, and green onions laced with hickory smoke-flavored almonds. Harvest Fruit Salad combines the sweetness of honey with plums, apples, and pears. Add one whole wheat dinner roll per person to balance the menu.

Fresh raspberries bring vibrant flavor and color to the Raspberry Chiffon Pie. The vanilla wafer crumb crust is easy to prepare in a matter of minutes using the microwave oven.

COUNTRY CHICKEN WITH CREAMY GRAVY

¾ cup whole grain corn flakes cereal, crushed
½ teaspoon paprika
½ teaspoon poultry seasoning
¼ teaspoon dried whole thyme
¼ teaspoon salt
¼ teaspoon pepper
2 tablespoons evaporated skimmed milk
6 (4-ounce) skinned, boned chicken breast halves
Creamy Gravy

Place cereal, paprika, poultry seasoning, thyme, salt, and pepper in a shallow dish, stirring well to combine. Pour milk into a shallow bowl. Dip chicken breast halves in milk; dredge in cereal mixture.

Place coated chicken breast halves in an 11- x 7- x 2-inch baking dish with thickest portions towards outside of dish. Cover with wax paper, and microwave at HIGH for 12 minutes or until chicken is done, rotating dish a half-turn every 4 minutes.

Remove chicken to a serving platter, and keep warm. Spoon Creamy Gravy evenly over

chicken. Serve immediately. Yield: 6 servings (218 calories per serving).

Creamy Gravy:

1 tablespoon margarine
1 tablespoon all-purpose flour
½ cup evaporated skimmed milk
¼ cup canned no-salt-added chicken broth, undiluted
1 teaspoon dry sherry
¼ teaspoon salt
¼ teaspoon ground white pepper
2 tablespoons chopped fresh chives

Place margarine in a 4-cup glass measure; microwave, uncovered, at HIGH for 30 seconds or until melted. Add flour; stir until smooth. Gradually add milk, broth, and sherry; stir until smooth. Microwave at HIGH for 3 to 5 minutes or until thickened, stirring once. Stir in salt, pepper, and chives. Serve immediately. Yield: 1 cup.

PROTEIN 29.7 / FAT 3.6 / CARBOHYDRATE 15.5 / CHOLESTEROL 67 / IRON 1.5 / SODIUM 416 / CALCIUM 100

CORN AND CELERY MINGLE

¼ cup sliced green onions
1 tablespoon reduced-calorie margarine
2 tablespoons chopped hickory smoke-flavored almonds, toasted
1 teaspoon lemon juice
1½ cups sliced celery
¼ cup water
1 (10-ounce) package frozen whole kernel corn

Place onions and margarine in a 2-cup glass measure. Cover with wax paper, and microwave at HIGH for 2 minutes, stirring once. Add almonds and lemon juice, stirring well; set aside.

Place celery and water in a 1½-quart casserole. Cover with heavy-duty plastic wrap, and microwave at HIGH for 3 minutes. Add corn; cover and microwave at HIGH for 6 to 7 minutes or until vegetables are crisp-tender, stirring once. Add reserved nut mixture, stirring well. Yield: 6 servings (77 calories per ½-cup serving).

PROTEIN 2.5 / FAT 3.2 / CARBOHYDRATE 11.6 / CHOLESTEROL 0 / IRON 0.5 / SODIUM 71 / CALCIUM 19

HARVEST FRUIT SALAD

¼ cup unsweetened orange juice
1 tablespoon honey
1 teaspoon grated orange rind
¼ teaspoon ground ginger
1 cup sliced fresh plums
1 cup coarsely chopped apple
1 cup coarsely chopped pear
Lettuce leaves (optional)

Combine first 4 ingredients in a jar. Cover tightly and shake vigorously. Chill dressing mixture thoroughly.

Place plums, apple, and pear in a large bowl; add dressing, tossing gently to combine. To serve, spoon fruit mixture onto individual lettuce-lined salad plates, if desired. Yield: 6 servings (64 calories per ½-cup serving).

PROTEIN 0.6 / FAT 0.4 / CARBOHYDRATE 16.0 / CHOLESTEROL 0 / IRON 0.3 / SODIUM 2 / CALCIUM 11

RASPBERRY CHIFFON PIE

2 tablespoons reduced-calorie margarine
1 cup crushed vanilla wafers
2 cups fresh raspberries
⅓ cup sugar
⅓ cup skim milk
2 egg yolks
1 envelope unflavored gelatin
½ teaspoon vanilla extract
¼ teaspoon salt
2 egg whites
¼ teaspoon cream of tartar
2 tablespoons sugar
Fresh raspberries (optional)
Fresh mint sprigs (optional)

Place margarine in a 9-inch pieplate. Microwave, uncovered, at HIGH for 30 seconds or until melted. Add crushed wafers, stirring well. Press mixture evenly over bottom and up sides of pieplate. Microwave, uncovered, at HIGH for 1 to 2 minutes or until firm, rotating pieplate a half-turn every 30 seconds. Set aside; let cool.

Place raspberries in container of an electric blender; top with cover, and process until smooth. Strain puree, discarding seeds. Combine puree, sugar, and next 5 ingredients in a 1½-quart baking dish. Microwave, uncovered, at MEDIUM (50% power) 4 to 6 minutes or until mixture boils, stirring every 2 minutes. Let stand 30 to 40 minutes or until mixture thickens slightly.

Beat egg whites (at room temperature) and cream of tartar at high speed of an electric mixer just until foamy. Gradually add 2 tablespoons sugar, 1 tablespoon at a time, beating until stiff peaks form and sugar dissolves (2 to 4 minutes). Gently fold raspberry mixture into meringue. Pour mixture into crust. Chill 2 hours or until firm. If desired, garnish with fresh raspberries and mint sprigs. Yield: 8 servings (168 calories per serving).

PROTEIN 3.6 / FAT 6.5 / CARBOHYDRATE 24.4 / CHOLESTEROL 68 / IRON 0.7 / SODIUM 185 / CALCIUM 33

TV Tailgate Party

Pepper-Cheese Spread
Celery Sticks
Turkey Joes
Hot Three-Bean Salad
Honey-Apple Crisp

Serves 8
Total calories per serving: 624

Whether you are wrapped up in the Super Bowl, World Series, or Olympics, it's great to have a meal that is quick and easy to prepare.

Start with Pepper-Cheese Spread made from low-fat cheese. Serve the spread on top of vegetables such as cucumber, summer squash, or celery sticks. (Menu calories were calculated to allow 3 tablespoons of spread and 6 celery sticks per person.)

Turkey Joes are a novel way to serve leftover turkey. Hot Three-Bean Salad is a colorful bean combination marinated in a vinaigrette dressing, then warmed in the microwave.

Nothing is more all-American than a TV Tailgate, and it is only

Colorful Hot Three-Bean Salad (page 66) is simple to prepare using the microwave oven.

fitting to serve an all-American dessert such as Honey-Apple Crisp. Freshly sliced apples,

golden raisins, honey, and orange rind make up the winning team of flavors.

PEPPER-CHEESE SPREAD

½ (8-ounce) package Neufchâtel cheese, softened
1 cup (4 ounces) shredded 40% less-fat Cheddar cheese
3 tablespoons light beer
⅓ cup chopped sweet red pepper
⅓ cup chopped green pepper
2 tablespoons grated onion
1 clove garlic, crushed
⅛ teaspoon hot sauce

Combine cheeses and beer in container of an electric blender; top with cover, and process until smooth. Transfer cheese mixture to a small bowl. Stir in sweet red pepper and remaining ingredients. Cover and chill thoroughly. Serve spread with fresh raw vegetables. Yield: 1½ cups (26 calories per tablespoon).

PROTEIN 1.4 / FAT 1.8 / CARBOHYDRATE 1.5 / CHOLESTEROL 4 / IRON 0.1 / SODIUM 44 / CALCIUM 37

TURKEY JOES

½ cup chopped onion
½ cup chopped celery
1 teaspoon vegetable oil
3 cups finely chopped cooked turkey (skinned before cooking and cooked without salt)
1 (8-ounce) can no-salt-added tomato sauce
1 (6-ounce) can no-salt-added tomato paste
2 tablespoons chopped fresh parsley
½ teaspoon chili powder
¼ teaspoon salt
¼ teaspoon ground cumin
⅛ teaspoon pepper
4 English muffins, split and toasted

Combine onion, celery, and oil in a 2-quart casserole. Cover with heavy-duty plastic wrap and microwave at HIGH for 2 to 3 minutes or until vegetables are tender. Drain vegetables, and pat dry with a paper towel. Wipe pan drippings from casserole with a paper towel.

Return vegetables to casserole; stir in turkey and next 7 ingredients. Cover and microwave at HIGH for 3 to 4 minutes or until thoroughly heated, stirring once. To serve, place ½ cup turkey mixture on each muffin half. Yield: 8 servings (215 calories per serving).

PROTEIN 19.5 / FAT 4.0 / CARBOHYDRATE 24.7 / CHOLESTEROL 40 / IRON 2.4 / SODIUM 302 / CALCIUM 81

HOT THREE-BEAN SALAD

1 (10-ounce) package frozen baby lima beans
½ cup water
1 (10-ounce) package frozen cut green beans
1 (15-ounce) can kidney beans, drained and rinsed
1 (4-ounce) jar sliced pimiento, drained
1 small purple onion, thinly sliced
½ cup cider vinegar
1 tablespoon sugar
2¾ teaspoons vegetable oil
½ teaspoon celery seeds
½ teaspoon dry mustard
¼ teaspoon salt
¼ teaspoon ground red pepper
¼ teaspoon paprika

Place lima beans in a 2-quart casserole; add water. Cover with wax paper, and microwave at HIGH for 10 minutes, stirring after 5 minutes. Add green beans; cover and microwave at HIGH for 6 minutes or until green beans are crisp-tender. Drain. Return beans to casserole; add kidney beans, pimiento, and sliced onion, stirring gently to combine.

Combine vinegar and remaining ingredients in a jar. Cover tightly and shake vigorously. Pour dressing mixture over vegetable mixture, stirring gently to combine. Cover and let stand at room temperature 30 minutes. Microwave at HIGH for 4 to 5 minutes or until thoroughly heated, stirring once. Serve warm. Yield: 8 servings (125 calories per ¾-cup serving).

PROTEIN 6.3 / FAT 2.0 / CARBOHYDRATE 21.9 / CHOLESTEROL 0 / IRON 2.7 / SODIUM 134 / CALCIUM 44

HONEY-APPLE CRISP

6 medium cooking apples, peeled, cored, and thinly sliced
¼ cup honey
2 tablespoons golden raisins
2 teaspoons grated orange rind
½ cup all-purpose flour
⅓ cup quick-cooking oats, uncooked
3 tablespoons brown sugar
½ teaspoon ground allspice
3 tablespoons reduced-calorie margarine

Combine apple slices, honey, raisins, and orange rind in a medium bowl; toss gently. Place apple mixture in an 8-inch square baking dish; set aside.

Combine flour, oats, brown sugar, and allspice in a small bowl; cut in margarine with a pastry blender until mixture resembles coarse meal. Spoon flour mixture evenly over apple mixture. Cover with heavy-duty plastic wrap, and microwave at HIGH for 8 to 10 minutes. Let stand 10 minutes. To serve, spoon crisp evenly into individual dessert dishes. Yield: 8 servings (200 calories per serving).

PROTEIN 2.2 / FAT 3.7 / CARBOHYDRATE 42.4 / CHOLESTEROL 0 / IRON 0.9 / SODIUM 44 / CALCIUM 16

Southwestern Dinner

Creamy Green Chile Soup
Barbecued Chicken
Cilantro-Seasoned Corn
Commercial Whole Wheat
Roll
Spiced Chocolate Sundaes

Serves 6
Total calories per serving: 646

The fresh herbs and spices commonly used in Southwestern cuisine are highlighted in this menu. Creamy Green Chili Soup is topped with shredded Cheddar cheese for an authentic touch. Barbecued Chicken (made with reduced-calorie catsup) is always popular. Use fresh corn on the cob to prepare Cilantro-Seasoned Corn. A whole wheat dinner roll and 1 teaspoon margarine per person balances the menu. Spiced Chocolate Sundaes give a spirited finale to the dinner.

Our Southwestern Dinner begins on a lively note with a hearty serving of Creamy Green Chile Soup.

CREAMY GREEN CHILE SOUP

1 cup chopped onion
1 cup chopped celery
2 cloves garlic, minced
1 tablespoon reduced-calorie margarine
3 tablespoons all-purpose flour
1 teaspoon chicken-flavored bouillon granules
2 cups hot water
2 cups skim milk
¼ teaspoon chili powder
⅛ teaspoon ground red pepper
2 (4-ounce) cans chopped green chiles, drained
¼ cup plus 2 tablespoons (1½ ounces) shredded
   40% less-fat Cheddar cheese

Combine onion, celery, garlic, and margarine in a 3-quart casserole. Cover with heavy-duty plastic wrap, and microwave at HIGH for 3 to 4 minutes or until crisp-tender. Add flour; stir well. Dissolve bouillon granules in hot water. Gradually add bouillon, milk, chili powder, and pepper to mixture, stirring well. Microwave at HIGH for 8 to 10 minutes or until slightly thickened, stirring every 3 minutes. Stir in chiles, and microwave at HIGH for 1 minute. Stir well before serving. To serve, ladle soup into individual serving bowls. Top each serving with 1 tablespoon cheese. Serve immediately. Yield: 6 cups (94 calories per 1-cup serving).

PROTEIN 5.1 / FAT 2.7 / CARBOHYDRATE 12.9 / CHOLESTEROL 2 / IRON 0.4 / SODIUM 282 / CALCIUM 166

BARBECUED CHICKEN

3 tablespoons brown sugar
3 tablespoons reduced-calorie catsup
2 tablespoons reduced-calorie chili sauce
1 tablespoon vinegar
2 teaspoons lemon juice
2 teaspoons low-sodium Worcestershire sauce
½ teaspoon salt
¼ teaspoon pepper
6 (4-ounce) skinned, boned chicken breast halves

Combine first 8 ingredients in a 2-cup glass measure. Microwave, uncovered, at HIGH for 1½ minutes or until mixture boils; set aside.

Arrange chicken in a 12- x 8- x 2-inch baking dish with thickest portions towards outside of dish. Cover with wax paper, and microwave at HIGH for 10 minutes. Drain off drippings, and rearrange chicken. Brush chicken with sauce. Cover and microwave at HIGH for 9 to 10 minutes or until chicken is done, rearranging chicken and brushing with sauce after 5 minutes. Let stand 2 minutes. Yield: 6 servings (163 calories per serving).

PROTEIN 25.7 / FAT 2.9 / CARBOHYDRATE 6.4 / CHOLESTEROL 70 / IRON 1.0 / SODIUM 270 / CALCIUM 18

CILANTRO-SEASONED CORN

3 cups fresh corn cut from cob
¼ cup water
¼ cup chopped fresh cilantro
¼ teaspoon salt
¼ teaspoon cumin seeds
⅛ teaspoon pepper
1 medium tomato, peeled, seeded,
    and chopped

Combine first 6 ingredients in a 2-quart baking dish; stir well. Cover with wax paper, and microwave at HIGH for 6 to 8 minutes. Stir in tomato; cover and microwave at HIGH for 1 to 2 minutes or until corn is tender. Yield: 6 servings (72 calories per ½-cup serving).

PROTEIN 2.8 / FAT 1.0 / CARBOHYDRATE 15.8 / CHOLESTEROL 0 / IRON 0.7 / SODIUM 111 / CALCIUM 9

SPICED CHOCOLATE SUNDAES

1 (8-ounce) carton plain nonfat yogurt
¼ cup sifted powdered sugar
3 tablespoons crème de cacao or other
    chocolate-flavored liqueur
½ teaspoon ground cinnamon
3 cups chocolate ice milk
Grated orange rind (optional)

Combine first 4 ingredients in a small bowl,

stirring with a wire whisk until well blended. Cover and chill.

Scoop ½ cup ice milk into each of 6 individual dessert dishes. Spoon sauce evenly over ice milk. Sprinkle grated orange rind over each serving, if desired. Yield: 6 servings (127 calories per ½-cup serving).

PROTEIN 3.3 / FAT 1.2 / CARBOHYDRATE 19.3 / CHOLESTEROL 1 / IRON 0.1 / SODIUM 29 / CALCIUM 78

MICROWAVE OVEN DRIES HERBS

Use the microwave oven to dry herbs quickly and easily. To dry fresh herbs in the microwave oven, first remove stems from cilantro, parsley, chives, basil, sage, and other herbs; rinse and pat dry. Then spread ½ to 1 cup of the rinsed herbs between two paper towels, and microwave at HIGH for 2 to 2½ minutes. Store dried herbs in airtight containers.

Last-Minute Company Dinner

Herbed Tomato Bouillon
Prize Chicken Cutlets
Lemony Baby Carrots
Green Salad with
Warm Brie Dressing
Ginger-Peach Parfaits
Blush Wine

Serves 4
Total calories per serving: 590

Unexpected dinner guests need not throw you into a panic-stricken spin towards the kitchen. Keep this quick and easy company dinner menu on file for last-minute occasions.

Get the meal off to a quick start with Herbed Tomato Bouillon, made from the basics on the spice rack and no-salt-added tomato juice. For your main course, serve Prize Chicken Cutlets prepared with chicken thighs that have been flavored with thyme and garlic.

Easily prepared Ginger-Peach Parfaits (page 70) look special enough to serve to company.

You'll find the microwave oven to be a real time saver when preparing Lemony Baby Carrots and Green Salad with Warm Brie Dressing. Offer your guests a favorite dry white wine (6 ounces per person) to complement the meal. Ginger-Peach Parfaits are a simple but special dessert appropriate for company.

HERBED TOMATO BOUILLON

1 teaspoon beef-flavored bouillon granules
1 cup hot water
3 cups no-salt-added tomato juice
2 tablespoons chopped fresh parsley
1 tablespoon lemon juice
1 teaspoon low-sodium Worcestershire sauce
½ teaspoon dried whole rosemary
¼ teaspoon dried whole thyme
¼ teaspoon pepper
Lemon slices (optional)

Dissolve bouillon granules in hot water; add tomato juice and next 6 ingredients, stirring well. Cover with heavy-duty plastic wrap, and microwave at HIGH for 3 to 5 minutes or until bouillon mixture is hot. To serve, ladle bouillon into soup bowls. Garnish each serving with a lemon slice, if desired. Yield: 4 cups (43 calories per 1-cup serving).

PROTEIN 1.9 / FAT 0.3 / CARBOHYDRATE 10.1 / CHOLESTEROL 0 / IRON 0.3 / SODIUM 262 / CALCIUM 7

PRIZE CHICKEN CUTLETS

4 (6-ounce) chicken thighs, skinned
    and boned
½ teaspoon dried whole thyme
¼ teaspoon garlic powder
¼ teaspoon salt
¼ teaspoon pepper
1 cup sliced fresh mushrooms
½ cup chopped sweet red pepper
½ cup sliced green onions
¼ cup Chablis or other dry white wine
2 tablespoons grated Parmesan cheese
Green onion fans (optional)

Place chicken thighs between 2 sheets of wax paper; flatten to ⅛-inch thickness using a meat mallet or rolling pin.

Combine thyme, garlic powder, salt, and pepper. Rub chicken on all sides with thyme mixture; let stand 5 minutes.

Arrange chicken thighs in a 1-quart casserole. Add mushrooms, sweet red pepper, green onions, and wine to chicken. Cover with heavy-duty plastic wrap and microwave at HIGH for 6 to 8 minutes or until chicken is done and vegetables are tender, rotating dish one-half turn after 3 minutes.

Remove chicken and vegetables to a serving platter. Sprinkle Parmesan cheese evenly over chicken. Garnish chicken with green onion fans, if desired. Yield: 4 servings (143 calories per serving).

PROTEIN 21.2 / FAT 4.8 / CARBOHYDRATE 3.1 / CHOLESTEROL 84 / IRON 2.0 / SODIUM 281 / CALCIUM 60

LEMONY BABY CARROTS

1 (16-ounce) package baby carrots, scraped
¼ cup water
1 tablespoon lemon juice
1 teaspoon grated lemon rind
½ teaspoon dried whole dillweed
¼ teaspoon ground white pepper
⅛ teaspoon chicken-flavored bouillon granules

Combine all ingredients in a 1½-quart casserole; stir well. Cover with heavy-duty plastic

wrap, and microwave at HIGH for 8 to 10 minutes or until crisp-tender, stirring after 4 minutes. Yield: 4 servings (37 calories per ½-cup serving).

PROTEIN 0.9 / FAT 0.2 / CARBOHYDRATE 8.8 / CHOLESTEROL 0 / IRON 0.5 / SODIUM 78 / CALCIUM 25

GREEN SALAD WITH WARM BRIE DRESSING

2 tablespoons coarsely chopped walnuts
1 ounce Brie cheese
1 cup torn Boston lettuce
1 cup torn romaine lettuce
⅓ cup commercial reduced-calorie Italian dressing

Spread walnuts in a 6-ounce custard cup. Microwave at HIGH for 3 to 4 minutes or until walnuts are lightly toasted, stirring after every minute. Set aside.

Remove rind from brie; cut into small pieces. Set aside. Place lettuce in a large bowl, tossing gently to combine. Arrange lettuce mixture evenly on individual salad plates. Set aside.

Place dressing in a 1-cup glass measure. Microwave, uncovered, at HIGH for 30 seconds or until thoroughly heated. Add brie, stirring until cheese melts. To serve, spoon dressing evenly over each salad. Top each serving with 1½ teaspoons chopped walnuts. Yield: 4 servings (60 calories per serving).

PROTEIN 2.8 / FAT 4.2 / CARBOHYDRATE 3.1 / CHOLESTEROL 7 / IRON 0.3 / SODIUM 227 / CALCIUM 21

GINGER-PEACH PARFAITS

2 cups vanilla ice milk
½ cup no-sugar-added peach conserve
1 tablespoon plus 1 teaspoon gingersnap crumbs

Spoon ¼ cup ice milk into each of 4 parfait glasses; top each serving with 2 tablespoons conserve. Spoon ¼ cup ice milk over each serving. Sprinkle 1 teaspoon gingersnap crumbs over each serving. Serve immediately. Yield: 4 servings (181 calories per serving).

PROTEIN 2.8 / FAT 3.3 / CARBOHYDRATE 34.6 / CHOLESTEROL 10 / IRON 0.3 / SODIUM 57 / CALCIUM 93

Indian Curry Feast

Curried Lamb and
Vegetable Medley
Savory Rice
Carrot-Mango Relish
Banana-Pineapple Frozen
Yogurt

Serves 6
Total calories per serving: 540

Curried Indian dishes demand that other foods on the menu be cool or bland. The Carrot-Mango Relish (¼ cup per person) and Savory Rice that accompany the curried lamb entrée help soothe the palate. To complete the feast, serve Banana-Pineapple Frozen Yogurt, and save remaining frozen yogurt and coconut for a snack.

Curried Lamb with Vegetables features a spicy flavor blend of coriander, cardamom, ginger, cumin, and curry.

CURRIED LAMB AND VEGETABLE MEDLEY

1½ pounds lean boneless lamb, cut into 1-inch
  cubes
½ cup chopped onion
1 tablespoon vegetable oil
1 clove garlic, minced
1 cup hot water
1 teaspoon minced fresh gingerroot
1 teaspoon chicken-flavored bouillon granules
1 teaspoon curry powder
½ teaspoon ground coriander
½ teaspoon dry mustard
½ teaspoon cumin seeds
¼ teaspoon ground cardamom
¼ teaspoon pepper
2 tablespoons water
2 teaspoons cornstarch
1 cup broccoli flowerets
1 sweet red pepper, cut into julienne strips
1 small yellow squash, cut into ¼-inch slices

Combine lamb, onion, oil, and garlic in a 3-quart baking dish. Cover with wax paper, and microwave at HIGH for 6 to 7 minutes or until meat is no longer pink, stirring every 2 minutes. Drain and pat dry with paper towels. Wipe pan drippings from dish with paper towels.

Return mixture to dish. Stir in 1 cup hot water and next 8 ingredients. Cover and microwave at MEDIUM (50% power) for 30 to 35 minutes, stirring twice. Combine 2 tablespoons water and cornstarch, stirring until smooth; stir into lamb mixture. Microwave at HIGH, uncovered, 2 to 3 minutes or until thickened, stirring once. Add broccoli, sweet red pepper, and squash. Cover and microwave at HIGH for 5 to 7 minutes or until vegetables are crisp-tender. Serve immediately. Yield: 6 servings (204 calories per serving).

PROTEIN 25.3 / FAT 8.7 / CARBOHYDRATE 5.4 / CHOLESTEROL 85 / IRON 2.6 / SODIUM 195 / CALCIUM 30

SAVORY RICE

1⅔ cups water
¼ cup grated onion
1 teaspoon margarine
¼ teaspoon salt
¼ teaspoon pepper
1½ cups uncooked instant rice
1 medium tomato, peeled, seeded, and chopped
2 tablespoons chopped fresh parsley
2 tablespoons unsalted sunflower kernels, toasted

Combine first 5 ingredients in a 2-quart casserole; stir in rice and tomato. Cover with heavy-duty plastic wrap, and microwave at HIGH for 8 to 10 minutes or until liquid is absorbed. Let stand 2 minutes. Fluff rice with a fork; sprinkle parsley and sunflower kernels over rice. Yield: 6 servings (130 calories per ½-cup serving).

PROTEIN 3.3 / FAT 3.1 / CARBOHYDRATE 22.4 / CHOLESTEROL 0 / IRON 1.3 / SODIUM 107 / CALCIUM 15

CARROT-MANGO RELISH

2 medium carrots, scraped and cut into ⅛-inch slices
¼ cup finely chopped onion
¼ cup unsweetened apple juice
¼ teaspoon ground cardamom
¼ teaspoon dry mustard
⅛ teaspoon ground red pepper
1 cup coarsely chopped mango
2 tablespoons raisins
1 tablespoon grated orange rind

Combine first 6 ingredients in a 1½-quart casserole. Cover with heavy-duty plastic wrap, and microwave at HIGH for 5 to 6 minutes. Add mango, raisins, and orange rind, stirring well. Cover and microwave at HIGH for 2 to 3 minutes or until carrots are tender. Let cool. Yield: 1½ cups (12 calories per tablespoon).

PROTEIN 0.2 / FAT 0.1 / CARBOHYDRATE 3.2 / CHOLESTEROL 0 / IRON 0.1 / SODIUM 2 / CALCIUM 4

BANANA-PINEAPPLE FROZEN YOGURT

2 (8-ounce) cartons vanilla low-fat yogurt
2 (8-ounce) cartons pineapple low-fat yogurt
1 cup mashed bananas
2 tablespoons crème de bananes or other banana-flavored liqueur
2 teaspoons lemon juice
½ teaspoon ground cinnamon
½ teaspoon ground nutmeg
¼ teaspoon ground ginger
1 tablespoon plus 2½ teaspoons unsweetened grated coconut, toasted

Place all ingredients except coconut in a large bowl, stirring well to combine. Pour yogurt mixture into freezer can of a hand-turned or electric freezer. Freeze according to manufacturer's instructions. To serve, scoop ½ cup frozen yogurt into individual dessert dishes. Top each serving of yogurt with ½ teaspoon coconut. Serve immediately. Yield: 5½ cups (157 calories per ½-cup serving).

PROTEIN 4.5 / FAT 1.9 / CARBOHYDRATE 31.5 / CHOLESTEROL 4 / IRON 0.3 / SODIUM 50 / CALCIUM 134

Cucumber and Watercress, Potted Shrimp, and Curried Chicken Sandwiches (page 88)—Tea Sandwiches in a Bread Bowl.

That's Entertaining

Elegant Autumn Dinner Party

Wild Mushroom Consommé
Burgundy Beef with Parslied Fettuccine
Plum-Wine Sorbet

Serves 8
Total calories per serving: 604

When the leaves begin turning color, kitchen inspirations turn to indoor entertaining. The first course of this elegant menu is Wild Mushroom Consommé, an aromatic, Asian-inspired broth. The centerpiece of the dinner is wonderful Burgundy Beef with Parslied Fettuccine. The stew is rich in vegetables: carrots, onions, artichoke hearts, and snow peas, all blanketed in a flavorful red wine broth and served on a bed of parslied fettuccine. The grand

Scoops of Plum-Wine Sorbet are elegantly garnished with champagne grapes and fresh mint sprigs.

finale, Plum-Wine Sorbet, can be served with a cluster of champagne grapes and fresh mint sprigs, if desired. The rich-tasting sorbet is definitely worth a little extra effort.

WILD MUSHROOM CONSOMMÉ

12 ounces fresh mushrooms, divided
6 (10½-ounce) cans no-salt-added chicken broth, undiluted
2 ounces dried porcini mushrooms
3 tablespoons minced shallots
1 ounce fresh gingerroot, peeled and sliced
¼ teaspoon salt
1 tablespoon dry sherry
1 teaspoon reduced-sodium soy sauce
1¾ ounces fresh enoki mushrooms
1 green onion, thinly sliced

Slice 4 ounces fresh mushrooms; set aside. Coarsely chop remaining 8 ounces fresh mushrooms; set aside.

Place chicken broth in a Dutch oven; bring to a boil. Add chopped fresh mushrooms, porcini mushrooms, shallots, gingerroot, and salt. Reduce heat, and simmer, uncovered, 30 minutes, stirring occasionally. Remove from heat. Strain mixture through a fine sieve; discard mushroom mixture. Return strained liquid to Dutch oven. Add sliced fresh mushrooms, stirring well. Cook over medium heat 5 minutes. Add sherry and soy sauce; cook 1 minute. To serve, ladle soup into individual serving bowls.

Top each serving evenly with enoki mushrooms and green onion slices. Yield: 6 cups (78 calories per ¾-cup serving).

PROTEIN 3.7 / FAT 2.1 / CARBOHYDRATE 9.2 / CHOLESTEROL 0 / IRON 0.8 / SODIUM 227 / CALCIUM 8

BURGUNDY BEEF WITH PARSLIED FETTUCCINE

2 pounds beef tenderloin
1 cup Burgundy or other dry red wine
2 tablespoons Cognac
1 tablespoon black peppercorns
2 bay leaves
1 teaspoon dried whole thyme
1 teaspoon Worcestershire sauce
Vegetable cooking spray
1 tablespoon olive oil
6 ounces pearl onions, peeled
1 cup canned low-sodium beef broth, undiluted
3 medium carrots, scraped and cut diagonally into
   ½-inch pieces
1 (9-ounce) package frozen artichoke hearts
½ pound fresh snow pea pods, trimmed
1 tablespoon cornstarch
1 tablespoon water
¼ teaspoon freshly ground pepper
4 cups hot cooked fettuccine (cooked without salt
   or fat)
1 tablespoon chopped fresh parsley

Trim fat from beef; cut beef into 1-inch cubes, and place in a large bowl. Combine wine and next 5 ingredients, stirring well; pour marinade mixture over beef. Cover and marinate in refrigerator 8 hours. Drain beef, reserving marinade. Set beef aside. Strain marinade, and set aside.

Coat a large nonstick skillet with cooking spray; add olive oil. Place over medium-high heat until hot. Add half the beef cubes, and cook 5 minutes or until browned, turning frequently. Remove beef from skillet, and set aside. Add remaining beef cubes to skillet, and cook until browned. Remove beef from skillet, and set aside.

Add onions to skillet, and sauté 5 minutes or until tender. Stir in reserved marinade and beef broth. Bring to a boil; reduce heat, and simmer, uncovered, 15 minutes. Add carrots, and cook 5 minutes. Add artichoke hearts, and cook 6 minutes. Add reserved beef cubes, and cook 5 minutes. Add snow peas, and cook 3 minutes or until crisp-tender. Combine cornstarch and water, stirring until smooth; stir cornstarch mixture into beef mixture. Add freshly ground pepper, stirring well to combine. Cook until vegetables and meat are tender, and mixture is slightly thickened.

Place fettuccine on a serving platter. Sprinkle parsley over fettuccine, and toss gently to combine. Top with beef mixture. Yield: 8 servings (334 calories per serving).

PROTEIN 28.9 / FAT 9.7 / CARBOHYDRATE 29.2 / CHOLESTEROL 70 / IRON 5.2 / SODIUM 94 / CALCIUM 52

PLUM-WINE SORBET

1 cup sugar
1 cup port wine
1½ pounds plums, pitted and halved
2 tablespoons lemon juice
Champagne grapes (optional)
Fresh mint sprigs (optional)

Combine sugar and wine in a medium saucepan. Bring to a boil; reduce heat, and simmer 5 minutes or until sugar dissolves, stirring occasionally. Remove from heat; let cool.

Position knife blade in food processor bowl; add plums and lemon juice. Top with cover, and process until smooth. Combine plum mixture and sugar syrup, stirring well. Pour mixture into an 8-inch square pan; freeze until almost firm. Break mixture into large pieces, and place in processor bowl; process until fluffy, but not thawed. Return mixture to pan; freeze until firm.

To serve, scoop sorbet into individual dessert bowls. If desired, garnish each serving with champagne grapes and fresh mint sprigs. Yield: 4 cups (192 calories per ½-cup serving).

PROTEIN 0.7 / FAT 0.5 / CARBOHYDRATE 39.9 / CHOLESTEROL 0 / IRON 0.2 / SODIUM 2 / CALCIUM 5

FINDING A NUTRITION EXPERT

The yes/no, on/off of nutrition advice can confuse even the most savvy eater. Obviously, sorting through all of the nutrition information available today is not an easy task. Because of the nature of science, research is bound to continue uncovering new information about nutrition. Therefore, your best source for accurate nutrition information is a registered dietitian (R.D.). One word of caution: the terms "nutritionist" and dietitian are not synonymous. Spot the real nutrition experts by the R.D. after their name.

A "Not-So-Traditional" Thanksgiving Dinner

We all look forward to our national celebration of food and abundance on Thanksgiving Day, but we may dread the guilty feelings that arise when we step on the scale the next day. This menu is the perfect antidote to the cycle of day-after remorse we often experience.

All of the traditional ingredients associated with Thanksgiving are included—turkey, pumpkin, and cranberries. However, these traditional holiday foods are presented in not-so-traditional guises and without the usual onslaught of calories.

Pumpkin appears as the first

Curried Pumpkin Soup
Turkey Breast with Wild Rice and Mushroom Stuffing
Carrot Puree
Cranberry Chutney
Apple Tart
White Wine

Serves 6
Total calories per serving: 723

course in a creamy, rich-tasting soup with a dash of curry. Lean turkey breast is boned and rolled

around a savory stuffing of wild rice and mushrooms. A sweet but tangy Cranberry Chutney is a perfect meal accompaniment (2 tablespoons per serving). Carrots are pureed without the usual additions of cream and butter. Instead, the richness comes from our homemade Light Fromage Blanc, a low-calorie substitute for cream. The Light Fromage Blanc can also be served as a topping for any fruit dessert such as Apple Tart, a perfect finish for a satisfying dinner. Serve a glass of dry white wine (6 ounces per person) to complement this not-so-traditional dinner.

The key to the striking appearance of the Apple Tart (page 78) lies in its simplicity.

CURRIED PUMPKIN SOUP

2 medium leeks
Vegetable cooking spray
1 tablespoon margarine
1 cup chopped onion
1 teaspoon curry powder
3½ cups canned low-sodium chicken broth, undiluted
1¼ cups canned pumpkin
1 bay leaf
½ teaspoon salt
¼ teaspoon ground white pepper
¾ cup skim milk
¼ cup Light Fromage Blanc (page 78)
Fresh parsley sprigs (optional)

Remove roots, tough outer leaves, and tops from leeks, leaving 2 inches of dark leaves. Slice leeks, and set aside.

Coat a large saucepan with cooking spray; add margarine. Place over low heat until margarine melts. Add sliced leeks, onion, and curry powder. Cover and cook 10 minutes or until vegetables are tender, stirring every 2 minutes. Add chicken broth and next 4 ingredients, stirring well. Bring to a boil; reduce heat, and simmer, uncovered, 20 minutes, stirring occasionally. Remove from heat, and let cool slightly. Remove and discard bay leaf.

Pour one-half of pumpkin mixture into container of an electric blender or food processor; top with cover, and process until smooth. Repeat procedure with remaining mixture. Return pumpkin mixture to saucepan.

Combine milk and Light Fromage Blanc in a small bowl; stir well. Add milk mixture to pumpkin mixture; stir well. Cook over low heat until thoroughly heated (do not boil). To serve, ladle soup into individual bowls. Garnish each serving with fresh parsley sprigs, if desired. Yield: 6 cups (90 calories per 1-cup serving).

PROTEIN 3.6 / FAT 2.5 / CARBOHYDRATE 12.6 / CHOLESTEROL 1 / IRON 1.5 / SODIUM 271 / CALCIUM 85

TURKEY BREAST WITH WILD RICE AND MUSHROOM STUFFING

1 (6-pound) whole turkey breast, boned and skinned
¼ teaspoon salt
⅛ teaspoon freshly ground pepper
Vegetable cooking spray
1 tablespoon margarine
1 cup chopped onion
1 cup chopped green onions
¾ cup canned low-sodium chicken broth, undiluted
¼ cup Madeira wine
3 cups cooked wild rice (cooked without salt or fat)
1 pound sliced fresh mushrooms
3 tablespoons chopped fresh parsley
½ teaspoon dried whole rosemary

Trim fat from turkey; remove tendons. Place turkey breast, boned side up, on heavy-duty plastic wrap. From center, slice horizontally through thickest part of each side almost to outer edge; flip cut piece over to enlarge breast. Place heavy-duty plastic wrap over turkey; flatten to ½-inch thickness using a meat mallet. (Place loose pieces of turkey over thin portions.) Sprinkle with salt and pepper; set aside.

Coat a nonstick skillet with cooking spray; add margarine. Place over medium heat until hot. Add onion and green onions; sauté until tender. Stir in broth and wine, cooking until liquid is absorbed. Combine onion mixture and rice in a bowl. Wipe skillet with a paper towel; coat with cooking spray. Place over medium heat until hot; add mushrooms, and sauté until liquid is evaporated. Stir in parsley and rosemary. Add to rice mixture, stirring well.

Spoon rice mixture in center of turkey breast, leaving a 2-inch border at sides; roll up jellyroll fashion, starting with short side. Tie turkey breast securely at 2-inch intervals with string. Place seam side down on a rack in a shallow roasting pan that has been coated with cooking spray. Insert meat thermometer. Bake, uncovered, at 350° for 1 hour or until meat thermometer registers 185°. Transfer turkey to a cutting board; remove string. Let stand 10 minutes before slicing. Yield: 12 servings (222 calories per serving).

PROTEIN 36.3 / FAT 2.7 / CARBOHYDRATE 11.8 / CHOLESTEROL 94 / IRON 2.9 / SODIUM 128 / CALCIUM 29

CARROT PUREE

1½ pounds carrots, scraped and sliced
¾ cup skim milk
3 tablespoons Light Fromage Blanc (recipe below)
2 teaspoons minced fresh chives
⅛ teaspoon salt
Dash of ground white pepper

Place carrots in a medium saucepan; add water to cover. Bring to a boil; cover, reduce heat, and simmer 20 minutes or until carrots are tender. Drain.

Place carrots, milk, and remaining ingredients in container of an electric blender or food processor; top with cover, and process until smooth. Return carrot puree to saucepan; cook over low heat until thoroughly heated. Yield: 6 servings (58 calories per ½-cup serving).

PROTEIN 2.8 / FAT 0.3 / CARBOHYDRATE 11.6 / CHOLESTEROL 1 / IRON 0.5 / SODIUM 119 / CALCIUM 71

CRANBERRY CHUTNEY

1 medium orange, peeled and coarsely chopped
½ cup sugar
½ cup water
1 tablespoon minced fresh gingerroot
1 tablespoon cider vinegar
1 (12-ounce) package frozen cranberries, thawed

Combine all ingredients except cranberries in a medium saucepan; bring to a boil. Reduce heat, and simmer, uncovered, 5 minutes. Add cranberries, and cook over medium-low heat 20 minutes or until cranberries pop and mixture thickens, stirring frequently. Let cool. Yield: 2½ cups (15 calories per tablespoon).

PROTEIN 0.1 / FAT 0.0 / CARBOHYDRATE 3.9 / CHOLESTEROL 0 / IRON 0.0 / SODIUM 0 / CALCIUM 2

APPLE TART

1 cup all-purpose flour
1½ teaspoons sugar
¼ cup margarine
2 to 3 tablespoons cold water
2 medium cooking apples, peeled, cored, and sliced
1 tablespoon lemon juice
3 tablespoons low-sugar apricot spread, melted
½ teaspoon ground cinnamon

Combine flour and sugar in a medium bowl; cut in margarine with a pastry blender until mixture resembles coarse meal. Sprinkle cold water, 1 tablespoon at a time, evenly over surface of flour mixture; stir with a fork until dry ingredients are moistened. Shape into a ball; cover and chill 10 minutes.

Roll dough between 2 sheets of heavy-duty plastic wrap into a 10-inch circle. Chill dough 10 minutes. Remove plastic wrap and fit pastry into a 9-inch tart pan. Chill 10 minutes. Prick bottom of pastry with a fork. Bake at 400° for 5 minutes. Remove from oven; let cool on a wire rack.

Place apple slices and lemon juice in a bowl; toss gently to combine. Arrange apple slices evenly over pastry. Brush apple slices evenly with melted apricot spread, and sprinkle with cinnamon. Bake at 400° for 30 minutes or until pastry is golden brown and apples are tender. Serve warm. Yield: 6 servings (199 calories per serving).

PROTEIN 2.6 / FAT 8.0 / CARBOHYDRATE 29.9 / CHOLESTEROL 0 / IRON 0.8 / SODIUM 98 / CALCIUM 11

LIGHT FROMAGE BLANC

½ cup low-fat cottage cheese
3 tablespoons plain nonfat yogurt

Position knife blade in food processor bowl; add cottage cheese and yogurt. Top with cover, and process until smooth, scraping sides occasionally. Cover and chill 4 hours. Yield: ¾ cup (10 calories per tablespoon).

PROTEIN 1.5 / FAT 0.2 / CARBOHYDRATE 0.6 / CHOLESTEROL 1 / IRON 0.0 / SODIUM 41 / CALCIUM 13

Celebrate the Chinese New Year with Beef with Broccoli, Spicy Carrots, and Chinese "Not Fried" Rice.

Chinese New Year Celebration

Whether you're celebrating the Chinese New Year or just a special winter occasion, this light Asian repast will fit the bill.

Most Chinese soups are composed of a light, flavorful broth that has been thickened with cornstarch. Hot and Sour Soup is a spicy version that usually includes strips of pork. Our lightened Hot and Sour Soup substitutes chicken breast meat and tofu for the pork.

Beef with Broccoli, served with "Chinese Not Fried" Rice, is a favorite Cantonese restaurant recipe that has been adapted for the main course. Instead of cooking the spicy, carbohydrate-rich

Hot and Sour Soup
Beef with Broccoli
Chinese "Not Fried" Rice
Spicy Carrots
Strawberries with Litchis
Commercial Fortune
Cookies
Hot Tea

Serves 6
Total calories per serving: 629

rice with oil, add flavor by braising the rice with reduced-sodium soy sauce, dry sherry, Chinese spices, and a dash of hot sauce for flavor.

Both the Beef with Broccoli

and the Spicy Carrots are stir-fried. To streamline the dinner preparation, have all of the ingredients for both dishes ready to cook and within reach of the cooktop. Stir-fry the Beef with Broccoli first, remove to a platter, cover with aluminum foil, and keep warm in the oven. Immediately rinse out the wok or skillet, then stir-fry the spicy carrot mixture.

A wonderful combination of fresh strawberries and litchis provides a refreshing conclusion to the celebration. Of course, no Chinese meal would be complete without hot tea and a fortune cookie. Gund hay fat choy! Happy New Year!

HOT AND SOUR SOUP

6 dried shiitake mushrooms
4 cups canned low-sodium chicken broth, undiluted
2 green onions, cut into 1-inch pieces
½ ounce fresh gingerroot, sliced
2 (4-ounce) skinned, boned chicken breast halves, cut into 2- x ¼-inch strips
½ pound firm tofu, drained and cut into ¼-inch strips
3 tablespoons cider vinegar
2 tablespoons reduced-sodium soy sauce
2 tablespoons water
1 tablespoon cornstarch
1 egg, lightly beaten
1 teaspoon dark sesame oil
¾ teaspoon ground white pepper
2 green onions, thinly sliced

Pour boiling water to cover over dried shiitake mushrooms; let stand 30 minutes. Drain; remove and discard mushroom stems. Slice mushroom caps into ¼-inch slices. Set aside.

Combine chicken broth, green onion pieces, and sliced gingerroot in a Dutch oven. Bring to a boil; reduce heat, and simmer, uncovered, 20 minutes. Remove and discard onions and gingerroot. Add reserved mushroom caps and chicken strips to broth, and cook 5 minutes. Stir in tofu, vinegar, and soy sauce; cook 2 minutes. Combine water and cornstarch, stirring until smooth; stir cornstarch mixture into broth mixture, and cook until slightly thickened. Slowly drizzle egg into soup, stirring soup constantly. Stir in sesame oil and pepper.

To serve, ladle soup into individual bowls, and top each serving evenly with thinly sliced green onions. Yield: 3 cups (123 calories per ½-cup serving).

PROTEIN 13.9 / FAT 3.9 / CARBOHYDRATE 6.5 / CHOLESTEROL 55 / IRON 2.9 / SODIUM 242 / CALCIUM 59

BEEF WITH BROCCOLI

1 pound lean round steak
2 tablespoons dry sherry, divided
1 tablespoon plus 2 teaspoons cornstarch, divided
2 teaspoons sugar, divided
2 teaspoons sesame oil, divided
2 teaspoons reduced-sodium soy sauce, divided
1 teaspoon salt, divided
1 pound fresh broccoli
½ cup canned low-sodium chicken broth, undiluted
1 tablespoon hoisin sauce
½ teaspoon ground white pepper
1 tablespoon safflower oil
1 tablespoon minced fresh gingerroot
2 teaspoons minced fresh garlic
1 medium-size sweet red pepper, cut into julienne strips
1 tablespoon sesame seeds, toasted

Partially freeze steak; slice diagonally across grain into 3- x ¼-inch strips.

Combine 1 tablespoon dry sherry, 2 teaspoons cornstarch, 1 teaspoon sugar, 1 teaspoon sesame oil, 1 teaspoon reduced-sodium soy sauce, and ½ teaspoon salt in a large bowl; stir well. Add meat, tossing gently; cover and marinate in refrigerator 1 to 4 hours, stirring occasionally.

Trim off large leaves of broccoli, and remove tough ends of lower stalks. Wash broccoli thoroughly. Cut off flowerets, and set aside. Cut stalks into ¼-inch slices; set aside.

Combine 1 tablespoon cornstarch and 1 tablespoon dry sherry in a small bowl; stir well. Add chicken broth, hoisin sauce, 1 teaspoon sugar, 1 teaspoon sesame oil, 1 teaspoon reduced-sodium soy sauce, ½ teaspoon salt, and white pepper; stir well and set aside.

Heat electric wok or nonstick skillet to 325°. Add safflower oil; allow to heat 1 minute. Add gingerroot and garlic; stir-fry 30 seconds. Add beef and marinade; stir-fry 1 minute. Add broccoli and sweet red pepper; stir-fry 2 minutes. Add cornstarch mixture, stirring constantly. Cover wok, reduce heat, and cook 2 minutes or until mixture is slightly thickened. Sprinkle with sesame seeds. Serve immediately. Yield: 6 servings (194 calories per serving).

PROTEIN 19.6 / FAT 8.7 / CARBOHYDRATE 9.7 / CHOLESTEROL 44 / IRON 2.8 / SODIUM 623 / CALCIUM 45

CHINESE "NOT FRIED" RICE

Vegetable cooking spray
½ cup finely chopped onion
2 cups canned low-sodium chicken broth, undiluted
1 tablespoon dry sherry
1 tablespoon reduced-sodium soy sauce
1 teaspoon dark sesame oil
4 drops of hot sauce
1 cup uncooked long-grain converted rice
⅓ cup diagonally sliced green onions
1 tablespoon pine nuts, toasted

Coat a medium saucepan with cooking spray. Place over medium heat until hot. Add onion, and sauté 2 minutes or until tender. Add chicken broth and next 4 ingredients; bring to a boil. Stir in rice; cover, reduce heat, and simmer 25 minutes or until rice is tender and liquid is absorbed. Remove from heat, and stir in green onions and pine nuts. Yield: 6 servings (145 calories per ½-cup serving).

PROTEIN 3.3 / FAT 2.2 / CARBOHYDRATE 27.8 / CHOLESTEROL 0 / IRON 1.3 / SODIUM 106 / CALCIUM 33

SPICY CARROTS

Vegetable cooking spray
2 teaspoons safflower oil
1 tablespoon minced garlic
1 tablespoon minced fresh gingerroot
½ teaspoon crushed red pepper
1½ pounds carrots, scraped and cut diagonally into ½-inch pieces
⅔ cup canned low-sodium chicken broth, undiluted
3 tablespoons reduced-sodium soy sauce
2 tablespoons cider vinegar
½ teaspoon sugar
1 tablespoon cornstarch
1 tablespoon water

Coat a large nonstick skillet or wok with cooking spray; add oil. Place over medium-high heat until hot. Add garlic, gingerroot, and crushed red pepper, stirring well. Add carrot, stirring well.

Combine chicken broth and next 3 ingredients, stirring well. Pour chicken broth mixture over carrot mixture, stirring well. Bring to a boil; cover, reduce heat, and simmer 10 minutes or until carrots are crisp-tender.

Combine cornstarch and water, stirring until smooth. Stir cornstarch mixture into carrot mixture, and cook 1 minute or until slightly thickened. Yield: 6 servings (81 calories per ½-cup serving).

PROTEIN 1.8 / FAT 1.8 / CARBOHYDRATE 15.3 / CHOLESTEROL 0 / IRON 0.8 / SODIUM 341 / CALCIUM 37

 ## TOO SPICY OR TOO HOT

Unless you have a "cast-iron" stomach, eating a highly-spiced meal may seem like asking for trouble. But it shouldn't be. At least that's the word from scientists at Baylor College of Medicine in Houston, Texas. Recently these researchers found no evidence that spicy foods cause injury to the stomach lining. Scientists fed a variety of spicy foods or one medication—aspirin—to volunteers. After meals, scientists used medical equipment to get a direct view of each stomach lining. The only substance that actually caused direct damage to the stomach lining was aspirin. None of the foods tested, even pepper, caused stomach injury.

Of course, this is not to say that spicy foods don't cause an increase in stomach acid. But extra acid in the stomach does not necessarily spell stomach injury. Moreover, other foods eaten along with a spicy meal often dilute the effects of one particular spicy food. All of this is good news for ulcer victims. Forced for years to follow bland diets, people with ulcers may now be able to enjoy a more varied diet.

STRAWBERRIES WITH LITCHIS

6 cups fresh strawberries, hulled and halved
1 (15-ounce) can litchis, drained
2 teaspoons brown sugar
1 teaspoon minced fresh gingerroot
Fresh mint sprigs (optional)

Combine strawberries and litchis in a large bowl; set aside.

Combine sugar and gingerroot; stir well. Add sugar mixture to strawberry mixture, tossing gently to combine. Cover and chill 1 hour. Toss gently before serving. Garnish with fresh mint sprigs, if desired. Yield: 6 servings (62 calories per 1-cup serving).

PROTEIN 1.0 / FAT 0.6 / CARBOHYDRATE 14.9 / CHOLESTEROL 0 / IRON 0.6 / SODIUM 2 / CALCIUM 18

Dine alfresco with Grilled Salmon Provençal, Green Bean Salad, and Herbed Croutons.

Alfresco Dining

When the days grow long and warm, dining outdoors under the stars becomes a special occasion that demands a memorable menu. Whether served poolside, on the porch, in the back yard, or under an arbor, guests will appreciate the summer-fresh flavors this menu provides.

Fresh green beans are blanched until crisp-tender ahead of time, and then dressed just before serving with a flavorful mixture of walnut oil and balsamic vinegar. Top the tender beans with chopped purple onion, and garnish with shredded fresh basil leaves.

Pristine salmon fillets are briefly

Grilled Salmon Provençal
Green Bean Salad
Herbed Croutons
Peaches with Cheese and
Pistachios
White Wine

Serves 4
Total calories per serving: 692

marinated in a mixture of dry white wine and olive oil flavored with grated orange rind, then grilled over a charcoal flame. To make things easier on the cook, the tomato and sweet red pepper sauce (reminiscent of a Mediterranean fish broth) is prepared

while the salmon is being marinated or cooked. If desired, fresh clams or mussels can be poached in the broth just before serving and placed alongside the salmon. Serve the saucy salmon entrée in shallow soup bowls or on dinner plates with a rim. Place the crisp Herbed Croutons, flavored with olive oil, garlic, and Italian seasonings alongside the grilled salmon for a stunning presentation.

What says summer more temptingly than a bounty of fresh peaches? Serve peaches Italian style—filled with a light ricotta cheese mixture and sprinkled with chopped pistachios.

GRILLED SALMON PROVENÇAL

⅓ cup unsweetened orange juice
1 tablespoon Chablis or other dry white wine
1 teaspoon olive oil
1 tablespoon grated orange rind
4 (3-ounce) salmon fillets with skin
Vegetable cooking spray
½ cup diced onion
2 cloves garlic, minced
1 (8-ounce) bottle clam juice
1 (16-ounce) can Italian-style tomatoes, drained and chopped
1 small sweet red pepper, diced
Dash of ground saffron
1 tablespoon margarine
1 tablespoon finely shredded fresh basil leaves
1 tablespoon chopped fresh parsley
2 drops of hot sauce
Fresh basil sprigs (optional)

Combine first 4 ingredients in a shallow baking dish. Add salmon, turning to coat well. Cover and marinate in refrigerator 1 hour.

Coat a medium saucepan with cooking spray; place over medium-high heat until hot. Add

onion, and garlic, and sauté 1 minute. Add clam juice, tomatoes, sweet red pepper, and saffron. Bring to a boil; reduce heat, and simmer 30 minutes, stirring occasionally. Bring to a boil, and cook 4 minutes or until liquid has been reduced by one-fourth. Stir in margarine, shredded basil leaves, parsley, and hot sauce. Set aside and keep warm.

Coat grill rack with cooking spray; place on grill over hot coals. Remove salmon from marinade, discarding marinade. Place salmon on rack skin side down. Cook 10 minutes or until fish flakes easily when tested with a fork (do not turn salmon). Remove salmon from grill by sliding a thin spatula between skin and flesh, leaving skin on the grill. Place each salmon fillet in a shallow soup bowl or on a dinner plate with a rim. Spoon sauce evenly over each serving of salmon. Garnish each serving with fresh basil sprigs, if desired. Yield: 4 servings (219 calories per serving).

PROTEIN 19.6 / FAT 11.5 / CARBOHYDRATE 8.7 / CHOLESTEROL 58 / IRON 1.1 / SODIUM 210 / CALCIUM 50

GREEN BEAN SALAD

1 pound fresh green beans
1 quart water
2 tablespoons water
2 tablespoons balsamic vinegar
1 tablespoon walnut oil
¼ teaspoon salt
⅛ teaspoon freshly ground pepper
½ cup chopped purple onion
2 tablespoons finely shredded fresh basil leaves

Wash beans; trim ends, and remove strings. Bring 1 quart water to a boil; add beans and cook, uncovered, 8 minutes or just until crisp-tender. Drain beans, and plunge into ice water. Drain again, and pat dry with paper towels.

Combine 2 tablespoons water and next 4 ingredients in a small bowl, stirring with a wire whisk until blended.

Divide green beans evenly among individual salad plates. Sprinkle each serving with 2 tablespoons chopped onion. Drizzle 1 tablespoon dressing mixture over each salad. Top each salad with 1½ teaspoons shredded basil leaves. Yield: 4 servings (73 calories per serving).

PROTEIN 2.3 / FAT 3.6 / CARBOHYDRATE 9.9 / CHOLESTEROL 0 / IRON 1.4 / SODIUM 155 / CALCIUM 51

HERBED CROUTONS

16 (½-inch) slices French bread
1 teaspoon olive oil
1 clove garlic, crushed
2 teaspoons dried Italian seasoning
1 tablespoon water

Place bread slices on an ungreased baking sheet. Bake at 350° for 15 minutes or until golden brown; set aside.

Place olive oil in a small nonstick skillet over medium heat until hot. Add garlic, and sauté until garlic is lightly browned. Remove from heat. Remove and discard garlic; add Italian seasoning and water to skillet. Lightly brush one side of each bread slice with oil mixture. Yield: 4 servings (138 calories per serving).

PROTEIN 4.1 / FAT 2.1 / CARBOHYDRATE 24.5 / CHOLESTEROL 1 / IRON 1.8 / SODIUM 247 / CALCIUM 41

PEACHES WITH CHEESE AND PISTACHIOS

1 tablespoon plus 1 teaspoon shelled pistachios
½ cup part-skim ricotta cheese
2 tablespoons powdered sugar
⅛ teaspoon vanilla extract
4 medium peaches, peeled and halved crosswise
Fresh mint sprigs (optional)

Blanch pistachios by submerging in boiling water 1 minute; remove and discard skins. Finely chop pistachios, and set aside.

Combine cheese, sugar, and vanilla in a small bowl; stir well. Spoon 1 tablespoon cheese mixture into each peach half. Sprinkle pistachios evenly over peach halves. Garnish each serving with fresh mint sprigs, if desired. Yield: 4 servings (138 calories per serving).

PROTEIN 5.1 / FAT 3.7 / CARBOHYDRATE 23.2 / CHOLESTEROL 10 / IRON 0.5 / SODIUM 39 / CALCIUM 95

 ### SHOPPING TIPS FOR QUALITY FOODS

When you shop, check foods closely to be sure they are not spoiled. Look for fresh, unblemished produce. Check expiration dates on dairy and refrigerated products. Do not buy cans that are badly dented, leaking, or bulging at the ends. Also, avoid packages that have broken seals.

Summer Luncheon

Roasted Eggplant Soup
Oriental Chicken Salad
Commercial Rice Cakes
Ginger Custard
Iced Tea

Serves 8
Total calories per serving: 592

The weather is delightful—occasion enough for a special luncheon. Start with delicious smoky-tasting Roasted Eggplant Soup. The main course, Oriental Chicken Salad, contains less fat than traditional chicken salad. Two rice cakes per person serve as a crunchy accompaniment. Ginger Custard must have time to cool before being served. So sit back and enjoy the sunshine.

Our colorful Oriental Chicken Salad (page 86) contains less fat than traditional chicken salads.

ROASTED EGGPLANT SOUP

2 medium eggplant (2 pounds)
1 teaspoon olive oil
Vegetable cooking spray
1 tablespoon margarine
1 cup chopped onion
2 large sweet red peppers, chopped
1 tablespoon plus 1½ teaspoons curry powder
6 cups canned no-salt-added chicken broth, undiluted
½ teaspoon salt
¼ teaspoon freshly ground pepper
½ cup low-fat sour cream
Fresh basil sprigs (optional)

Slice eggplant in half lengthwise; place cut side up on a baking sheet. Lightly brush cut surfaces of eggplant with olive oil. Bake at 450° for 40 minutes or until eggplant is soft. Remove from oven, and let cool on baking sheet. Cut into ½-inch pieces; set aside.

Coat a large Dutch oven with cooking spray; add margarine. Place over medium heat until hot; add onion, and sauté 3 minutes. Add sweet red pepper and curry powder, and sauté 3 minutes, stirring often. Add eggplant, and sauté 30 seconds. Stir in chicken broth, salt, and pepper; bring to a boil. Reduce heat, and simmer, uncovered, 30 minutes. Let cool.

Transfer mixture in batches to container of an electric blender or food processor; top with cover, and process until smooth. To serve, ladle soup into individual bowls. Top each serving with 1 tablespoon sour cream. Garnish each serving with fresh basil sprigs, if desired. Yield: 8 cups (102 calories per 1-cup serving).

PROTEIN 3.4 / FAT 5.7 / CARBOHYDRATE 9.7 / CHOLESTEROL 6 / IRON 1.3 / SODIUM 275 / CALCIUM 59

ORIENTAL CHICKEN SALAD

½ cup plus 1 tablespoon reduced-sodium soy sauce, divided
¼ cup dry sherry
2 tablespoons coarse-grained Dijon mustard
6 (4-ounce) skinned, boned chicken breast halves
Vegetable cooking spray
9 ounces vermicelli, uncooked
1 tablespoon rice wine vinegar
1 teaspoon dark sesame oil
¼ teaspoon crushed red pepper
5 cups fresh spinach leaves, washed and shredded
2 cups finely shredded red cabbage
1 small sweet yellow pepper, cut into julienne strips
1¾ cups thinly sliced English cucumber
½ cup fresh bean sprouts, rinsed and drained
2 green onions, thinly sliced on the diagonal
¼ cup canned low-sodium chicken broth, undiluted
¼ cup vinegar
2 tablespoons sugar
1 tablespoon dark sesame oil
1 tablespoon minced fresh gingerroot
1 tablespoon minced fresh garlic
1 teaspoon crushed red pepper
2 tablespoons sesame seeds, toasted

Combine ½ cup soy sauce, dry sherry, and mustard in a small bowl; stir well. Place chicken breast halves in a 13- x 9- x 2-inch baking dish. Pour marinade mixture over chicken; cover and marinate in refrigerator 8 hours.

Coat rack of a broiler pan with cooking spray. Drain chicken, and discard marinade. Place chicken on rack. Broil 4 inches from heat for 4 minutes; turn and broil an additional 4 minutes or until chicken is done. Let cool. Shred chicken into ¼-inch strips, and set aside.

Cook vermicelli according to package directions, omitting salt and fat. Drain; rinse with cold water, and drain again. Place vermicelli in a medium bowl, and set aside.

Combine rice wine vinegar, remaining 1 tablespoon soy sauce, 1 teaspoon sesame oil, and ¼ teaspoon crushed red pepper in a small bowl; stir well. Pour vinegar mixture over cooked vermicelli, tossing gently to combine. Set aside.

Combine chicken, spinach, cabbage, sweet yellow pepper, cucumber, bean sprouts, and green onions in a large bowl; toss gently.

Place chicken broth and next 6 ingredients in a jar; cover tightly and shake vigorously. Pour dressing mixture over chicken mixture, tossing gently to combine.

To serve, place ½ cup vermicelli mixture on individual serving plates. Top each serving with 1½ cups chicken mixture. Sprinkle sesame seeds evenly over each serving. Yield: 8 servings (297 calories per serving).

PROTEIN 25.7 / FAT 6.5 / CARBOHYDRATE 33.3 / CHOLESTEROL 53 / IRON 3.0 / SODIUM 259 / CALCIUM 64

GINGER CUSTARD

3 cups skim milk
3 tablespoons chopped fresh gingerroot
2 eggs
5 egg yolks
¼ cup sugar
2 teaspoons vanilla extract
½ teaspoon ground cinnamon

Place milk in a heavy saucepan; cook over medium heat until thoroughly heated. Stir in gingerroot; remove from heat, and chill 1 hour.

Combine eggs and egg yolks in a medium bowl; stir with a wire whisk until well blended. Gradually add sugar, stirring until mixture is slightly thickened. Set aside.

Place milk mixture in saucepan over low heat; cook until thoroughly heated. Gradually stir milk mixture into egg mixture with a wire whisk. Stir in vanilla. Strain; discard gingerroot.

Pour custard mixture into 8 (6-ounce) custard cups. Set custard cups in 2 (8-inch square) baking dishes; pour hot water into baking dishes to a depth of 1 inch. Bake at 300° for 45 minutes or until knife inserted halfway between center and edge of custard comes out clean. Remove custard cups from water; sprinkle evenly with cinnamon. Serve warm or chilled. Yield: 8 servings (121 calories per serving).

PROTEIN 6.5 / FAT 4.9 / CARBOHYDRATE 12.2 / CHOLESTEROL 222 / IRON 0.9 / SODIUM 70 / CALCIUM 138

Delicate and diminutive Lemon Tea Cakes (page 89) make a delightful addition to a Victorian tea party.

Afternoon Tea Party

One of the most delightful food trends to hit American shores in recent years is the revival of the Victorian afternoon tea time. The traditional tea, as it is served in England, can be a simple break from the day's routine or a full evening meal. With today's stress-filled and frantic lifestyles, an afternoon tea can serve to nourish our psyches as well as our bodies.

This light menu for an afternoon tea party offers an assortment of small tea sandwiches that are creatively served in a round bread loaf that has been hollowed. The three sandwich

Tea Sandwiches in a Bread Bowl
Lemon Tea Cakes
Green-Green Fruit Salad
Hot Tea

Serves 8
Total calories per serving: 441

fillings—Cucumber and Watercress, Potted Shrimp, and Curried Chicken—can be prepared in advance. However, don't assemble the sandwiches until an hour before serving; otherwise, the bread will become soggy. The bread that is removed from the round

loaf can be used for another purpose, such as making homemade breadcrumbs.

Accompanying the sandwiches are tiny Lemon Tea Cakes that resemble delicious, but higher calorie, scones (two per serving). An all green fruit salad and an assortment of teas complete the party menu.

Serve the hot tea from your best tea service, whether it be pottery or silver. Put out a tray of your favorite teas, cold milk, and cut lemons, if desired. Crisp linens and an arrangement of fresh and fragrant flowers are all you need to complete the setting.

TEA SANDWICHES IN A BREAD BOWL

1 (9- to 10-inch) round loaf Italian or French bread
Cucumber and Watercress Sandwiches
Potted Shrimp Sandwiches
Curried Chicken Sandwiches
1 bunch watercress (optional)

Cut a ½-inch slice off top of loaf; set aside. Hollow out center of loaf. Reserve top slice and inside of loaf for other uses.

Place hollowed out bread loaf on a serving platter; fill with Cucumber and Watercress, Potted Shrimp, and Curried Chicken Sandwiches. Arrange watercress around outside of filled bread loaf, if desired. Yield: 8 servings (250 calories per serving).

PROTEIN 16.7 / FAT 9.3 / CARBOHYDRATE 25.4 / CHOLESTEROL 70 / IRON 2.3 / SODIUM 638 / CALCIUM 77

CUCUMBER AND WATERCRESS SANDWICHES

1½ cups thinly sliced English cucumber
1 teaspoon tarragon vinegar
½ teaspoon salt
2 teaspoons minced fresh dillweed
8 slices pumpernickel bread, trimmed
2 tablespoons reduced-calorie mayonnaise
¼ cup torn watercress
2 tablespoons low-fat sour cream

Place cucumber slices in a colander. Sprinkle vinegar and salt over cucumber slices, tossing gently. Place colander over a bowl to drain; let stand 30 minutes. Press cucumber slices between layers of paper towels to remove excess moisture. Place cucumber slices in a bowl; add dillweed, tossing gently to combine. Set cucumber slices aside.

Spread 4 slices of pumpernickel bread evenly with mayonnaise; top evenly with reserved cucumber slices and watercress. Spread remaining 4 slices of pumpernickel bread evenly with sour cream, and place on top of cucumber and watercress-topped bread slices. Cut each sandwich into 4 triangles or squares. Yield: 8 servings (58 calories per serving).

PROTEIN 1.8 / FAT 1.7 / CARBOHYDRATE 9.6 / CHOLESTEROL 3 / IRON 0.5 / SODIUM 268 / CALCIUM 24

POTTED SHRIMP SANDWICHES

4 cups water
¾ pound unpeeled medium-size fresh shrimp
2 ounces Neufchâtel cheese, softened
1 tablespoon margarine
2 teaspoons minced fresh dillweed
1 teaspoon lemon juice
1 teaspoon prepared horseradish
¼ teaspoon salt
Dash of ground white pepper
8 slices white bread, trimmed

Bring water to a boil; add shrimp, and cook 3 to 5 minutes. Drain; rinse with cold water. Chill. Peel, devein, and chop shrimp. Set aside.

Combine Neufchâtel cheese and next 6 ingredients in a bowl; stir well. Add chopped shrimp, stirring well. Spread 4 slices of bread evenly with shrimp mixture; top with remaining bread slices. Cut each sandwich into 4 triangles or squares. Yield: 8 servings (100 calories per serving).

PROTEIN 7.7 / FAT 4.0 / CARBOHYDRATE 7.8 / CHOLESTEROL 49 / IRON 1.1 / SODIUM 233 / CALCIUM 32

CURRIED CHICKEN SANDWICHES

Vegetable cooking spray
3 tablespoons finely chopped onion
2 teaspoons curry powder
¼ cup reduced-calorie mayonnaise
2 teaspoons chutney, chopped
¾ cup chopped cooked chicken breast (skinned before cooking and cooked without salt)
1 tablespoon chopped blanched almonds, toasted
8 slices whole wheat bread, trimmed

Coat a small nonstick skillet with cooking spray. Place over medium heat until hot. Add onion, and sauté 3 minutes or until tender. Add curry powder, and cook 1 minute, stirring constantly. Remove from heat; let cool.

Combine onion mixture, mayonnaise, and chutney in a bowl, stirring well. Add chicken and almonds, stirring well to combine. Spread 4 slices of bread evenly with chicken mixture; top with remaining bread slices. Cut each sandwich into 4 triangles or squares. Yield: 8 servings (92 calories per serving).

PROTEIN 7.2 / FAT 3.6 / CARBOHYDRATE 8.0 / CHOLESTEROL 18 / IRON 0.7 / SODIUM 137 / CALCIUM 21

LEMON TEA CAKES

¾ cup all-purpose flour
1 teaspoon baking powder
⅛ teaspoon salt
1 (10½-ounce) package firm tofu, drained
1 egg, beaten
2 tablespoons sugar
1 tablespoon grated lemon rind
1 tablespoon safflower oil
Vegetable cooking spray
¼ cup reduced-calorie strawberry jam

Combine flour, baking powder, and salt in a medium bowl; make a well in center of mixture, and set aside.

Position knife blade in food processor bowl; add tofu. Top with cover, and process until smooth. Combine tofu, egg, sugar, lemon rind, and oil in a small bowl; stir well. Add tofu mixture to dry ingredients, stirring just until dry ingredients are moistened.

Spoon 2 tablespoons batter into 2-inch fluted tart pans or miniature (1¾-inch) muffin pans that have been coated with cooking spray. Bake at 400° for 20 to 25 minutes or until a wooden pick inserted in center comes out clean. Immediately remove tea cakes from pans; serve warm. Spread ¾ teaspoon jam over each tea cake. Yield: 16 tea cakes (65 calories each).

PROTEIN 2.6 / FAT 2.4 / CARBOHYDRATE 8.8 / CHOLESTEROL 12.5 / IRON 1.3 / SODIUM 46.5 / CALCIUM 35

GREEN-GREEN FRUIT SALAD

2 medium kiwifruit, peeled
1 cup seedless green grapes
1 small fresh pear, cored and cut into ½-inch pieces
1 cup honeydew melon balls
¼ cup kiwifruit nectar
¼ cup white grape juice
¼ cup tightly packed fresh mint leaves, crushed
Fresh mint sprigs (optional)

Cut kiwifruit in half lengthwise, and thinly slice. Combine kiwifruit, grapes, pear, and melon balls in a large bowl; toss gently. Cover and chill 1 hour.

Combine kiwifruit nectar, grape juice, and crushed mint leaves in a small bowl. Cover and chill 1 hour. Strain liquid, discarding mint leaves. Pour liquid over chilled fruit mixture, tossing gently to combine. Garnish with fresh mint sprigs, if desired. Yield: 8 servings (59 calories per ½-cup serving).

PROTEIN 0.7 / FAT 0.4 / CARBOHYDRATE 14.2 / CHOLESTEROL 0 / IRON 0.4 / SODIUM 4 / CALCIUM 16

INCREASING EXERCISE CAPACITY

Whether you're a weekend athlete or a trained competitor, the key to increased stamina lies in a few simple strategies.
• Capitalize on individual strengths. Certain people are better suited to certain activities as a result of body structure and muscles.
• Emphasize the positive. A positive attitude only enhances achievements.
• Set realistic goals. Striving to improve your distance record or aiming for a specific amount of weight loss may motivate you to succeed.
• Develop a game plan for exercise, but be flexible.

Planning for exercise is the way to make it an integral part of your life.
• Vary training strategies. Switch from swimming to bicycling to calisthenics. Change your exercise schedule occasionally to prevent boredom and to reduce the chance for injury.
• Keep exercise in perspective. While exercise requires some devotion, there's no need to exclude other leisure activities.
• Develop a rhythm. Balance workouts so that you don't overdo one week and loaf the next. Muscles respond best to regular exercise.

Light Recipes

A hearty appetite and a healthy heart go hand in hand when meals are composed of colorful, nutritious recipes: (Clockwise from right) Cappellini with Broccoli and Cheese (page 124), Papaya and Avocado Salad (page 181), Oriental Beef Salad (page 187), and Garden Fresh Cocktail (page 103).

Cooking Light Cookbook 1990 offers hundreds of recipes from appetizers to main dishes to desserts, so you will have plenty from which to choose. And, best of all, you will find that the light touch in cooking results in foods that are higher in nutrients, fiber, and complex carbohydrates, but lower in fat, cholesterol, sugar, and salt.

With a little planning you can turn these healthy recipes into nutritionally balanced meals whose taste and appearance say delicious. Planning healthy meals begins with nutrient-dense recipes. This does not mean, however, that you'll have to spend more time or money to purchase or prepare food.

Attention to the principles of sound nutrition, freshness, variety, and presentation will give you confidence as a cook. But even more important, you will have the satisfaction of serving your family and friends the healthiest, freshest, and most attractive meals possible.

Cooking Light's attention to presentation and flavor will invite success as you plan lightened meals. Remember that appearance of the food counts, especially when introducing new and different items to family and guests. Enhance the visual appeal of your meal by including foods of contrasting color and texture.

Whether you are having an intimate fireside supper, a backyard gathering, a formal dinner, or a holiday celebration, you will find many ideas in the following recipe sections to help you create exciting meals that meet today's high standards for the best in nutrition. And you will be pleased to discover that many of them are as economical and time-efficient as they are appealing and wholesome.

Many nutritious recipes are as close as your own recipe files. Trimming the fat, calories, and cholesterol from your favorite recipes can be done by implementing cooking and seasoning methods used in our *Cooking Light* recipes.

Plan your next party to include Marinated Mussels (page 102) and Fresh Tomato and Pesto Croutons (page 96).

Appetizers & Beverages

HUMMUS DIP

3 cloves garlic, halved
1 (15-ounce) can garbanzo beans, drained
¾ cup chopped onion
1 teaspoon olive oil
¼ cup minced fresh parsley
½ cup soft tofu
2 tablespoons lemon juice
½ teaspoon salt
¼ teaspoon ground cumin
2 teaspoons sesame oil
¼ teaspoon hot sauce

Position knife blade in food processor; add garlic. Top with cover, and process garlic until minced. Add garbanzo beans; process until smooth.

Sauté onion in oil in a small nonstick skillet over low heat until tender. Add onion to bean mixture; process until smooth. Add parsley and remaining ingredients. Transfer dip to a small bowl; cover and chill 1 hour. Serve with fresh raw vegetables. Yield: 2 cups (19 calories per tablespoon).

PROTEIN 0.7 / FAT 0.7 / CARBOHYDRATE 2.6 / CHOLESTEROL 0 / IRON 0.2 / SODIUM 64 / CALCIUM 12

ROASTED GARLIC WITH HERBED YOGURT CHEESE

4 whole heads garlic
¼ cup canned low-sodium chicken broth, undiluted
1 tablespoon olive oil
1 (18-inch) French bread baguette
Herbed Yogurt Cheese

Cut stem end off each head of garlic, exposing individual cloves. Place each garlic head on a square of aluminum foil to make individual bundles. Combine chicken broth and olive oil; pour evenly over garlic. Fold foil edges over, and wrap securely. Place bundles in a shallow baking dish. Bake at 275° for 1 hour and 15 minutes, or until garlic is soft.

Cut French bread into ¼-inch diagonal slices. Spread each bread slice with a squeezed garlic clove and 1 teaspoon Herbed Yogurt Cheese. Yield: 6 dozen appetizers (22 calories each).

Herbed Yogurt Cheese:

3 (8-ounce) cartons plain nonfat yogurt
1½ teaspoons dried whole dillweed
1½ teaspoons dried whole thyme
½ teaspoon salt
¼ teaspoon ground white pepper

Line a colander or sieve with a double layer of cheesecloth that has been rinsed out and squeezed dry; allow cheesecloth to overlap side of colander. Stir yogurt until smooth; pour into colander, and fold edges of cheesecloth over to cover yogurt. Place colander in a large bowl; refrigerate 12 to 24 hours. Remove yogurt from colander, and set aside. Discard liquid.

Place drained yogurt, dillweed, thyme, salt, and white pepper in a small bowl, stirring well to combine. Refrigerate yogurt mixture 4 hours or until firm. Yield: 1½ cups.

PROTEIN 1.0 / FAT 0.3 / CARBOHYDRATE 3.7 / CHOLESTEROL 0 / IRON 0.2 / SODIUM 49 / CALCIUM 24

MUSHROOM CAVIAR

¼ cup minced shallots
1 tablespoon margarine
2 tablespoons canned no-salt-added chicken broth, undiluted
1 pound fresh mushrooms, minced
1 tablespoon dry sherry
1 tablespoon minced fresh parsley
½ teaspoon dried whole thyme
¼ teaspoon salt
⅛ teaspoon pepper

Sauté minced shallots in margarine in a large nonstick skillet over medium-high heat until tender. Add chicken broth and fresh mushrooms; cook over high heat 5 minutes or until all liquid evaporates, stirring constantly. Add sherry, and stir gently. Stir in fresh parsley, dried whole thyme, salt, and pepper. Remove from heat, and allow mixture to cool.

Pack mushroom mixture into a small crock or container, and chill at least 2 hours. Serve with toasted French bread rounds. Yield: 1½ cups (11 calories per tablespoon).

PROTEIN 0.4 / FAT 0.6 / CARBOHYDRATE 1.1 / CHOLESTEROL 0 / IRON 0.3 / SODIUM 32 / CALCIUM 3

CHOPPED LIVER

1 pound chicken livers
Vegetable cooking spray
2 medium onions, sliced
⅓ cup canned no-salt-added chicken broth,
   undiluted
1 (½-ounce) package powdered butter flavor
2 hard-cooked eggs
2 tablespoons chopped fresh parsley
¼ teaspoon salt
⅛ teaspoon freshly ground pepper
⅛ teaspoon ground nutmeg

Place chicken livers on rack of a broiler pan that has been coated with cooking spray. Broil 4 to 6 inches from heating element 5 minutes on each side or until done. Set aside.

Spray a large nonstick skillet with cooking spray; place over medium heat until hot. Add sliced onion, and sauté until tender. Increase heat to medium-high, and cook until onion begins to brown. Set aside.

Place chicken broth in a small saucepan; cook over medium heat until thoroughly heated. Stir in powdered butter flavor. Remove from heat.

Position knife blade in food processor bowl; add chicken livers, onion, eggs, and next 4 ingredients. Top with cover, and process until coarsely chopped. With processor running, pour chicken broth mixture through food chute in a slow, steady stream until mixture is combined. Transfer mixture to a small bowl. Cover and chill thoroughly. Serve with unsalted crackers. Yield: 3 cups (16 calories per tablespoon).

PROTEIN 1.7 / FAT 0.6 / CARBOHYDRATE 0.8 / CHOLESTEROL 44 / IRON 0.5 / SODIUM 37 / CALCIUM 4

SMOKED SALMON PÂTÉ

¼ pound smoked salmon
½ (8-ounce) package Neufchâtel cheese
2 tablespoons minced onion
2 tablespoons low-fat sour cream
1 tablespoon minced fresh chives
1 tablespoon dried whole dillweed
⅛ teaspoon ground white pepper
4 to 5 drops of hot sauce
Fresh dill sprigs (optional)

Position knife blade in food processor bowl; add first 8 ingredients. Top with cover, and process until smooth. Transfer salmon mixture to a small serving bowl. Cover and chill. Garnish with fresh dill sprigs, if desired. Serve pâté with unsalted crackers. Yield: 1¼ cups (24 calories per tablespoon).

PROTEIN 1.7 / FAT 1.8 / CARBOHYDRATE 0.4 / CHOLESTEROL 6 / IRON 0.1 / SODIUM 68 / CALCIUM 10

HAM-STUFFED PINWHEELS

2 cups water
12 slices thin crisp bread
⅓ cup minced lean cooked
   ham
2 tablespoons Neufchâtel cheese,
   softened
2 tablespoons (½ ounce) shredded Swiss
   cheese
1 tablespoon unsweetened crushed
   pineapple, drained
½ teaspoon Dijon mustard
½ cup minced fresh parsley

Place water in a small saucepan, and bring to a boil; remove from heat. Dip each bread slice into hot water; remove and lay flat on wax paper. Cover with wax paper, and set aside.

Combine ham and next 4 ingredients; stir well. Spread 2 teaspoons ham mixture evenly over each bread slice. Roll up jellyroll fashion, starting at narrow end. Dip each end in parsley. Cover and chill at least 8 hours before serving. Yield: 12 appetizers (36 calories each).

PROTEIN 1.9 / FAT 1.1 / CARBOHYDRATE 4.9 / CHOLESTEROL 5 / IRON 0.2 / SODIUM 80 / CALCIUM 17

FRESH TOMATO AND PESTO CROUTONS

1 (24-inch) French bread baguette
1 tablespoon olive oil
2 cups packed fresh basil
1 cup packed fresh parsley
¼ cup pine nuts, toasted
¼ cup canned no-salt-added chicken broth, undiluted
3 tablespoons grated Parmesan cheese
1 tablespoon olive oil
1 clove garlic, cut in half
1 pint firm, red or yellow cherry tomatoes
48 small fresh basil leaves

Slice bread diagonally into 48 (½-inch) slices. Place on a baking sheet. Brush slices evenly on one side with 1 tablespoon olive oil. Bake at 350° for 15 minutes or until golden. Set aside.

Remove stems from basil. Wash leaves thoroughly in lukewarm water, and pat dry.

Position knife blade in food processor bowl; add basil and next 6 ingredients. Top with cover, and process 30 seconds or until smooth, scraping sides of processor bowl occasionally.

Slice tomatoes crosswise into thin slices. Arrange tomato slices on croutons. Top each with 1 teaspoon pesto mixture and a small basil leaf. Yield: 4 dozen appetizers (30 calories each).

PROTEIN 1.0 / FAT 1.3 / CARBOHYDRATE 4.1 / CHOLESTEROL 0 / IRON 0.8 / SODIUM 36 / CALCIUM 39

CHERRY TOMATOES STUFFED WITH TABBOULEH

1 cup bulgur wheat
1 cup boiling water
¼ cup lemon juice
1 tablespoon olive oil
1 (.19-ounce) envelope instant chicken-flavored broth
60 cherry tomatoes (about 3 pints)
1 cup finely chopped green onions
2 tablespoons minced fresh mint
2 tablespoons minced fresh parsley
1 clove garlic, minced
1 teaspoon salt
¼ teaspoon freshly ground pepper
Fresh parsley sprigs (optional)

Combine first 5 ingredients; let stand 1 hour.

Cut off top of each cherry tomato, and scoop out pulp, leaving shells intact (reserve pulp for other uses). Invert tomato shells on paper towels to drain.

Add onions and next 5 ingredients to bulgur mixture, stirring well. Spoon mixture evenly into tomato cups. Chill thoroughly before serving. Garnish with fresh parsley sprigs, if desired. Yield: 5 dozen appetizers (16 calories each).

PROTEIN 0.5 / FAT 0.3 / CARBOHYDRATE 2.9 / CHOLESTEROL 0 / IRON 0.2 / SODIUM 40 / CALCIUM 3

CAPONATA WITH PITA WEDGES

1 small eggplant, unpeeled and finely chopped (about ¾ pound)
1 teaspoon olive oil, divided
Vegetable cooking spray
¼ cup finely chopped onion
1 (16-ounce) can whole tomatoes, undrained and chopped
2 tablespoons chopped ripe olives
2 tablespoons raisins
2 tablespoons pine nuts, toasted
2 teaspoons capers, drained
2 tablespoons chopped fresh parsley
3 (6-inch) whole wheat pita bread rounds

Sauté half of eggplant in a large nonstick skillet with ½ teaspoon olive oil over high heat 6 minutes or until lightly browned, stirring occasionally. Remove eggplant, and set aside. Repeat with remaining eggplant and oil.

Coat skillet with cooking spray; add onion, and sauté over medium heat until tender. Combine eggplant, onion, tomatoes, olives, and raisins in a large saucepan. Cook over low heat 25 minutes, stirring occasionally. Stir in pine nuts, capers, and parsley. Set aside.

Separate each pita bread into 2 rounds; cut each round into 8 wedges to make 48 triangles. Place on 2 ungreased baking sheets; bake at 350° for 8 to 10 minutes or until lightly browned.

Serve caponata warm or cold with pita wedges. Yield: 3 cups (17 calories per 1 tablespoon caponata and 1 pita wedge).

PROTEIN 0.5 / FAT 0.5 / CARBOHYDRATE 2.7 / CHOLESTEROL 0 / IRON 0.3 / SODIUM 18 / CALCIUM 8

For an appetizer that is as colorful as it is tasty, serve Polenta with Sweet Red Pepper Dip.

POLENTA WITH SWEET RED PEPPER DIP

3 cups water
1 teaspoon salt
1 cup instant polenta, uncooked
¼ cup chopped fresh basil
Vegetable cooking spray
¼ cup freshly grated Parmesan cheese
Sweet Red Pepper Dip

Combine water and salt in a saucepan; bring to a boil. Add polenta in a slow, steady stream, stirring constantly. Reduce heat; cook, uncovered, over low heat 20 minutes or until mixture pulls away from sides of pan. Stir in basil.

Pour half of mixture into a 13- x 9- x 2-inch baking pan that has been coated with cooking spray, working quickly. Repeat procedure, pouring polenta into a second pan. Cool.

Cut each pan into 48 pieces. Place on baking sheets that have been coated with cooking spray; sprinkle with cheese. Broil 3 inches from heat 6 minutes or until browned. Serve with Sweet Red Pepper Dip. Yield: 96 appetizers (8 calories per piece and 1 teaspoon dip).

Sweet Red Pepper Dip:

1¼ pounds sweet red peppers, seeded (about 3 large)
Vegetable cooking spray
1 tablespoon sherry vinegar
¼ teaspoon salt
⅛ teaspoon pepper
⅛ teaspoon hot sauce
Fresh basil sprigs (optional)

Cut sweet red peppers into 1-inch pieces. Place in a 2-quart casserole that has been coated with cooking spray. Cover and bake at 400° for 20 minutes or until soft, stirring once.

Position knife blade in food processor bowl; add sweet red pepper. Top with cover, and process until smooth. Add vinegar and next 3 ingredients; process until blended. Transfer pepper mixture to serving dish. Garnish with basil sprigs, if desired. Yield: 2 cups.

PROTEIN 0.3 / FAT 0.2 / CARBOHYDRATE 1.3 / CHOLESTEROL 0 / IRON 0.1 / SODIUM 36 / CALCIUM 4

CURRIED EGG CUPS

6 hard-cooked eggs
¼ cup plus 1 tablespoon light process
    cream cheese product
1 tablespoon reduced-calorie mayonnaise
1 teaspoon grated onion
1 teaspoon minced fresh parsley
¼ teaspoon curry powder
Dash of red pepper

Slice eggs in half lengthwise; carefully remove yolks, and reserve for other uses.

Combine cream cheese and remaining ingredients, stirring well. Divide cheese mixture evenly among egg whites. Chill. Yield: 12 appetizers (51 calories each).

PROTEIN 3.7 / FAT 3.8 / CARBOHYDRATE 0.9 / CHOLESTEROL 104 / IRON 0.5 / SODIUM 74 / CALCIUM 21

POTATO SKINS

4 large baking potatoes (about 3 pounds)
Butter-flavored vegetable cooking spray
½ teaspoon salt
1 teaspoon paprika
¼ teaspoon freshly ground pepper
¼ cup plain low-fat yogurt
¼ cup low-fat sour cream
2 tablespoons minced fresh chives

Scrub potatoes thoroughly, and prick several times with a fork. Bake at 450° for 45 minutes to 1 hour or until done. Allow potatoes to cool to touch.

Cut potatoes in half lengthwise; carefully scoop out pulp, leaving ⅛-inch-thick shells. (Reserve pulp for other uses.) Cut each potato shell lengthwise into 4 strips, and place on an ungreased baking sheet. Spray potato strips lightly with cooking spray. Combine salt, paprika, and pepper. Sprinkle over potato strips. Bake at 425° for 14 minutes or until crisp.

Combine yogurt and sour cream in a small bowl; stir in chives. Serve potato skins with sour cream mixture. Yield: 32 appetizers (11 calories per potato skin and ¾ teaspoon dip).

PROTEIN 0.4 / FAT 0.4 / CARBOHYDRATE 1.5 / CHOLESTEROL 1 / IRON 0.4 / SODIUM 40 / CALCIUM 9

ROLLED CRÊPES

1 (8-ounce) package Neufchâtel cheese, softened
¾ cup part-skim ricotta cheese
½ cup finely chopped lean cooked ham
3 tablespoons grated Parmesan cheese
1 tablespoon chopped fresh parsley
1 teaspoon dried whole thyme
1 clove garlic, minced
Spinach Crêpes

Combine Neufchâtel and ricotta cheese in a medium bowl; beat at medium speed of an electric mixer until smooth. Stir in ham and next 4 ingredients. Spread 2 tablespoons cheese mixture on each Spinach Crêpe; roll crêpes tightly, and refrigerate 1 hour.

Slice each crêpe diagonally into 6 pieces with an electric knife. Yield: 84 appetizers (20 calories each).

Spinach Crêpes:

1 cup unbleached flour
¾ cup skim milk
¼ cup chopped, cooked spinach
¼ cup chopped green onions
2 eggs
⅛ teaspoon salt
⅛ teaspoon ground nutmeg
Vegetable cooking spray

Combine first 7 ingredients in container of an electric blender or food processor. Top with cover; process until smooth. Refrigerate batter at least 1 hour. (This allows flour particles to swell and soften so that crêpes are light in texture.)

Coat a 6-inch crêpe pan with cooking spray; place over medium heat until just hot, not smoking. Spoon 2 tablespoons crêpe batter into pan; quickly spread batter in all directions so batter covers pan. Cook 1 minute or until lightly browned.

Lift edge of crêpe to test for doneness. Crêpe is ready for flipping when it can be shaken loose from pan. Flip crêpe, and cook about 30 seconds on other side. (This side is usually spotty brown and is the side on which filling is placed.)

Place crêpes on a towel to cool. Stack between layers of wax paper to prevent sticking. Repeat until all batter is used. Yield: 14 crêpes.

PROTEIN 1.2 / FAT 1.0 / CARBOHYDRATE 1.4 / CHOLESTEROL 8 / IRON 0.1 / SODIUM 38 / CALCIUM 15

ONION FOCCACIA

5 medium onions (about 1¾ pounds)
Vegetable cooking spray
1 tablespoon olive oil
⅓ cup canned no-salt-added chicken broth,
　undiluted
2 tablespoons balsamic vinegar
1 tablespoon fresh rosemary
1½ teaspoons salt, divided
¼ teaspoon pepper
1 package dry yeast
¼ cup warm water (105° to 115°)
1 teaspoon honey
3 cups unbleached flour
1 cup warm skim milk (105° to 115°)
2 tablespoons grated Parmesan cheese

Peel onions; cut in half lengthwise, and thinly slice crosswise. Coat a large nonstick skillet with cooking spray; add olive oil. Place over medium heat until hot. Add onions. Cover and cook 20 minutes or until onions are tender and begin to brown, stirring occasionally.

Stir in chicken broth. Cook over high heat 1 minute or until liquid evaporates, stirring constantly. Add vinegar; cook 4 minutes or until onions are golden and glazed. Stir in rosemary, ½ teaspoon salt, and pepper. Cool completely.

Combine yeast, water, and honey in a small bowl; let stand 5 minutes.

Position knife blade in food processor bowl. Add flour and remaining 1 teaspoon salt; top with cover, and process 10 seconds. Pour yeast mixture and milk through food chute with processor running; process until dough forms a ball. Process dough an additional 5 seconds. Remove dough from bowl, and knead 1 to 2 minutes. Place in a bowl that has been coated with cooking spray, turning to grease top. Cover and let rise in a warm place (85°), free from drafts, 45 minutes or until doubled in bulk.

Punch dough down; return to bowl. Cover and let rise in a warm place 20 minutes or until almost doubled in bulk. Knead 1 to 2 minutes or until smooth and elastic. Pat dough evenly onto a 14- x 16-inch baking sheet that has been coated with cooking spray, spreading to edges. Cover with plastic wrap that has been coated with cooking spray, and let rise in a warm place 30 minutes or until doubled in bulk.

Gently spread onion mixture over dough. Sprinkle with cheese. Bake at 400° on lower rack of oven 25 minutes or until crust is golden. Cool on a wire rack. Cut into 2-inch squares. Serve warm or at room temperature. Yield: 56 appetizers (32 calories each).

PROTEIN 1.1 / FAT 0.5 / CARBOHYDRATE 6.1 / CHOLESTEROL 0 / IRON 0.3 / SODIUM 70 / CALCIUM 12

MINI PIZZAS

1 package dry yeast
¼ cup warm water (105° to 115°)
2 teaspoons honey
2 cups unbleached flour
1 cup whole wheat flour
1 teaspoon salt
¾ cup water
Vegetable cooking spray
2 tablespoons cornmeal
½ cup plus 3 tablespoons no-salt-added
　tomato sauce
½ teaspoon dried whole basil
½ teaspoon dried whole oregano
½ teaspoon dried whole thyme
¼ teaspoon freshly ground pepper
2 cups (8 ounces) shredded mozzarella cheese

Dissolve yeast in ¼ cup warm water; add honey, and let stand 5 minutes.

Position knife blade in food processor bowl; add flours, salt, and yeast mixture. With processor running, pour ¾ cup water through food chute in a slow, steady stream. Process until well blended. Place dough in a bowl that has been coated with cooking spray, turning to grease top. Cover and let rise in a warm place (85°), free from drafts, 30 minutes.

Punch dough down, and divide into 32 equal pieces. Roll each piece into a 3-inch circle. Place circles on baking sheets that have been coated with cooking spray and sprinkled with cornmeal.

Combine tomato sauce and next 4 ingredients. Spread 1 teaspoon tomato sauce mixture on each pizza round. Sprinkle with cheese. Bake at 500° for 5 to 6 minutes or until cheese melts. Yield: 32 appetizers (64 calories each).

PROTEIN 2.8 / FAT 1.7 / CARBOHYDRATE 9.5 / CHOLESTEROL 6 / IRON 0.5 / SODIUM 101 / CALCIUM 40

MINCED TURKEY-CABBAGE ROLLS

1 teaspoon cornstarch
1 teaspoon sugar
1 teaspoon dry sherry
1 teaspoon water
1 teaspoon oyster sauce
1 teaspoon reduced-sodium soy sauce
½ teaspoon salt
1¼ pounds fresh raw lean ground turkey
4 dried wood ear mushrooms
Vegetable cooking spray
1 teaspoon sesame oil
2 tablespoons minced green onions
2 teaspoons minced fresh gingerroot
2 cloves garlic, minced
1 (8-ounce) can sliced water chestnuts, drained and minced
½ cup frozen English peas, thawed
¼ cup canned no-salt-added chicken broth, undiluted
1 tablespoon oyster sauce
1 tablespoon dry sherry
2 teaspoons cornstarch
1 teaspoon reduced-sodium soy sauce
½ teaspoon salt
¼ teaspoon ground white pepper
32 Chinese cabbage leaves

Combine first 7 ingredients; stir well. Stir in turkey. Cover; marinate in refrigerator 1 hour.

Soak mushrooms in hot water 30 minutes. Drain well; press mushrooms between paper towels to remove excess moisture. Chop mushrooms, and set aside.

Coat a nonstick skillet with cooking spray. Add marinated turkey mixture; cook over medium-high heat 4 to 5 minutes or until done, stirring to crumble. Transfer to a large bowl; set aside.

Add 1 teaspoon sesame oil to skillet. Add green onions, gingerroot, and garlic; sauté over medium-high heat until onions are tender. Add water chestnuts, reserved chopped mushrooms, and peas. Cook 1 minute. Stir in turkey mixture. Combine chicken broth and next 6 ingredients. Add broth mixture to skillet. Cook over medium heat until thoroughly heated. Remove from heat; cover and keep warm.

Cook cabbage leaves in boiling water 4 minutes or until wilted; drain. Place 2 tablespoons turkey mixture in center of each cabbage leaf;
fold ends over, and roll up. Serve warm. Yield: 32 appetizers (37 calories each).

PROTEIN 4.8 / FAT 0.8 / CARBOHYDRATE 2.7 / CHOLESTEROL 12 / IRON 0.7 / SODIUM 156 / CALCIUM 49

CHICKEN SATE

6 (4-ounce) skinned, boned chicken breast halves
¼ cup canned no-salt-added chicken broth, undiluted
¼ cup reduced-sodium soy sauce
1 tablespoon curry powder
1 tablespoon safflower oil
2 teaspoons sugar
1 clove garlic, minced
Vegetable cooking spray
Peanut Sauce

Cut chicken into ½-inch-thick strips. Combine chicken broth and next 5 ingredients in a large bowl. Add chicken; toss gently to coat. Cover and marinate in refrigerator 6 hours.

Remove chicken from marinade mixture, discarding marinade. Weave chicken strips lengthwise onto thirty (6-inch) bamboo skewers that have been soaked in water overnight. Arrange skewers of chicken on a broiler rack that has been coated with cooking spray. Broil 4 inches from heat 4 minutes. Turn chicken, and broil an additional 4 minutes or until done. Serve warm with Peanut Sauce. Yield: 30 appetizers (43 calories per chicken strip and 1 teaspoon sauce).

Peanut Sauce:

¼ cup canned no-salt-added chicken broth, undiluted
1 tablespoon minced fresh cilantro
2 tablespoons peanut butter
2 tablespoons reduced-sodium soy sauce
1 tablespoon balsamic vinegar
1 tablespoon honey
1 teaspoon sesame oil
½ teaspoon minced garlic
⅛ teaspoon ground red pepper

Position knife blade in food processor bowl; add all ingredients. Top with cover, and process until smooth. Transfer to a serving bowl. Cover and chill. Yield: ⅔ cup.

PROTEIN 5.6 / FAT 1.6 / CARBOHYDRATE 1.3 / CHOLESTEROL 14 / IRON 0.3 / SODIUM 114 / CALCIUM 4

"BUFFALO" CHICKEN DRUMMETTES

½ cup canned low-sodium chicken broth, undiluted
1 tablespoon paprika
2 tablespoons lime juice
1 tablespoon reduced-sodium soy sauce
1 tablespoon honey
1 teaspoon safflower oil
½ teaspoon salt
¼ teaspoon hot sauce
⅛ teaspoon ground red pepper
⅛ teaspoon black pepper
24 chicken drummettes (about 2 pounds), skinned
Vegetable cooking spray
Blue Cheese Dip

Combine first 10 ingredients in a medium-size nonaluminum bowl; stir well. Add drummettes to chicken broth mixture. Cover and marinate in refrigerator 12 hours.

Remove drummettes from marinade, discarding marinade. Arrange drummettes on rack of a broiler pan that has been coated with cooking spray. Broil 20 minutes, turning frequently.

Arrange chicken drummettes on a serving platter, and serve with Blue Cheese Dip. Yield: 12 appetizers (76 calories per 2 drummettes and 1 tablespoon dip).

Blue Cheese Dip:

⅓ cup reduced-calorie mayonnaise
2 tablespoons minced onion
2 tablespoons nonfat buttermilk
1 clove garlic, minced
1 tablespoon vinegar
1 ounce blue cheese, crumbled
1 tablespoon minced fresh parsley
⅛ teaspoon pepper
Dash of hot sauce

Combine all ingredients in container of an electric blender or food processor; top with cover, and process until smooth. Transfer to a small serving bowl. Yield: ¾ cup.

PROTEIN 7.3 / FAT 4.1 / CARBOHYDRATE 2.2 / CHOLESTEROL 25 / IRON 0.4 / SODIUM 191 / CALCIUM 18

LAMB MEATBALLS WITH CURRY DIP

2 pounds lean ground lamb
¼ cup finely minced onion
¼ cup chopped pine nuts
2 tablespoons minced fresh gingerroot
2 tablespoons chopped fresh mint
1 teaspoon ground cumin
¼ teaspoon salt
¼ teaspoon pepper
¼ teaspoon ground cinnamon
Vegetable cooking spray
2 tablespoons lemon juice
Curry Dip

Combine first 9 ingredients; stir well. Shape mixture into 60 (1¼-inch) meatballs. Cover and refrigerate 1 hour.

Arrange meatballs on rack of a broiler pan that has been coated with cooking spray. Broil 8 to 10 minutes or until browned, turning frequently. Remove from oven, and sprinkle with lemon juice. Serve immediately with Curry Dip. Yield: 60 meatballs (98 calories per 3 meatballs and 1 tablespoon dip).

Curry Dip:

½ cup soft tofu
½ cup plain nonfat yogurt
¼ cup mango chutney
1 tablespoon plus ½ teaspoon minced green onions
1 tablespoon plus ½ teaspoon minced fresh cilantro
2 teaspoons curry powder

Combine all ingredients in container of an electric blender or food processor; top with cover, and process until smooth. Transfer to a serving bowl. Cover and chill. Yield: 1¼ cups.

PROTEIN 10.7 / FAT 4.6 / CARBOHYDRATE 3.8 / CHOLESTEROL 34 / IRON 1.1 / SODIUM 67 / CALCIUM 31

MARINATED MUSSELS

4 dozen fresh mussels
½ cup cornmeal
1 cup water
1 cup Chablis or other dry white wine
1 cup thinly sliced onion
2 bay leaves
⅓ cup champagne vinegar
1 egg yolk
2 tablespoons Dijon mustard
2 tablespoons olive oil
1 teaspoon fresh lemon juice
1 tablespoon minced green onions
1 tablespoon minced fresh parsley
1 tablespoon minced fresh cilantro
1 tablespoon minced fresh basil
⅛ teaspoon ground white pepper
Rock salt
Cilantro sprigs (optional)

Remove beards on mussels; scrub shells with a brush. Discard open or cracked mussels, or heavy ones (they're filled with sand). Place mussels in a large bowl; cover with cold water. Sprinkle with cornmeal; let stand 30 minutes.

Drain and rinse mussels. Discard cornmeal.

Combine water, wine, onion, and bay leaves in a large Dutch oven. Add mussels; cover and simmer 5 minutes or until shells open, shaking pot several times. Transfer mussels to a bowl using a slotted spoon; reserve liquid in pan. Let mussels cool. Discard halves of shells to which mussels are not attached. Remove mussels from shells, and place in a bowl; reserve shells.

Strain reserved cooking liquid through several layers of cheesecloth, reserving ⅓ cup. Combine ⅓ cup cooking liquid, vinegar, and next 9 ingredients in container of an electric blender. Top with cover, and process 30 seconds or until emulsified; pour over mussels. Cover and marinate in refrigerator at least 8 hours.

Drain mussels, reserving ½ cup marinade. Sprinkle rock salt on a serving platter. Arrange reserved shells on rock salt. Place one mussel in each shell. Top each with ½ teaspoon reserved marinade. Garnish with cilantro sprigs, if desired. Yield: 48 appetizers (14 calories each).

PROTEIN 0.9 / FAT 0.9 / CARBOHYDRATE 0.4 / CHOLESTEROL 8 / IRON 0.3 / SODIUM 39 / CALCIUM 4

OYSTERS WRAPPED IN SPINACH

2 dozen unshucked oysters
2 quarts water
24 large fresh spinach leaves
¼ cup clam juice
¼ teaspoon freshly ground pepper
1 teaspoon hot sauce
2 tablespoons lemon juice
1 tablespoon margarine
Lemon zest (optional)

Wash oysters thoroughly in cold water. Shuck oysters, reserving ¼ cup oyster liquid and deep half of shells. Set aside.

Bring water to a boil in a large Dutch oven. Place spinach in a metal basket, and plunge basket into boiling water. Cook 10 seconds, and remove immediately. Quickly place spinach in ice-cold water to cover. Let stand 1 minute; drain well. Carefully press spinach leaves between paper towels to remove excess moisture.

Combine reserved ¼ cup oyster liquid and clam juice in a medium saucepan. Bring liquid to a boil; add oysters, and reduce heat. Simmer 3 minutes or until edges of oysters begin to curl. Drain, reserving liquid.

Place an oyster on each spinach leaf. Sprinkle each evenly with pepper and hot sauce. Fold tip of leaf over oyster, and fold in sides of leaf. Roll up to make a neat package. Place each into a deep oyster shell half. Arrange shells on a serving platter.

Place reserved cooking liquid in a small saucepan; add lemon juice. Bring mixture to a boil; cook mixture, uncovered, about 10 minutes or until reduced to ¾ cup. Remove from heat; add margarine, and stir with a wire whisk until combined. Pour mixture evenly over spinach-wrapped oysters in shells. Sprinkle with lemon zest, if desired. Serve immediately. Yield: 24 appetizers. (22 calories each).

PROTEIN 1.8 / FAT 1.1 / CARBOHYDRATE 1.2 / CHOLESTEROL 13 / IRON 1.7 / SODIUM 43 / CALCIUM 17

BUTTERED CRANAPPLE PUNCH

3 cups cranapple juice
¼ teaspoon ground cinnamon
¼ teaspoon ground nutmeg
¼ teaspoon ground allspice
⅛ teaspoon ground cloves
2 teaspoons reduced-calorie
  margarine
Dash of nutmeg (optional)
4 (3-inch) sticks cinnamon (optional)

Combine first 5 ingredients in a saucepan. Bring to a boil over medium heat; stir frequently. Reduce heat; simmer 15 minutes. Pour into mugs. Top each serving with ½ teaspoon margarine. If desired, garnish with nutmeg and add cinnamon stick for stirring. Yield: 3 cups (135 calories per ¾-cup serving).

PROTEIN 0.2 / FAT 1.3 / CARBOHYDRATE 31.7 / CHOLESTEROL 0 / IRON 0.2 / SODIUM 22 / CALCIUM 16

GARDEN FRESH COCKTAIL

3 cups no-salt-added tomato juice
½ cup peeled, seeded, and coarsely chopped
  cucumber
1 small carrot, scraped and sliced
¼ cup chopped onion
2 tablespoons lemon juice
2 teaspoons low-sodium Worcestershire sauce
1 teaspoon dried whole dillweed
¼ teaspoon hot sauce
Cucumber slices (optional)

Combine tomato juice, chopped cucumber, carrot, onion, lemon juice, Worcestershire sauce, dillweed, and hot sauce in container of an electric blender; top with cover, and process vegetable mixture until smooth. Serve vegetable mixture over ice. Garnish each serving with a cucumber slice, if desired. Yield: 4 cups (53 calories per 1-cup serving).

PROTEIN 2.3 / FAT 0.1 / CARBOHYDRATE 13.2 / CHOLESTEROL 0 / IRON 0.3 / SODIUM 38 / CALCIUM 15

REFRESHING LIMEADE SPRITZER

¾ cup lime juice
⅓ cup superfine sugar
5 cups club soda, chilled
Lime wedges (optional)

Combine lime juice and sugar in a pitcher; stir until sugar dissolves. Add club soda, and stir well. Serve over ice. Garnish each glass with a lime wedge, if desired. Yield: 6 cups (51 calories per 1-cup serving).

PROTEIN 0.1 / FAT 0.0 / CARBOHYDRATE 13.8 / CHOLESTEROL 0 / IRON 0.0 / SODIUM 42 / CALCIUM 13

AMBROSIA CUP COOLER

1 cup fresh tangerine juice
1 cup unsweetened pineapple juice
2 medium bananas, peeled and sliced
2 tablespoons cherry-flavored liqueur or
  brandy
¼ teaspoon coconut extract
8 ice cubes

Combine first 5 ingredients in container of an electric blender; top with cover, and process until smooth. Add ice cubes, and process until smooth. Serve immediately. Yield: 4 cups (69 calories per ½-cup serving).

PROTEIN 0.6 / FAT 0.2 / CARBOHYDRATE 15.7 / CHOLESTEROL 0 / IRON 0.2 / SODIUM 1 / CALCIUM 13

(From left): Strawberry-Champagne Cocktail, Honeybees, and Chocolate Mocha-Mint Shake are delicious and refreshing beverages.

HONEYBEES

4 cups unsweetened orange juice
1 cup freshly squeezed lemon juice
¼ cup bourbon
3 tablespoons honey
Lemon rind curls (optional)

Combine first 4 ingredients in container of an electric blender; top with cover, and process until blended. Serve over ice. Garnish each serving with a lemon curl, if desired. Yield: 6 cups (140 calories per 1-cup serving).

PROTEIN 1.3 / FAT 0.1 / CARBOHYDRATE 30.1 / CHOLESTEROL 0 / IRON 0.2 / SODIUM 3 / CALCIUM 18

ISLAND COOLER

1 (6-ounce) can frozen orange juice
  concentrate, thawed and undiluted
2 cups unsweetened pineapple juice
2 teaspoons rum extract
2 cups lime-flavored sparkling mineral
  water, chilled
Fresh pineapple spears (optional)
Fresh mint sprigs (optional)

Combine orange juice concentrate, pineapple juice, and rum extract in a large pitcher. Chill thoroughly. Stir in mineral water just before serving. Serve over ice. If desired, garnish with fresh pineapple spears and fresh mint sprigs. Yield: 5 cups (118 calories per 1-cup serving).

PROTEIN 1.1 / FAT 0.2 / CARBOHYDRATE 26.8 / CHOLESTEROL 0 / IRON 0.4 / SODIUM 22 / CALCIUM 28

STRAWBERRY-CHAMPAGNE COCKTAIL

1½ cups sliced fresh strawberries
¼ cup Triple Sec or other orange-flavored liqueur
¾ cup unsweetened orange juice
1 cup champagne, chilled
½ cup club soda, chilled
Whole fresh strawberries (optional)

Combine sliced strawberries and liqueur in a small bowl; let stand 2 hours.

Combine strawberry mixture and orange juice in container of an electric blender; top with cover, and process until smooth. Stir in champagne and club soda. Pour into glasses, and garnish with whole strawberries, if desired. Serve immediately. Yield: 4 cups (130 calories per 1-cup serving).

PROTEIN 0.8 / FAT 0.3 / CARBOHYDRATE 13.9 / CHOLESTEROL 0 /
IRON 0.5 / SODIUM 10 / CALCIUM 15

BAHAMIAN COCOA

¼ cup firmly packed brown sugar
¼ cup unsweetened cocoa
1 cup water
4½ cups skim milk
1 tablespoon grated orange rind
1 teaspoon rum extract

Combine sugar and cocoa in a medium saucepan; stir until blended. Stir in water. Bring

to a boil over medium heat. Reduce heat; slowly stir in milk. Cook until thoroughly heated, stirring constantly.

Remove from heat, and stir in orange rind and rum extract. Beat at medium speed of an electric mixer until frothy. Serve immediately. Yield: 6 cups (118 calories per 1-cup serving).

PROTEIN 7.3 / FAT 0.8 / CARBOHYDRATE 19.7 / CHOLESTEROL 4 /
IRON 1.0 / SODIUM 99 / CALCIUM 241

CHOCOLATE MOCHA-MINT SHAKE

2 cups strong cold coffee
1 cup chocolate ice milk
1 cup skim milk
4 ice cubes
½ teaspoon peppermint extract
2 tablespoons crushed hard peppermint candy

Combine cold coffee, ice milk, skim milk, ice

cubes, and peppermint extract in container of an electric blender; top with cover, and process until smooth. Pour into serving glasses, and sprinkle evenly with crushed peppermint candy. Serve immediately. Yield: 4 cups (86 calories per 1-cup serving).

PROTEIN 2.8 / FAT 0.7 / CARBOHYDRATE 14.9 / CHOLESTEROL 1 /
IRON 0.6 / SODIUM 37 / CALCIUM 79

WINE COOLER SMARTS

Packaged to look like soda and fruit drinks, and promoted almost as furiously, wine coolers have fast become popular additions to the alcohol beverage industry. At last count, these liquids made up a full 25 percent of total industry sales. But if you think these beverages are healthy alternatives to other alcoholic drinks, think again. Unbeknown to most consumers, wine coolers actually contain more alcohol than beer or mixed drinks.

One 12-ounce bottle of wine cooler contains more alcohol than a mixed drink made with 1 ounce of hard liquor. Wine coolers average 6 percent alcohol

by volume. Most beers, however, contain only 4 percent alcohol. In addition, wine coolers are higher in calories. Each 12-ounce bottle typically packs 200 calories.

One 6-ounce glass of wine itself averages 110 calories and 11.5 percent alcohol by weight, making it an even more concentrated source of alcohol and calories. Wine coolers have added sugar and sometimes fruit juice to dilute the wine, but they are still rich in alcohol. While there is no reason not to enjoy wine coolers, it is important to know what you are drinking.

SPICY ORANGE-ALMOND TEA

2 cups boiling water
4 orange spice tea bags
1 cup water
2 (1-inch) sticks cinnamon
1 tablespoon sugar
½ teaspoon pumpkin pie spice
1 cup unsweetened orange juice
3 tablespoons amaretto
12 whole cloves
4 orange slices

Pour 2 cups boiling water over tea bags; cover and steep 5 minutes. Remove and discard tea bags. Set steeped tea aside.

Combine 1 cup water, cinnamon sticks, sugar, and pumpkin pie spice in a saucepan; bring to a boil. Reduce heat, and simmer 10 minutes. Remove and discard cinnamon sticks. Add reserved tea, orange juice, and amaretto; stir well. Cook over medium heat until thoroughly heated (do not boil). Pour into mugs. Insert 3 cloves into each orange slice and float on top of tea. Serve immediately. Yield: 4 cups (79 calories per 1-cup serving).

PROTEIN 0.4 / FAT 0.1 / CARBOHYDRATE 14.3 / CHOLESTEROL 0 / IRON 0.1 / SODIUM 1 / CALCIUM 7

FLAMING SPICED COFFEE BRÛLOT

¼ cup brandy
2 tablespoons brown sugar
2 (2- x ¼-inch) strips orange rind
2 (2- x ¼-inch) strips lemon rind
2 teaspoons whole cloves
1 (4-inch) stick cinnamon,
  quartered
2 cups hot coffee
Orange rind curls (optional)

Combine first 6 ingredients in a small, long-handled saucepan. Cook over medium heat until mixture is warm (do not boil). Remove from heat, and ignite with a long match. Pour over hot coffee. Ladle into 8 demitasse cups. Garnish with orange curls, if desired. Yield: 2 cups (28 calories per ¼-cup serving).

PROTEIN 0.1 / FAT 0.0 / CARBOHYDRATE 7.1 / CHOLESTEROL 0 / IRON 0.7 / SODIUM 4 / CALCIUM 8

COFFEE DIABLE

¼ cup brandy
2 tablespoons sugar
1 teaspoon grated lemon rind
½ teaspoon ground cinnamon
¼ teaspoon ground cloves
3¾ cups strong, hot coffee
Lemon rind twists (optional)
4 (3-inch) sticks cinnamon (optional)

Combine first 5 ingredients in a small bowl; stir until sugar dissolves. Divide mixture evenly among 4 coffee mugs. Add hot coffee; stir well. If desired, garnish each serving with a lemon twist and a cinnamon stick for stirring. Yield: 4 cups (64 calories per 1-cup serving).

PROTEIN 0.3 / FAT 0.0 / CARBOHYDRATE 7.5 / CHOLESTEROL 0 / IRON 1.1 / SODIUM 5 / CALCIUM 10

(Clockwise from top): Enjoy the home-baked goodness of Whole Wheat-Apricot Twist (page 114), Orange Rye Rolls (page 117), and Easy Cucumber-Dill Loaf (page 115).

Breads, Grains & Pasta

CURRY WHEAT THINS

1 cup all-purpose flour
1 cup whole wheat flour
3 tablespoons sugar
¾ teaspoon salt
¾ teaspoon curry powder
½ teaspoon baking powder
½ teaspoon baking soda
¼ cup unsalted margarine
1 cup plain nonfat yogurt
Vegetable cooking spray

Combine first 7 ingredients; stir well. Cut in margarine with a pastry blender until mixture resembles coarse meal. Add yogurt, stirring until dry ingredients are moistened. Turn dough out onto a lightly floured surface, and knead 20 times. Cover and freeze 15 minutes.

Divide dough into 8 equal portions. Roll each portion into a 10- x 6-inch rectangle on a baking sheet that has been coated with cooking spray. Cut each portion into fifteen 2-inch squares. Pierce squares with a fork. Bake at 450° for 10 minutes or until golden brown. Remove from pan; cool completely on wire racks. Store in an airtight container. Yield: 120 crackers (13 calories each).

PROTEIN 0.4 / FAT 0.4 / CARBOHYDRATE 2.0 / CHOLESTEROL 0 / IRON 0.1 / SODIUM 21 / CALCIUM 6

EASY BREADSTICKS

2 whole wheat rolls
3 tablespoons plus 1½ teaspoons reduced-calorie margarine, melted
2 tablespoons grated Parmesan cheese
2 teaspoons minced fresh parsley

Split each roll in half lengthwise. Cut each half into 4 breadsticks. Place breadsticks 1 inch apart on a baking sheet.

Combine remaining ingredients, mixing well. Brush butter mixture over tops of bread. Bake at 200° for 1½ hours or until crisp and lightly browned. Cool completely. Store breadsticks in an airtight container. Yield: 16 breadsticks (42 calories each).

PROTEIN 1.1 / FAT 2.2 / CARBOHYDRATE 4.8 / CHOLESTEROL 0 / IRON 0.0 / SODIUM 67 / CALCIUM 9

SPICY PUMPKIN PONES

2 cups cornmeal
1 cup skim milk
1 (15½-ounce) can pumpkin
2 tablespoons margarine, melted
1 egg, beaten
1 tablespoon sugar
¼ teaspoon salt
¼ teaspoon ground cinnamon
⅛ teaspoon ground nutmeg
⅛ teaspoon ground cloves
Vegetable cooking spray

Combine first 10 ingredients in a large bowl; stir well. Drop mixture by level tablespoonfuls onto a griddle or electric skillet that has been coated with cooking spray. Bake at 400° for 15 to 20 minutes or until lightly browned. Yield: 53 pones (28 calories each).

PROTEIN 0.8 / FAT 0.6 / CARBOHYDRATE 4.8 / CHOLESTEROL 4 / IRON 0.3 / SODIUM 20 / CALCIUM 9

CINNAMON-PEAR PANCAKES

¾ cup all-purpose flour
¾ cup whole wheat flour
¼ cup unprocessed oat bran
1½ teaspoons baking powder
½ teaspoon baking soda
¼ teaspoon salt
½ teaspoon ground cinnamon
¼ teaspoon ground nutmeg
1½ cups nonfat buttermilk
1 egg, beaten
2 tablespoons water
½ cup peeled, shredded fresh pear
Vegetable cooking spray

Combine first 8 ingredients in a large bowl; make a well in center of mixture. Combine buttermilk, egg, and water; add to dry ingredients, stirring until moistened. Fold in shredded pear.

For each pancake, pour ¼ cup batter onto a hot griddle or skillet that has been coated with cooking spray. (Batter will be thick.) Turn pancakes when tops are covered with bubbles and edges look cooked. Yield: 12 (4-inch) pancakes (92 calories each).

PROTEIN 4.0 / FAT 1.1 / CARBOHYDRATE 17.1 / CHOLESTEROL 17 / IRON 0.8 / SODIUM 158 / CALCIUM 42

(From top): Applesauce and shredded pears give Oatmeal Pancakes and Cinnamon-Pear Pancakes light texture. Both can be served topped with sliced fresh fruit and reduced-calorie maple syrup.

OATMEAL PANCAKES

¾ cup quick-cooking oats, uncooked
1½ cups skim milk
2 eggs, beaten
¾ cup unsweetened applesauce
1 tablespoon vegetable oil
1¼ cups all-purpose flour
1 tablespoon baking powder
1 tablespoon sugar
½ teaspoon salt
½ teaspoon ground cinnamon
Vegetable cooking spray

Combine oats and milk in a medium bowl; let stand 5 minutes. Add eggs, applesauce, and oil to oat mixture, stirring well.

Combine flour, baking powder, sugar, salt, and cinnamon in a large bowl; add oat mixture to dry ingredients, stirring just until moistened.

For each pancake, pour ¼ cup batter onto a hot griddle or skillet that has been coated with cooking spray. Turn pancakes when tops are covered with bubbles and edges look cooked. Yield: 14 (4-inch) pancakes (121 calories each).

PROTEIN 4.4 / FAT 2.6 / CARBOHYDRATE 19.8 / CHOLESTEROL 29 / IRON 1.0 / SODIUM 172 / CALCIUM 85

CHEESY CHIVE BISCUITS

1¼ cups all-purpose flour
½ cup unprocessed oat bran
1 tablespoon minced fresh parsley
1½ teaspoons baking powder
2 teaspoons minced fresh chives
⅛ teaspoon dried whole oregano
2 tablespoons unsalted margarine, softened
¾ cup low-fat cottage cheese
2 egg whites, lightly beaten
1 tablespoon all-purpose flour
1 tablespoon cornmeal

Combine first 6 ingredients in a large bowl; cut in margarine with a pastry blender until mixture resembles coarse meal. Add cottage cheese and egg whites, stirring just until dry ingredients are moistened.

Sprinkle 1 tablespoon flour evenly over work surface. Turn dough out onto floured surface, and knead lightly 3 to 4 times. Roll dough to ⅞-inch thickness; cut into rounds with a 2-inch biscuit cutter. Sprinkle a baking sheet with cornmeal; transfer dough rounds to baking sheet. Bake at 400° for 10 to 13 minutes or until golden brown. Serve warm. Yield: 1 dozen (103 calories each).

PROTEIN 4.8 / FAT 2.5 / CARBOHYDRATE 14.9 / CHOLESTEROL 1 / IRON 0.8 / SODIUM 104 / CALCIUM 40

CRACKED WHEAT-APPLESAUCE MUFFINS

½ cup boiling water
¼ cup cracked wheat
1 cup unsweetened applesauce
⅓ cup unsalted margarine
⅔ cup sugar
1 egg, beaten
2 cups all-purpose flour
1 teaspoon baking soda
1½ teaspoons ground cinnamon
1 teaspoon ground allspice
½ teaspoon salt
½ cup raisins
Vegetable cooking spray

Pour boiling water over cracked wheat; let stand 20 minutes. Stir in applesauce.

Cream margarine; gradually add sugar, beating at medium speed of an electric mixer until light and fluffy. Add egg; beat well. Combine flour, soda, ground cinnamon, ground allspice, and salt in a small bowl. Add flour mixture to creamed mixture alternately with applesauce mixture, beginning and ending with flour mixture. Fold in raisins.

Spoon batter into muffin pans that have been coated with cooking spray, filling three-fourths full. Bake at 375° for 15 minutes or until golden brown. Remove from pans immediately. Yield: 1½ dozen (147 calories each).

PROTEIN 2.3 / FAT 4.1 / CARBOHYDRATE 25.7 / CHOLESTEROL 15 / IRON 0.8 / SODIUM 116 / CALCIUM 21

RHUBARB NUT BREAD

1¼ cups all-purpose flour
¼ cup sugar
¼ cup firmly packed brown sugar
1½ teaspoons baking powder
¼ teaspoon baking soda
¼ teaspoon salt
¼ teaspoon ground cloves
1 egg, beaten
½ cup plain nonfat yogurt
¼ cup vegetable oil
1 teaspoon almond extract
1½ cups diced fresh rhubarb
Vegetable cooking spray
2 tablespoons finely chopped almonds
1 tablespoon sugar

Combine first 7 ingredients in a large bowl; stir well. Combine egg, yogurt, oil, and almond extract. Add to dry ingredients, stirring well. Fold in rhubarb.

Spoon batter into an 8½- x 4½- x 3-inch loafpan that has been coated with cooking spray. Combine almonds and 1 tablespoon sugar. Sprinkle over batter. Bake at 350° for 55 minutes or until a wooden pick inserted near center comes out clean. Let cool in pan 10 minutes. Remove from pan, and let cool on a wire rack. Cover and chill 8 hours. Yield: 16 servings (115 calories per ½-inch slice).

PROTEIN 2.2 / FAT 4.5 / CARBOHYDRATE 16.8 / CHOLESTEROL 13 / IRON 0.6 / SODIUM 89 / CALCIUM 54

FIVE-GRAIN LOAF

1 cup 5-grain cereal
1½ cups nonfat buttermilk
1 egg, beaten
2 tablespoons brown sugar
2 tablespoons plus 1½ teaspoons vegetable oil
2 cups unbleached flour
1 teaspoon baking powder
1 teaspoon baking soda
½ teaspoon ground cinnamon
¼ teaspoon salt
Vegetable cooking spray

Combine cereal and buttermilk in a small bowl; let stand 5 minutes. Add egg, sugar, and vegetable oil; stir well.

Combine flour and next 4 ingredients in a large bowl, stirring well. Add cereal mixture to flour mixture, stirring just until dry ingredients are moistened. Spoon batter into an 8½- x 4½- x 3-inch loafpan that has been coated with cooking spray. Bake at 350° for 45 to 50 minutes or until a wooden pick inserted in center comes out clean. Cool in pan 10 minutes; remove from pan, and let cool on a wire rack. Yield: 15 servings (117 calories per ½-inch slice).

PROTEIN 3.4 / FAT 3.3 / CARBOHYDRATE 18.8 / CHOLESTEROL 18 / IRON 0.8 / SODIUM 161 / CALCIUM 29

APPLE-SOUR CREAM COFFEE CAKE

1 cup peeled, chopped cooking apples
1⅓ cups all-purpose flour, divided
¾ teaspoon baking powder
¾ teaspoon baking soda
¾ teaspoon ground cinnamon, divided
½ teaspoon ground nutmeg
⅓ cup unsalted margarine, softened
½ cup sugar
2 eggs
⅔ cup low-fat sour cream
2 tablespoons brandy
½ teaspoon vanilla extract
Vegetable cooking spray
3 tablespoons chopped raisins
2 tablespoons brown sugar
2 teaspoons lemon juice
1 tablespoon powdered sugar

Toss apples with 2 tablespoons flour; set aside. Combine remaining flour, baking powder, soda, ½ teaspoon cinnamon, and nutmeg in a small bowl; set aside. Cream margarine; gradually add sugar, beating at medium speed of an electric mixer until light and fluffy. Add eggs, one at a time, beating well after each addition. Add reserved flour mixture alternately with sour cream, beginning and ending with flour mixture. Mix after each addition. Stir in brandy and vanilla.

Spread one-half of batter into a 9-inch square baking pan that has been coated with cooking spray. Combine reserved apples, remaining ¼ teaspoon cinnamon, raisins, brown sugar, and lemon juice; sprinkle evenly over batter. Spread remaining batter evenly over apple mixture. Bake at 350° for 40 minutes or until a wooden pick inserted in center comes out clean. Cool in pan on a wire rack. Dust top of cake with powdered sugar. Yield: 16 servings (139 calories per serving).

PROTEIN 2.4 / FAT 5.8 / CARBOHYDRATE 19.7 / CHOLESTEROL 29 / IRON 0.6 / SODIUM 66 / CALCIUM 37

WINTER WORKOUTS

To stay warm during outdoor winter workouts, dress in layers: a T-shirt under a sweatshirt under a jacket. Not only do layers trap in body heat but also they are easy to pull off as your body warms up. Make use of outdoor apparel accessories. Cover your head and hands to prevent chapping. Use a scarf over your mouth to prevent loss of moisture from the lungs.

Surprise your family with familiar flavors in Peanut Butter and Jelly Coffee Cake.

PEANUT BUTTER AND JELLY COFFEE CAKE

3 cups all-purpose flour, divided
1 package dry yeast
½ teaspoon salt
¾ teaspoon ground ginger, divided
½ cup skim milk
½ cup water
3 tablespoons brown sugar
3 tablespoons no-sugar-added peanut butter
1 tablespoon unsalted margarine
1 egg, beaten
3 tablespoons all-purpose flour, divided
Vegetable cooking spray
¾ cup no-sugar-added strawberry spread

Combine 2 cups flour, yeast, salt, and ½ teaspoon ginger in a large bowl; stir well. Set aside.

Combine skim milk and next 4 ingredients in a medium saucepan; cook over medium heat until very warm (120° to 130°). Remove mixture from heat.

Gradually add milk mixture to flour mixture, beating at medium speed of an electric mixer 3 minutes. Add egg; beat an additional 3 minutes at medium speed. Stir in enough remaining flour to make a soft dough.

Sprinkle 2 tablespoons flour evenly over work surface. Turn dough out onto floured surface, and knead until dough is smooth and elastic (about 8 to 10 minutes). Place dough in a large bowl that has been coated with cooking spray, turning to grease top. Cover and let rise in a warm place (85°), free from drafts, 1½ hours or until doubled in bulk.

Punch dough down; cover and let stand 10 minutes. Sprinkle remaining 1 tablespoon flour evenly over work surface. Place dough on floured surface, and roll into a 22- x 12-inch rectangle. Combine strawberry spread and remaining ¼ teaspoon ginger; spread over rectangle, leaving a 1-inch margin at sides.

Roll up dough, jellyroll fashion, starting at long side; pinch ends and seam to seal. Place dough, seam side down, in a 9-inch round cakepan that has been coated with cooking spray, beginning at outer edge and making concentric circles toward center of pan. Cover and let rise in a warm place, free from drafts, 30 minutes or until doubled in bulk. Bake at 350° for 35 minutes. Cover with aluminum foil the last 15 minutes of baking, if necessary, to prevent excessive browning. Cool in pan 10 minutes; remove from pan, and let cool on a wire rack. Yield: 18 servings (132 calories per serving).

PROTEIN 4.0 / FAT 2.6 / CARBOHYDRATE 22.9 / CHOLESTEROL 11 / IRON 0.9 / SODIUM 74 / CALCIUM 17

RAISIN BRAN ENGLISH MUFFIN LOAF

2 cups whole wheat flour
2 packages dry yeast
¾ teaspoon salt
¼ teaspoon baking powder
2 cups skim milk
½ cup water
1 tablespoon honey
1 cup unprocessed wheat bran
⅓ cup raisins, chopped
2½ cups all-purpose flour
Vegetable cooking spray
2 tablespoons cornmeal, divided

Combine whole wheat flour, yeast, salt, and baking powder; stir well. Combine milk, water, and honey in a small saucepan; cook over medium heat until very warm (120° to 130°). Gradually add milk mixture to flour mixture, beating at medium speed of an electric mixer 3 minutes. Gradually stir in bran, raisins, and enough all-purpose flour to make a stiff dough.

Coat two 8½- x 4½- x 3-inch loafpans with cooking spray; sprinkle each pan with 2 teaspoons cornmeal. Spoon batter evenly into pans. (Batter will be thin in pans.) Sprinkle remaining 2 teaspoons cornmeal evenly over batter in pans. Cover and let rise in a warm place (85°), free from drafts, 30 to 45 minutes or until doubled in bulk. Bake at 400° for 25 minutes. Remove from pans immediately, and let cool on wire racks. Yield: 32 servings (83 calories per ½-inch slice).

PROTEIN 3.1 / FAT 0.4 / CARBOHYDRATE 17.0 / CHOLESTEROL 0 / IRON 1.0 / SODIUM 66 / CALCIUM 29

APPLE CINNAMON ROLLS

5½ cups all-purpose flour, divided
⅓ cup sugar
2 packages dry yeast
2 teaspoons ground cinnamon
1 teaspoon salt
1 cup unsweetened apple juice
⅔ cup water
3 tablespoons unsalted margarine
2 eggs
¼ cup all-purpose flour, divided
Vegetable cooking spray
2 tablespoons unsalted margarine, melted and
   divided
¼ cup raisins, chopped
2 tablespoons sugar
¼ teaspoon ground cinnamon
½ cup sifted powdered sugar
2 tablespoons unsweetened apple juice

Combine 2 cups flour, ⅓ cup sugar, yeast, 2 teaspoons cinnamon, and salt; stir well. Combine 1 cup apple juice, water, and 3 tablespoons margarine in a saucepan; cook over medium heat until very warm (120° to 130°).

Gradually add hot liquid mixture to dry ingredients. Beat at medium speed of an electric mixer 2 minutes or until smooth. Add eggs and ½ cup flour. Beat an additional 2 minutes at high speed. Gradually stir in enough of the remaining 3 cups flour to make a soft dough.

Sprinkle 3 tablespoons flour evenly over work surface. Turn dough out onto floured surface; knead until smooth and elastic (about 8 to 10 minutes). Place in a large bowl that has been coated with cooking spray, turning to grease top. Cover and let rise in a warm place (85°), free from drafts, 1 hour or until doubled in bulk.

Punch dough down, and divide in half. Sprinkle 1½ teaspoons flour evenly over work surface. Place half of dough on floured surface, and roll into an 18- x 5-inch rectangle; brush with 1 tablespoon melted margarine. Combine raisins, 2 tablespoons sugar, and ¼ teaspoon cinnamon. Sprinkle half of raisin mixture evenly over rectangle. Roll up dough jellyroll fashion, starting at long side. Pinch seam to seal. Cut roll into 1-inch slices. Repeat procedure with remaining 1½ teaspoons flour, dough, 1 tablespoon melted margarine, and raisin mixture.

Place slices, cut side down, in two 13- x 9- x 2-inch baking pans that have been coated with cooking spray. Cover and let rise in a warm place, free from drafts, 30 minutes or until doubled in bulk.

Bake at 375° for 20 to 25 minutes or until golden brown. Combine powdered sugar and 2 tablespoons apple juice; stir well. Drizzle over warm rolls. Yield: 3 dozen (122 calories each).

PROTEIN 2.8 / FAT 2.1 / CARBOHYDRATE 22.8 / CHOLESTEROL 11 / IRON 0.9 / SODIUM 70 / CALCIUM 9

WHOLE WHEAT-APRICOT TWIST

1 package dry yeast
¼ cup warm water (105° to 115°)
¾ cup nonfat buttermilk
3 tablespoons molasses
2 tablespoons margarine
½ cup bran flakes cereal
1½ cups whole wheat flour
½ teaspoon salt
2 cups chopped, dried apricots
1¼ cups all-purpose flour
1 tablespoon all-purpose flour
Vegetable cooking spray

Dissolve yeast in warm water; let stand 5 minutes. Combine buttermilk, molasses, and margarine in a saucepan; cook over medium heat until margarine melts, stirring constantly. Transfer buttermilk mixture to a large bowl; add bran cereal, and stir well. Cool to 105° to 115°. Add yeast mixture, whole wheat flour, and salt. Beat at low speed of an electric mixer until well blended. Beat an additional 3 minutes at high speed. Stir in apricots and enough of the 1¼ cups all-purpose flour to make a soft dough.

Sprinkle 1 tablespoon all-purpose flour evenly over work surface. Turn dough out onto floured surface, and knead until smooth and elastic (about 8 to 10 minutes). Place dough in a large bowl that has been coated with cooking spray, turning to grease top. Cover and let rise in a warm place (85°), free from drafts, 1½ hours or until doubled in bulk.

Punch dough down, and divide into 3 equal portions. Shape each portion into an 11-inch rope. Braid ropes, pinching ends to seal. Place braided loaf in a 9- x 5- x 3-inch loafpan that has been coated with cooking spray. Cover and let rise in a warm place, free from drafts, 45 minutes or until doubled in bulk. Bake at 350° for 30 to 40 minutes or until loaf sounds hollow when tapped. Remove from pan, and let cool completely on a wire rack. Yield: 18 servings (105 calories per ½-inch slice).

PROTEIN 3.2 / FAT 1.7 / CARBOHYDRATE 20.2 / CHOLESTEROL 0 / IRON 1.3 / SODIUM 103 / CALCIUM 19

EASY CUCUMBER-DILL LOAF

1½ cups peeled, shredded cucumber
3 cups all-purpose flour, divided
1 package dry yeast
¼ cup warm water (105° to 115°)
1 (8-ounce) carton plain nonfat yogurt
¼ teaspoon baking soda
1 egg
1 tablespoon sugar
½ teaspoon salt
3 tablespoons minced fresh parsley
1 tablespoon minced fresh dillweed or 1 teaspoon dried whole dillweed
1 tablespoon minced fresh chives
Vegetable cooking spray

Press cucumber between paper towels to remove excess moisture. Toss cucumber with 2 tablespoons flour; set aside.

Dissolve yeast in warm water; let stand 5 minutes. Combine yogurt and soda in a small bowl; stir well.

Combine egg, sugar, salt, yeast mixture, yogurt mixture, and 2 cups flour in a large bowl. Beat at low speed of an electric mixer until smooth. Beat an additional 3 minutes at high speed. Add remaining ¾ cup plus 2 tablespoons flour; stir well. Stir in reserved cucumber, parsley, dillweed, and chives.

Spoon mixture into a 2-quart soufflé dish that has been coated with cooking spray. Cover and let rise in a warm place (85°), free from drafts, 1 hour or until doubled in bulk. Uncover and bake at 350° for 45 minutes or until loaf sounds hollow when tapped. Remove from dish, and let cool on a wire rack. Yield: 14 servings (129 calories per ½-inch wedge).

PROTEIN 4.8 / FAT 0.8 / CARBOHYDRATE 25.4 / CHOLESTEROL 15 / IRON 1.2 / SODIUM 118 / CALCIUM 48

HEARTY CALIFORNIA BREAD

3 cups whole wheat flour, divided
1 cup all-purpose flour
2 packages dry yeast
½ teaspoon salt
1 cup water
½ cup unsweetened orange juice
1 tablespoon honey
¼ cup millet
¼ cup unsalted sunflower kernels, toasted
¼ cup currants
1 teaspoon grated orange rind
1 tablespoon all-purpose flour
Vegetable cooking spray

Combine 1 cup whole wheat flour, all-purpose flour, yeast, and salt in a large bowl; stir well. Set aside.

Combine water, orange juice, and honey in a small saucepan; cook over medium heat until very warm (120° to 130°). Add orange juice mixture to reserved flour mixture, and beat at low speed of an electric mixer until well blended. Beat an additional 3 minutes at medium speed. Stir in remaining 2 cups whole wheat flour, millet, sunflower kernels, currants, and grated orange rind.

Sprinkle 1 tablespoon all-purpose flour evenly over work surface. Turn dough out onto floured surface, and knead until smooth and elastic (about 8 to 10 minutes). Place dough in a large bowl that has been coated with cooking spray, turning to grease top. Cover and let rise in a warm place (85°), free from drafts, 1 hour or until doubled in bulk.

Punch dough down, and shape into a round, slightly flat loaf. Place loaf on a baking sheet that has been coated with cooking spray. Cover and let rise in a warm place, free from drafts, 45 minutes or until doubled in bulk.

Place a 13- x 9- x 2-inch pan of boiling water on lower rack of oven. Place baking sheet on middle rack of oven. Bake at 375° for 45 minutes or until loaf sounds hollow when tapped. Remove from baking sheet, and let cool on a wire rack. Yield: 16 servings (145 calories per 1-inch wedge).

PROTEIN 5.1 / FAT 1.9 / CARBOHYDRATE 28.7 / CHOLESTEROL 0 / IRON 1.5 / SODIUM 76 / CALCIUM 18

MIXED GRAINS-BUTTERMILK BREAD

2 cups whole wheat flour
½ cup cornmeal
¼ cup wheat germ
2 packages dry yeast
½ teaspoon baking soda
2¼ cups nonfat buttermilk
¼ cup honey
2 tablespoons margarine
½ teaspoon salt
1 cup bulgur wheat, divided
2¼ cups all-purpose flour
1 tablespoon all-purpose flour
Vegetable cooking spray
2 tablespoons water

Combine first 5 ingredients in a large bowl; stir well. Combine buttermilk, honey, margarine, and salt in a saucepan; cook over medium heat until very warm (120° to 130°). Add buttermilk mixture to flour mixture; beat at low speed of an electric mixer until well blended. Beat an additional 3 minutes at high speed. Stir in ¾ cup plus 2 tablespoons bulgur and 2¼ cups all-purpose flour to make a soft dough.

Sprinkle 1 tablespoon flour evenly over work surface. Turn dough out onto floured surface, and knead until smooth and elastic (about 8 to 10 minutes). Place in a large bowl that has been coated with cooking spray, turning to grease top. Cover and let rise in a warm place (85°), free from drafts, 1 hour and 15 minutes or until doubled in bulk.

Punch dough down; divide into 2 equal portions. Roll each portion into a 15- x 8½-inch rectangle. Roll up dough jellyroll fashion, starting with narrow end; pinch seam and ends to seal. Place loaves, seam side down, in two 8½- x 4½- x 3-inch loafpans that have been coated with cooking spray. Brush loaves with water; sprinkle remaining 2 tablespoons bulgur evenly over loaves.

Cover and let rise in a warm place, free from drafts, 45 minutes or until doubled in bulk. Bake at 375° for 35 minutes or until loaves sound hollow when tapped. Remove from pans, and let cool completely on wire racks. Yield: 34 servings (105 calories per ½-inch slice).

PROTEIN 3.7 / FAT 1.2 / CARBOHYDRATE 20.6 / CHOLESTEROL 0 / IRON 0.9 / SODIUM 72 / CALCIUM 10

PESTO SWIRL-YOGURT BREAD

1 cup packed fresh basil
1 tablespoon plus 2 teaspoons pine nuts
1 tablespoon grated Parmesan cheese
3 cloves garlic
¼ teaspoon freshly ground pepper
¼ cup plain non-fat yogurt
1 package dry yeast
¼ cup warm water (105° to 115°)
½ cup skim milk
1 (8-ounce) carton plain non-fat yogurt
4 cups all-purpose flour, divided
1 tablespoon vegetable oil
1 tablespoon sugar
½ teaspoon salt
1 tablespoon all-purpose flour
Vegetable cooking spray
1 egg white, lightly beaten
1 tablespoon water

Remove stems from basil. Wash leaves thoroughly in lukewarm water; drain well. Position knife blade in food processor bowl; add basil and next 4 ingredients. Top with cover; process until smooth. Stir in ¼ cup yogurt; set aside.

Dissolve yeast in warm water in a bowl; let stand 5 minutes. Place milk in a saucepan; cook over medium heat until very warm (120° to 130°). Combine 8-ounce carton yogurt and milk in a bowl. Add yeast mixture, 2 cups flour, oil, sugar, and salt; stir well. Stir in enough remaining 2 cups flour to make a soft dough.

Sprinkle 1 tablespoon flour over work surface. Turn dough out onto floured surface; knead until smooth and elastic (about 8 to 10 minutes). Place dough in a large bowl that has been coated with cooking spray, turning to grease top. Cover; let rise in a warm place (85°), free from drafts, 1 hour or until doubled in bulk.

Punch dough down. Roll into a 16- x 8-inch rectangle; spread reserved pesto mixture over rectangle, leaving a 1-inch margin on all sides. Roll up jellyroll fashion, starting with short end. Pinch seam and ends to seal. Tuck ends under, and place seam side down in a 9- x 5- x 3-inch loafpan that has been coated with cooking spray. Cover; let rise in a warm place, free from drafts, 45 minutes or until doubled in bulk.

Combine egg white and water; brush over top of loaf. Bake at 375° for 30 minutes or until loaf sounds hollow when tapped. Remove from pan, and let cool on a wire rack. Yield: 18 servings (149 calories per ½-inch slice).

PROTEIN 5.2 / FAT 2.1 / CARBOHYDRATE 27.3 / CHOLESTEROL 1 / IRON 1.7 / SODIUM 91 / CALCIUM 84

ORANGE RYE ROLLS

2 cups rye flour
1 package dry yeast
½ teaspoon salt
1 cup light beer
1 cup plus 1 tablespoon water, divided
2 tablespoons unsalted margarine
3 tablespoons molasses, divided
1 tablespoon grated orange rind
2 teaspoons fennel seeds
3½ cups all-purpose flour
2 tablespoons all-purpose flour
Vegetable cooking spray

Combine first 3 ingredients in a large bowl; stir well. Set aside.

Combine beer, 1 cup water, margarine, and 2 tablespoons molasses in a saucepan; cook over medium heat until very warm (120° to 130°). Add beer mixture to flour mixture; beat at medium speed of an electric mixer 2 minutes or until smooth. Stir in orange rind, fennel, and 3½ cups all-purpose flour to make a soft dough.

Sprinkle 2 tablespoons flour over work surface. Turn dough out onto floured surface; knead until smooth and elastic (about 8 to 10 minutes). Place in a large bowl that has been coated with cooking spray, turning to grease top. Cover; let rise in a warm place (85°), free from drafts, 1½ hours or until doubled in bulk.

Punch dough down; divide into 32 portions. Shape each portion into a ball. Place in two 9-inch square baking pans that have been coated with cooking spray. Cover and let rise in a warm place, free from drafts, 45 minutes or until doubled in bulk.

Bake at 350° for 15 minutes. Combine 1 tablespoon molasses and 1 tablespoon water; stir well. Brush rolls gently with molasses mixture. Bake an additional 10 to 15 minutes or until golden. Remove from pans, and cool on wire racks. Yield: 32 rolls (90 calories each).

PROTEIN 2.3 / FAT 1.0 / CARBOHYDRATE 17.7 / CHOLESTEROL 0 / IRON 0.7 / SODIUM 38 / CALCIUM 12

ROSEMARY FLATBREAD

Vegetable cooking spray
¼ cup minced onion
1 clove garlic, minced
1 package dry yeast
¼ cup warm water (105° to 115°)
1⅓ cups warm skim milk (105° to 115°)
2 tablespoons olive oil
1 tablespoon honey
1 teaspoon dried whole rosemary, crushed
½ teaspoon salt
1½ cups whole wheat flour
2½ cups all-purpose flour
3 tablespoons all-purpose flour, divided

Coat a small nonstick skillet with cooking spray; place over medium heat until hot. Add onion and garlic; sauté until tender. Remove from heat, and set aside.

Dissolve yeast in warm water in a large bowl, and let stand 5 minutes. Add warm skim milk, reserved onion mixture, olive oil, honey, rosemary, and salt, stirring well. Add whole wheat flour, and stir until smooth. Gradually stir in enough of the 2½ cups all-purpose flour to make a soft dough.

Sprinkle 1 tablespoon all-purpose flour evenly over work surface. Turn dough out onto floured surface, and knead 1 minute. Cover and let rest 10 minutes. Knead until smooth and elastic (about 8 to 10 minutes). Place dough in a large bowl that has been coated with cooking spray, turning to grease top. Cover and let rise in a warm place (85°), free from drafts, 1 hour or until doubled in bulk.

Punch dough down, and divide into 2 equal portions. Sprinkle 1 tablespoon all-purpose flour evenly over work surface. Roll one portion of dough into a 15-inch circle, and place on a 15-inch pizza pan that has been coated with cooking spray; press to edges. Repeat procedure with remaining 1 tablespoon all-purpose flour and dough. Prick dough generously with a fork. Cover and let rise in a warm place, free from drafts, 30 minutes or until doubled in bulk. Bake at 350° for 10 to 15 minutes or until golden brown. Serve warm. Yield: 28 servings (86 calories per wedge).

PROTEIN 2.8 / FAT 1.3 / CARBOHYDRATE 16.0 / CHOLESTEROL 0 / IRON 0.7 / SODIUM 49 / CALCIUM 21

SESAME-PARMESAN CRESCENTS

1 package dry yeast
1¼ cups warm water (105° to 115°), divided
¼ cup unsalted margarine
2 tablespoons brown sugar
¼ teaspoon salt
1 cup quick-cooking oats, uncooked
2 egg whites
1½ cups whole wheat flour
2¼ cups all-purpose flour, divided
Vegetable cooking spray
3 tablespoons unsalted margarine, melted
¼ cup plus 1½ teaspoons grated Parmesan cheese
3 tablespoons sesame seeds

Dissolve yeast in ¼ cup warm water; let stand 5 minutes. Combine remaining 1 cup water, ¼ cup margarine, brown sugar, and salt in a saucepan. Cook over medium heat until very warm (120° to 130°). Place oats in a large bowl. Pour warm margarine mixture over oats; stir well. Let cool to 105° to 115°.

Add yeast mixture and egg whites to oatmeal mixture, stirring well. Gradually add whole wheat flour, beating at low speed of an electric mixer. Add 2 cups all-purpose flour, beating at low speed until mixture forms a soft dough.

Sprinkle 1 tablespoon all-purpose flour evenly over work surface. Turn dough out onto floured surface; knead until smooth and elastic (about 8 to 10 minutes). Place dough in a large bowl that has been coated with cooking spray, turning to grease top. Cover and let rise in a warm place (85°), free from drafts, 1½ hours or until doubled in bulk.

Punch dough down; cover and let rest 10 minutes. Divide dough into 3 equal portions. Roll each portion into a 12-inch circle on a surface sprinkled with remaining 3 tablespoons flour. Evenly brush circles with melted margarine, and sprinkle with cheese and sesame seeds. Cut each circle into 12 wedges. Roll up wedges, beginning at wide end. Place point side down on a baking sheet that has been coated with cooking spray. Cover with plastic wrap, and let rise in a warm place, free from drafts, 30 minutes or until doubled in bulk. Bake at 375° for 10 minutes or until lightly browned. Yield: 3 dozen (99 calories each).

PROTEIN 3.0 / FAT 3.5 / CARBOHYDRATE 14.4 / CHOLESTEROL 0 / IRON 0.8 / SODIUM 32 / CALCIUM 17

SESAME-WHOLE WHEAT PRETZELS

1 package dry yeast
⅔ cup warm water (105° to 115°)
1 cup whole wheat flour
2 tablespoons unsalted margarine, melted
2 teaspoons sugar
½ teaspoon salt
1 cup plus 1 tablespoon all-purpose flour, divided
Vegetable cooking spray
1 egg white, lightly beaten
2 teaspoons water
2 tablespoons sesame seeds

Dissolve yeast in warm water in a large mixing bowl; let stand 5 minutes. Add whole wheat flour, margarine, sugar, and salt, stirring until blended. Stir in enough of the 1 cup all-purpose flour to make a soft dough.

Sprinkle 1 tablespoon flour over work surface. Turn dough out onto floured surface; knead until smooth and elastic (8 to 10 minutes). Place dough in a large bowl that has been coated with cooking spray, turning to grease top. Cover and let rise in a warm place (85°), free from drafts, 1 hour or until doubled in bulk.

Using kitchen shears dipped in flour, cut dough into 12 pieces; roll each piece into a ball. With floured hands, roll each ball to form a 14-inch rope. Twist each rope into a pretzel shape. Place pretzels 1½ inches apart on aluminum foil-lined baking sheets that have been coated with cooking spray.

Combine egg white and 2 teaspoons water, stirring well; brush over pretzels. Sprinkle sesame seeds over pretzels. Bake at 400° for 8 to 10 minutes or until golden. Remove from baking sheets, and let cool on wire racks. Yield: 1 dozen (111 calories each).

PROTEIN 3.4 / FAT 3.2 / CARBOHYDRATE 17.7 / CHOLESTEROL 0 / IRON 1.0 / SODIUM 103 / CALCIUM 23

COUSCOUS WITH SUMMER VEGETABLES

Vegetable cooking spray
1 teaspoon olive oil
1¼ cups shredded zucchini
1¼ cups shredded carrot
½ cup chopped onion
1 small sweet red pepper, seeded and cut into
   ¼-inch strips
¼ cup chopped fresh parsley
1 tablespoon lemon juice
¼ teaspoon dried whole savory
¼ teaspoon dried whole rosemary, crumbled
¼ cup plus 2 tablespoons water
¼ teaspoon salt
½ cup uncooked couscous

Coat a large nonstick skillet with cooking spray; add oil, and place over medium heat until hot. Add zucchini, carrot, onion, and red pepper; sauté until crisp-tender. Transfer to a large bowl; stir in parsley, lemon juice, savory, and rosemary. Set aside, and keep warm.

Combine water and salt in a small saucepan, and bring to a boil. Remove from heat. Add couscous; cover and let stand 5 minutes or until couscous is tender and liquid is absorbed. Add to vegetable mixture, and stir well. Yield: 8 servings (35 calories per ½-cup serving).

PROTEIN 1.1 / FAT 0.8 / CARBOHYDRATE 6.5 / CHOLESTEROL 0 / IRON 0.5 / SODIUM 81 / CALCIUM 16

Couscous with Summer Vegetables will complement all types of entrées, from mildly seasoned to spicy.

SPICED COUSCOUS

2 tablespoons currants
Vegetable cooking spray
2 teaspoons olive oil
¾ cup chopped yellow onion
1 clove garlic, minced
1 tablespoon plus 1½ teaspoons curry powder
1 (14½-ounce) can low-sodium chicken broth, undiluted
⅓ cup water
1 tablespoon reduced-sodium soy sauce
1 cup uncooked couscous
1¾ cups chopped Red Delicious apple
¼ cup pine nuts, toasted
2 green onions, diagonally sliced

Place currants in a small bowl. Cover with hot water 1 inch above currants; let soak 10 minutes. Drain and set aside.

Coat a nonstick skillet with cooking spray; add oil, and place over medium heat until hot. Add ¾ cup chopped onion, garlic, and curry powder; sauté until tender. Set aside.

Combine chicken broth, water, and soy sauce in a medium saucepan; bring to a boil. Remove from heat. Add couscous and reserved onion mixture; cover and let stand 5 minutes or until couscous is tender and liquid is absorbed. Stir in chopped apple, pine nuts, and currants. Top with green onions. Yield: 12 servings (105 calories per ½-cup serving).

PROTEIN 2.7 / FAT 3.9 / CARBOHYDRATE 16.0 / CHOLESTEROL 0 /
IRON 0.8 / SODIUM 55 / CALCIUM 15

CONFETTI GRITS CROQUETTES

½ cup regular grits, uncooked
1 (10-ounce) package frozen mixed vegetables, cooked and drained
½ teaspoon dried whole dillweed
½ teaspoon pepper
¼ teaspoon salt
¼ teaspoon red pepper
¾ cup fine, dry breadcrumbs
2 tablespoons grated Parmesan cheese
1 egg
2 tablespoons water
Vegetable cooking spray
1 tablespoon vegetable oil

Cook grits according to package directions, omitting salt. Combine cooked grits and next 5 ingredients in a medium bowl; cover grits mixture and chill 2 hours.

Divide mixture into 16 portions. Shape into cones. Combine breadcrumbs and Parmesan cheese in a small bowl. Roll croquettes in breadcrumb mixture, pressing firmly so crumbs adhere. Beat egg with water. Dip each croquette in egg mixture; roll in breadcrumb mixture again. Coat a large nonstick skillet with cooking spray; add oil. Place over medium-high heat until hot. Cook croquettes in hot oil, turning frequently, until golden brown. Yield: 8 servings (127 calories per serving).

PROTEIN 4.5 / FAT 3.4 / CARBOHYDRATE 19.4 / CHOLESTEROL 26 /
IRON 1.1 / SODIUM 191 / CALCIUM 43

GRITS FLORENTINE

1 (10-ounce) package frozen chopped spinach
½ cup sliced green onions
¼ teaspoon ground white pepper
¼ teaspoon ground nutmeg
2½ cups water
¼ teaspoon salt
¾ cup quick-cooking grits, uncooked
½ cup plain nonfat yogurt

Cook chopped spinach according to package directions, omitting salt and adding onions. Drain well; stir in pepper and nutmeg. Set aside.

Combine water and salt in a medium saucepan; bring to a boil. Stir in grits. Cover, reduce heat, and simmer 5 minutes or until thickened. Stir in reserved spinach mixture and yogurt. Continue cooking until thoroughly heated. Yield: 8 servings (69 calories per ½-cup serving).

PROTEIN 3.2 / FAT 0.3 / CARBOHYDRATE 14.1 / CHOLESTEROL 0 /
IRON 1.3 / SODIUM 111 / CALCIUM 72

GOLDEN OAT SLICES

2 cups quick-cooking oats, uncooked
½ teaspoon salt
½ cup ground lean cooked ham
1 teaspoon brown sugar
⅛ teaspoon ground cloves
Vegetable cooking spray
1 tablespoon reduced-calorie margarine, divided

Cook oats according to package directions, omitting fat, and using ½ teaspoon salt. Add ham, brown sugar, and ground cloves to hot cooked oats; stir well. Spoon oat mixture into an 8½- x 4½- x 3-inch loafpan that has been coated with cooking spray. Cover and chill at least 8 hours.

Remove from pan, and cut into 16 slices. Coat a large nonstick skillet with cooking spray; add ¾ teaspoon margarine. Place over medium-high heat until hot. Add 4 oat slices, and cook 5 minutes on each side or until browned. Repeat procedure with remaining margarine and oat slices. Serve immediately. Yield: 8 servings (104 calories per serving).

PROTEIN 5.8 / FAT 3.6 / CARBOHYDRATE 12.5 / CHOLESTEROL 11 / IRON 0.9 / SODIUM 168 / CALCIUM 12

PEACHY RICE

Vegetable cooking spray
1 teaspoon margarine
½ cup chopped celery
¼ cup chopped green onions
1 cup hot cooked long-grain rice (cooked without salt or fat)
1 cup hot cooked brown rice (cooked without salt or fat)
1 (16-ounce) can unsweetened peach slices, chopped and drained
¼ teaspoon salt
¼ teaspoon curry powder
¼ teaspoon ground ginger
Fresh parsley sprigs (optional)

Coat a large nonstick skillet with cooking spray; add margarine, and place over medium-high heat until hot. Add chopped celery and chopped green onions; sauté until vegetables are tender. Stir in long-grain rice, brown rice, chopped peaches, salt, curry powder, and ground ginger.

Cover and cook over low heat 5 minutes or until thoroughly heated. Transfer rice mixture to a serving dish, and garnish with fresh parsley sprigs, if desired. Serve warm. Yield: 6 servings (108 calories per ½-cup serving).

PROTEIN 2.0 / FAT 1.0 / CARBOHYDRATE 22.9 / CHOLESTEROL 0 / IRON 0.9 / SODIUM 118 / CALCIUM 15

THE GRAIN WITH A GRIP ON CHOLESTEROL

Oats are a "hot" addition to more than cereals these days. Ever since Americans learned that oat bran can lower blood cholesterol levels, they can't seem to get enough of this soluble fiber-rich grain. It's popping up in everything from muffins to croissants to potato chips. The problem is that "oat" on the label is no guarantee of a healthful product. Some points to consider:
• Read the label on products you plan to purchase and look for oats and oat bran to be first, or near the top, of the list of ingredients.
• Search for any variety of oats: steel-cut, rolled, quick cooking, or instant. Any of the varieties will provide generous amounts of soluble fiber.
• Steer clear of oat bran products that contain saturated fats such as lard, coconut oil, or palm oil.
• Add oats to your own recipes: pancakes, meat loaf, and baked goods, for example.
• Buy oat flour or make your own by processing oatmeal in an electric blender or food processor.
• Understand that oat products vary in the amount of soluble fiber. Read the label to get the specifics. For example, the following foods all have at least 2 grams of fiber: 1 slice of oatmeal bread, 3 tablespoons of oat bran, ⅓ cup oatmeal, or ⅔ cup oat flake cereal.

GREEK TOMATOES WITH RICE

8 medium tomatoes (about 3½ pounds)
Vegetable cooking spray
½ cup chopped onion
1 cup uncooked instant rice
½ cup hot water
¼ teaspoon salt
¼ cup chopped ripe olives
2 tablespoons pine nuts
2 tablespoons chopped fresh parsley
¼ teaspoon dried whole basil
¼ teaspoon pepper
2 ounces feta cheese, crumbled

Cut top quarter off each tomato. Scoop out pulp, leaving ¼-inch-thick shells. Discard seeds, and chop pulp. Reserve 2 cups chopped pulp; discard remaining pulp or reserve for other uses.

Coat a large nonstick skillet with cooking spray; place over medium-high heat until hot. Add onion, and sauté until tender. Stir in rice, water, and salt. Cook, uncovered, for 2 minutes or until rice is tender. Stir in reserved chopped tomatoes, olives, and next 4 ingredients. Spoon rice mixture evenly into tomato shells. Arrange tomatoes in a large shallow dish that has been coated with cooking spray. Cover and bake at 350° for 20 to 25 minutes. Uncover and sprinkle with feta cheese before serving. Yield: 8 servings (117 calories per serving).

PROTEIN 3.6 / FAT 4.5 / CARBOHYDRATE 17.5 / CHOLESTEROL 6 / IRON 1.4 / SODIUM 212 / CALCIUM 55

ZUCCHINI AND CARROT SPAGHETTI

3 medium carrots
2 small zucchini
½ cup canned low-sodium chicken broth, undiluted
1 tablespoon margarine
4 ounces spaghetti, uncooked
¼ cup grated Parmesan cheese
¼ teaspoon salt
¼ teaspoon freshly ground pepper

Cut carrots and zucchini into 5- x ⅛-inch strips. Combine chicken broth and margarine in a large skillet. Place over medium heat, and bring to a boil; add carrots. Reduce heat, and simmer 3 minutes. Add zucchini, and continue cooking until vegetables are crisp-tender. Drain vegetables and set aside.

Cook spaghetti according to package directions, omitting salt and fat; drain. Combine spaghetti, reserved vegetables, and remaining ingredients, tossing gently. Yield: 10 servings (75 calories per ½-cup serving).

PROTEIN 2.8 / FAT 2.0 / CARBOHYDRATE 11.7 / CHOLESTEROL 2 / IRON 0.6 / SODIUM 118 / CALCIUM 41

SPAGHETTINI WITH SUN-COOKED TOMATO SAUCE

3 cups peeled, seeded, and chopped tomatoes
12 Calamata olives, pitted and quartered
2 tablespoons capers
1 tablespoon olive oil
1 clove garlic, minced
¼ teaspoon salt
¼ teaspoon crushed red pepper
⅛ teaspoon freshly ground pepper
8 ounces spaghettini, uncooked
¼ cup shredded fresh basil

Combine first 8 ingredients in a large glass bowl; toss gently. Cover and place in a warm place outside in sun or in kitchen for 3 hours.

Cook pasta according to package directions, omitting salt and fat; drain well.

Add hot pasta and basil to sun-cooked tomato sauce; toss well. Yield: 8 servings (150 calories per 1-cup serving).

PROTEIN 4.8 / FAT 3.0 / CARBOHYDRATE 26.9 / CHOLESTEROL 0 / IRON 2.2 / SODIUM 363 / CALCIUM 56

Garlic and two types of cheese add flavor and creaminess to Straw and Hay.

STRAW AND HAY

1 cup skim milk
½ cup low-fat cottage cheese
1 tablespoon cornstarch
½ cup freshly grated Parmesan cheese, divided
¼ teaspoon salt
⅛ teaspoon freshly ground pepper
⅛ teaspoon ground nutmeg
Vegetable cooking spray
4 ounces diced lean cooked ham
1 clove garlic, crushed
½ cup frozen English peas
4 ounces fettuccine, uncooked
4 ounces spinach fettuccine, uncooked

Combine milk, cottage cheese, and cornstarch in container of a food processor or electric blender. Top with cover, and process until smooth. Transfer milk mixture to a medium non-stick skillet. Place over medium heat; add ¼ cup Parmesan cheese, salt, pepper, and nutmeg, stirring until cheese melts. Set aside.

Coat a large nonstick skillet with cooking spray; place over medium heat until hot. Add ham and garlic; sauté 2 minutes. Stir in peas, and sauté 2 minutes. Remove from heat, and stir in reserved milk mixture. Set aside.

Cook fettuccine and spinach fettuccine according to package directions, omitting salt and fat; drain. Place in a large bowl; pour ham mixture over pasta, tossing gently until well combined. Sprinkle with remaining ¼ cup Parmesan cheese. Serve immediately. Yield: 12 servings (118 calories per ½-cup serving).

PROTEIN 8.6 / FAT 3.0 / CARBOHYDRATE 14.6 / CHOLESTEROL 30 / IRON 1.1 / SODIUM 325 / CALCIUM 108

CAPPELLINI WITH BROCCOLI AND CHEESE

6 ounces cappellini, uncooked
1 pound fresh broccoli
Vegetable cooking spray
2 teaspoons olive oil
1 cup canned low-sodium chicken broth, undiluted
2 cups peeled, seeded, and chopped tomatoes
½ cup (2 ounces) goat cheese
2 tablespoons sesame seeds, toasted
¼ teaspoon freshly ground pepper

Prepare cappellini according to package directions, omitting salt and fat. Drain; set aside.
Wash and trim fresh broccoli; cut into small flowerets, and cut stems diagonally into 1-inch pieces.

Coat a large nonstick skillet with cooking spray; add oil. Place over medium heat until hot. Add broccoli, and sauté 3 minutes or until crisp-tender. Add chicken broth, and bring to a boil; stir in tomatoes and goat cheese. Reduce heat, and stir until cheese melts. Stir in reserved cappellini. Add sesame seeds and pepper; toss gently. Serve immediately. Yield: 16 servings (69 calories per ½-cup serving).

PROTEIN 2.6 / FAT 2.1 / CARBOHYDRATE 9.9 / CHOLESTEROL 3 / IRON 0.7 / SODIUM 44 / CALCIUM 40

WINE-BRAISED BELL PEPPERS AND ONIONS WITH BROAD NOODLES

1 large sweet red pepper
1 large sweet yellow pepper
Vegetable cooking spray
1½ teaspoons olive oil
1 medium-size yellow onion, cut into
   ¾-inch-thick slices
¼ cup Chablis or other dry white wine
4 ounces pappardelle, uncooked
1 tablespoon minced fresh parsley
1 tablespoon chopped fresh basil
1 teaspoon balsamic vinegar
¼ teaspoon salt
¼ teaspoon freshly ground pepper

Wash and dry peppers. Place peppers on a baking sheet. Broil 4 inches from heat 2 to 3 minutes on each side or until skins are blackened and charred. Immediately transfer peppers to a large brown paper bag. Roll top tightly to trap steam; let peppers steam 20 minutes. Unroll top, and allow steam to escape; carefully remove peppers. Remove and discard skins and seeds. Cut peppers into ¾-inch strips; set aside.

Coat a large nonstick skillet with cooking spray; add oil. Place over medium-high heat until hot. Add onion, and sauté until tender. Add reserved pepper strips and wine. Bring to a boil; reduce heat, and simmer 1 minute. Cover and simmer an additional 5 minutes.

Cook pasta according to package directions, omitting salt and fat; drain. Combine pasta, pepper mixture, and remaining ingredients, tossing gently. Yield: 8 servings (81 calories per ½-cup serving).

PROTEIN 2.5 / FAT 1.8 / CARBOHYDRATE 14.1 / CHOLESTEROL 13 / IRON 1.2 / SODIUM 76 / CALCIUM 23

Green onion fans are an attractive garnish for Salmon Steaks with Pimento Sauce (page 129), an impressive entrée that company is sure to enjoy.

Fish & Shellfish

BASS WITH CHAMPAGNE SAUCE

8 (4-ounce) bass fillets
Vegetable cooking spray
2 tablespoons lemon juice
2 tablespoons reduced-calorie margarine
1 green onion, sliced
2 tablespoons all-purpose flour
1 cup champagne
2 teaspoons grated lemon rind
¼ teaspoon salt
⅛ teaspoon ground white pepper

Place fillets on rack of a broiler pan that has been coated with cooking spray. Brush fillets with lemon juice. Broil 4 to 5 inches from heat 7 to 9 minutes or until fish flake easily when tested with a fork. Transfer fillets to a serving platter, and keep warm.

Melt margarine in a small saucepan over medium heat; add onion and sauté until tender. Add flour, stirring until smooth. Cook 1 minute, stirring constantly. Gradually stir in champagne. Cook over medium heat, stirring constantly, until mixture is thickened. Remove from heat; stir in lemon rind, salt, and pepper. Spoon 2 tablespoons sauce over each fillet. Yield: 8 servings (108 calories per serving).

PROTEIN 17.4 / FAT 3.0 / CARBOHYDRATE 2.1 / CHOLESTEROL 48 / IRON 0.3 / SODIUM 175 / CALCIUM 16

WHAT'S YOUR FAT QUOTA?

As medical and health organizations continue to emphasize reducing fat in the diet to less than 30 percent, it becomes increasingly more important for consumers to understand how to determine their fat consumption. The best way is to look at the total picture. If you consume 1,500 calories a day, no more than 30 percent of that total—450 calories—should come from fat. Each gram of fat has 9 calories, so divide 450 by 9 to determine your fat quota—50 grams per day.

Packaged and convenience foods typically list the grams of fat per serving on the label. Add up these numbers and use the analysis with *Cooking Light* recipes to determine your intake. Not every food you eat needs to be less than 30 percent fat. But over the course of a day, higher fat foods should be balanced with low-fat choices.

MONTAUK POACHED BLUEFISH

1½ cups Chablis or other dry white wine
½ cup water
2 tablespoons lemon juice
1 bay leaf
½ teaspoon salt
½ teaspoon dried whole thyme
¼ teaspoon dried whole basil
⅛ teaspoon pepper
4 (4-ounce) bluefish fillets
1 small onion, sliced
1 medium tomato, peeled and sliced
½ cup sliced fresh mushrooms

Combine first 8 ingredients in a 10-inch skillet, stirring well; bring mixture to a boil. Reduce heat; cover and simmer 10 minutes. Layer fillets, onion, tomato, and mushrooms in wine mixture; cover and simmer 8 minutes or until fish flakes easily when tested with a fork. Transfer fish and vegetables to a serving platter. Yield: 4 servings (148 calories per serving).

PROTEIN 21.0 / FAT 4.4 / CARBOHYDRATE 5.3 / CHOLESTEROL 59 / IRON 1.1 / SODIUM 357 / CALCIUM 26

ZESTY BAKED CATFISH

½ cup fine, dry breadcrumbs
½ teaspoon dried whole tarragon
¼ teaspoon lemon and pepper seasoning
4 (4-ounce) farm-raised catfish fillets
3 tablespoons commercial reduced-calorie French dressing
Vegetable cooking spray
¼ cup (1 ounce) shredded Swiss cheese

Combine breadcrumbs, tarragon, and seasoning; stir well.

Brush fillets with French dressing; dredge in breadcrumb mixture.

Arrange fillets on rack of a broiler pan that has been coated with cooking spray. Bake, uncovered, at 450° for 10 minutes. Sprinkle fillets evenly with cheese, and bake an additional 2 minutes or until fish flakes easily when tested with a fork. Yield: 4 servings (211 calories per serving).

PROTEIN 24.2 / FAT 7.6 / CARBOHYDRATE 9.7 / CHOLESTEROL 73 / IRON 1.6 / SODIUM 324 / CALCIUM 129

Add fresh ears of corn and lemonade to flavorful Catfish Barbecue, and let the cookout begin.

CATFISH BARBECUE

⅓ cup reduced-calorie catsup
1 tablespoon lemon juice
1 teaspoon brown sugar
2 teaspoons vegetable oil
1 teaspoon low-sodium Worcestershire sauce
½ teaspoon dried whole marjoram
¼ teaspoon garlic powder
¼ teaspoon ground red pepper
6 (4-ounce) farm-raised catfish fillets
Vegetable cooking spray

Combine first 8 ingredients in a small bowl. Arrange fillets in a 13- x 9- x 2-inch baking dish that has been coated with cooking spray. Pour catsup mixture over fillets; cover and marinate in refrigerator 30 minutes, turning once.

Remove fillets from marinade, reserving marinade. Bring marinade to a boil in a small saucepan; boil 2 minutes. Place fillets on rack of a broiler pan that has been coated with cooking spray. Broil 6 inches from heat 14 to 15 minutes or until fish flakes easily when tested with a fork, basting occasionally with marinade. Transfer to a serving platter. Yield: 6 servings (156 calories per serving).

PROTEIN 20.7 / FAT 6.4 / CARBOHYDRATE 2.1 / CHOLESTEROL 66 / IRON 1.2 / SODIUM 78 / CALCIUM 47

FLOUNDER ROLLS WITH VEGETABLE FILLING

Vegetable cooking spray
½ cup shredded carrot
½ cup chopped fresh mushrooms
¼ cup finely chopped onion
½ cup soft whole wheat breadcrumbs
¼ cup minced fresh parsley
2 teaspoons lemon juice
½ teaspoon dried whole thyme
¼ teaspoon ground sage
¼ teaspoon salt
⅛ teaspoon pepper
6 (4-ounce) flounder fillets
Carrot flowers (optional)

Coat a large nonstick skillet with cooking spray; place over medium-high heat until hot.

Add carrot, mushrooms, and onion; sauté until crisp-tender. Remove from heat. Add breadcrumbs and next 6 ingredients; stir well.

Place 3 tablespoons vegetable mixture in center of each flounder fillet; roll up jellyroll fashion, beginning at narrow end. Place rolls, seam side down, in a 12- x 8- x 2-inch baking dish that has been coated with cooking spray. Bake, uncovered, at 350° for 20 minutes or until fish flakes easily when tested with a fork. Transfer rolls to a serving platter, and garnish with carrot flowers, if desired. Yield: 6 servings (138 calories per serving).

PROTEIN 22.7 / FAT 1.9 / CARBOHYDRATE 6.7 / CHOLESTEROL 55 / IRON 1.1 / SODIUM 244 / CALCIUM 41

HALIBUT WITH GOLDEN FRUIT SAUCE

4 (4-ounce) halibut steaks
Vegetable cooking spray
1½ cups finely chopped Golden Delicious apple (about 1 medium)
¼ cup unsweetened orange juice
2 tablespoons golden raisins
1 tablespoon brandy
1 tablespoon reduced-calorie margarine, melted
¼ teaspoon salt
¼ teaspoon curry powder
⅛ teaspoon ground white pepper
1 tablespoon chopped chives

Arrange halibut steaks in an 8-inch square baking dish that has been coated with cooking spray. Combine chopped apple and next 7 ingredients; stir well. Pour apple mixture over steaks in baking dish. Bake, uncovered, at 350° for 20 to 25 minutes or until fish flakes easily when tested with a fork. Transfer steaks to a serving platter, and sprinkle with chives. Serve immediately. Yield: 4 servings (189 calories per serving).

PROTEIN 24.0 / FAT 4.7 / CARBOHYDRATE 12.4 / CHOLESTEROL 53 / IRON 1.2 / SODIUM 236 / CALCIUM 65

ORANGE ROUGHY WITH ASPARAGUS

1 pound fresh asparagus spears
1 (2-ounce) jar diced pimiento, drained
2 tablespoons lemon juice
1 tablespoon reduced-calorie margarine, melted
¼ teaspoon dried whole thyme
⅛ teaspoon garlic powder
⅛ teaspoon pepper
6 (4-ounce) orange roughy fillets
Vegetable cooking spray
2 tablespoons chopped unsalted cashews

Snap off tough ends of asparagus. Remove scales with a knife or vegetable peeler, if

desired. Cut asparagus into 1-inch pieces. Combine asparagus and next 6 ingredients; set aside.

Arrange fillets in a 13- x 9- x 2-inch baking dish that has been coated with cooking spray. Spoon asparagus mixture over fillets. Bake, uncovered, at 350° for 20 minutes or until fish flakes easily when tested with a fork.

Transfer fillets and asparagus to a serving platter; sprinkle with cashews. Yield: 6 servings (158 calories per serving).

PROTEIN 15.6 / FAT 9.3 / CARBOHYDRATE 3.3 / CHOLESTEROL 19 / IRON 0.8 / SODIUM 81 / CALCIUM 12

SALMON BALLS IN DILL SAUCE

1 (15½-ounce) can salmon, drained and flaked
1 cup soft whole wheat breadcrumbs
2 eggs, lightly beaten
¼ cup minced onion
2 tablespoons finely chopped green pepper
2 tablespoons lemon juice
¼ teaspoon pepper
Vegetable cooking spray
1 tablespoon reduced-calorie margarine
2 tablespoons all-purpose flour
1 cup water
½ cup Chablis or other dry white wine
1 teaspoon dried whole dillweed
¼ cup plain nonfat yogurt
1 teaspoon grated lemon rind

Combine first 7 ingredients. Shape mixture into 24 salmon balls. Place salmon balls in a 13- x 9- x 2-inch baking dish that has been coated with cooking spray. Bake, uncovered, at 350° for 25 to 30 minutes or until browned. Transfer to a serving platter, and keep warm.

Melt margarine in a small saucepan over medium heat; add flour, stirring until smooth. Cook 1 minute, stirring constantly. Combine water, wine, and dillweed; stir well. Gradually add wine mixture to saucepan; cook over medium heat, stirring constantly, until mixture is thickened and bubbly. Remove from heat, and stir in yogurt. Spoon sauce over salmon balls, and sprinkle with lemon rind. Serve immediately. Yield: 6 servings (129 calories per serving).

PROTEIN 13.2 / FAT 5.0 / CARBOHYDRATE 8.0 / CHOLESTEROL 92 / IRON 1.1 / SODIUM 118 / CALCIUM 41

SALMON STEAKS WITH PIMIENTO SAUCE

6 (4-ounce) salmon steaks (½-inch thick)
1 tablespoon lemon juice
Vegetable cooking spray
1 tablespoon reduced-calorie margarine
2 tablespoons chopped green onions
1 tablespoon all-purpose flour
½ cup skim milk
2 tablespoons Chablis or other dry white wine
1 (2-ounce) jar sliced pimiento, drained
⅛ teaspoon salt
⅛ teaspoon freshly ground pepper

Brush salmon with lemon juice. Arrange salmon on rack of a broiler pan that has been coated with cooking spray. Broil 6 inches from heat 10 to 12 minutes or until fish flakes easily when tested with a fork. Transfer to a serving platter, and keep warm.

Melt margarine in a small saucepan over low heat. Add green onions, and sauté until tender. Add flour, stirring until smooth. Cook 1 minute, stirring constantly. Gradually add skim milk; cook over medium heat, stirring constantly, until thickened and bubbly. Stir in wine and remaining ingredients. Spoon pimiento sauce evenly over salmon steaks. Serve immediately. Yield: 6 servings (262 calories per serving).

PROTEIN 30.4 / FAT 13.2 / CARBOHYDRATE 2.8 / CHOLESTEROL 94 / IRON 0.8 / SODIUM 151 / CALCIUM 36

MINTY SNAPPER FILLETS

1 tablespoon reduced-calorie margarine, melted
1 clove garlic, minced
¼ cup Chablis or other dry white wine
2 tablespoons lemon juice
1 tablespoon finely chopped fresh mint leaves
1 teaspoon grated lemon rind
⅛ teaspoon pepper
4 (4-ounce) red snapper fillets (½-inch thick)
Vegetable cooking spray
Lemon slices (optional)
Fresh mint sprigs (optional)

Melt margarine in a small saucepan over medium heat. Add garlic, and sauté until tender. Stir in wine, lemon juice, fresh mint leaves, grated lemon rind, and pepper. Bring to a boil; reduce heat, and simmer, uncovered, 5 minutes. Remove wine mixture from heat, and let stand 15 minutes.

Arrange red snapper fillets in a single layer in an 11- x 7- x 2-inch baking dish that has been coated with cooking spray. Pour wine mixture over fillets. Bake, uncovered, at 350° for 20 to 25 minutes or until fish flakes easily when tested with a fork. Transfer fillets to a serving platter. If desired, garnish with lemon slices and fresh mint sprigs. Yield: 4 servings (119 calories per serving).

PROTEIN 22.6 / FAT 2.3 / CARBOHYDRATE 0.5 / CHOLESTEROL 41 / IRON 0.3 / SODIUM 82 / CALCIUM 37

SOLE WITH ORANGES AND GRAPES

4 (4-ounce) sole fillets
Vegetable cooking spray
4 orange slices
½ cup red seedless grapes, halved
¼ cup unsweetened orange juice
1 tablespoon margarine, melted
¼ teaspoon salt
⅛ teaspoon ground cloves

Arrange fillets in a 12- x 8- x 2-inch baking dish that has been coated with cooking spray. Top each fillet with an orange slice. Combine grapes and remaining ingredients; stir well, and pour over fillets. Bake, covered, at 400° for 15 minutes or until fish flakes easily when tested with a fork. Remove to a serving platter. Serve immediately. Yield: 4 servings (158 calories per serving).

PROTEIN 21.8 / FAT 4.5 / CARBOHYDRATE 6.9 / CHOLESTEROL 54 / IRON 0.5 / SODIUM 273 / CALCIUM 32

CITRUS GRILLED SWORDFISH

¼ cup unsweetened grapefruit juice
2 tablespoons reduced-calorie margarine, melted
1 teaspoon grated grapefruit rind
¼ teaspoon celery salt
⅛ teaspoon pepper
2 (12-ounce) swordfish steaks (1-inch thick)
Vegetable cooking spray
2 tablespoons finely chopped hazelnuts, toasted
Fresh grapefruit sections (optional)

Combine first 5 ingredients in a small bowl. Place swordfish steaks in a shallow dish; pour grapefruit juice mixture over steaks. Cover and marinate in refrigerator 1 hour.

Remove steaks from marinade; set aside. Bring marinade to a boil in a small saucepan; boil 2 minutes.

Coat grill rack with cooking spray; place on grill over medium-hot coals. Place steaks on rack, and cook 8 to 10 minutes on each side or until fish flakes easily when tested with a fork, basting frequently with marinade. Transfer to a serving platter, and sprinkle with hazelnuts. Garnish with grapefruit sections, if desired. Yield: 6 servings (177 calories per serving).

PROTEIN 22.8 / FAT 8.6 / CARBOHYDRATE 1.4 / CHOLESTEROL 44 / IRON 1.2 / SODIUM 226 / CALCIUM 12

TANDOORI SWORDFISH STEAKS

4 (4-ounce) swordfish steaks (¾-inch thick)
3 tablespoons lime juice
1 teaspoon minced garlic
¾ teaspoon freshly grated gingerroot
½ cup plain nonfat yogurt
½ teaspoon chili powder
½ teaspoon ground cumin
¼ teaspoon curry powder
¼ teaspoon crushed red pepper
¼ teaspoon salt
⅛ teaspoon ground coriander
Vegetable cooking spray
Fresh mint leaves (optional)

Place swordfish steaks in a shallow baking dish. Combine lime juice, minced garlic, and grated gingerroot, stirring well; pour over steaks. Cover and marinate in refrigerator 30 minutes, basting once with lime juice mixture.

Combine yogurt and next 6 ingredients in a small bowl; stir well. Spoon half of yogurt mixture evenly over steaks. Cover and marinate in refrigerator 1½ hours, basting occasionally with yogurt mixture. Refrigerate remaining yogurt mixture.

Remove steaks from marinade; discard marinade. Coat grill rack with cooking spray; place on grill over medium-hot coals. Place steaks on rack, and cook 8 minutes on each side or until fish flakes easily when tested with a fork.

Transfer steaks to a warm serving platter; spoon reserved yogurt mixture evenly over steaks. Garnish with mint leaves, if desired. Yield: 4 servings (162 calories per serving).

PROTEIN 24.3 / FAT 4.9 / CARBOHYDRATE 4.0 / CHOLESTEROL 45 / IRON 1.2 / SODIUM 274 / CALCIUM 69

GINGER-LIME SWORDFISH

2 (12-ounce) swordfish steaks (1-inch thick)
¼ cup lime juice
1 tablespoon honey
1 (⅛-inch-thick) slice fresh gingerroot
Vegetable cooking spray

Place swordfish steaks in an 11- x 7- x 2-inch baking dish. Combine lime juice and honey; stir with a wire whisk until blended. Add gingerroot. Pour mixture over steaks. Cover and marinate in refrigerator 1 hour.

Remove steaks from marinade; set aside. Remove and discard gingerroot. Bring marinade to a boil in a small saucepan; boil 2 minutes. Remove from heat.

Coat grill rack with cooking spray; place on grill over medium-hot coals. Grill steaks 8 minutes on each side or until fish flakes easily when tested with a fork, basting often with marinade. Yield: 6 servings (151 calories per serving).

PROTEIN 22.5 / FAT 4.6 / CARBOHYDRATE 3.8 / CHOLESTEROL 44 / IRON 0.9 / SODIUM 102 / CALCIUM 6

SEASHELL TUNA BAKE

1 cup medium shell macaroni, uncooked
Vegetable cooking spray
2 tablespoons margarine, divided
½ cup minced onion
½ cup minced green pepper
2 tablespoons all-purpose flour
1½ cups skim milk
2 (6½-ounce) cans spring water-packed white tuna, drained
¼ cup reduced-calorie chili sauce
¼ cup sliced pimiento-stuffed olives
¼ teaspoon salt
¼ teaspoon dried whole basil
¼ teaspoon dried whole oregano
⅛ teaspoon ground red pepper
Avocado slices (optional)
Lemon twists (optional)
Fresh oregano sprigs (optional)

Cook macaroni according to package directions, omitting salt and fat. Drain; set aside.

Coat a large nonstick skillet with cooking spray; add 1 teaspoon margarine, and place over medium heat until hot. Add onion and green pepper; sauté until tender. Remove from skillet, and set aside.

Melt remaining margarine in skillet. Add flour, and cook over medium heat, stirring constantly, 1 minute. Gradually add milk; cook over medium heat, stirring constantly, until mixture is thickened and bubbly. Remove mixture from heat; stir in pasta, onion mixture, tuna and next 6 ingredients.

Place tuna mixture in a 2-quart baking dish that has been coated with cooking spray. Bake, uncovered, at 350° for 30 minutes. If desired, garnish with avocado slices, lemon twists, and fresh oregano sprigs. Yield: 6 servings (188 calories per serving).

PROTEIN 15.6 / FAT 5.9 / CARBOHYDRATE 17.4 / CHOLESTEROL 19 / IRON 0.8 / SODIUM 409 / CALCIUM 90

 ## LOOK OUT FOR LEAD

Serving a dinner casserole in a pretty ceramic dish may make it appear more special, but it could be dangerous. The glazes used on many decorative ceramics—plates, cups, bowls—often contain unhealthy levels of lead. You won't see or taste the lead, but this metal can leach out and contaminate food or drinks. Once the lead accumulates in body tissues, it tends to wreak havoc on nerves, kidneys, and the brain. The damage, unfortunately, is often irreversible. Children are particularly susceptible to lead poisoning. For them, exposure to excessive levels of lead can stunt growth and may cause mental retardation.

Fortunately, the FDA has set strict standards for lead levels allowed in dishware. Periodically, it spot-checks to make sure manufacturers follow these guidelines. Still, FDA can't be everywhere. In addition, many ceramic pottery items are purchased outside the U.S., and the FDA has no way of checking these items.

To make sure you're eating and drinking from safe dishware, take the following precautions:
• Purchase American-made dinnerware unless you can be assured of the safety of a foreign variety.
• Refrain from storing food in ceramic ware. The longer food sits in a glazed container, the more lead can leach into it.
• Steer clear of hand-crafted or imported pottery items, at least for cooking purposes.
• Never serve food or beverages in antique pewter. It contains enormously high amounts of lead.

KEDGEREE

2 hard-cooked eggs
Vegetable cooking spray
½ cup chopped green onions
2 (6½-ounce) cans water-packed Albacore tuna, drained
2 cups hot cooked rice (cooked without salt or fat)
¼ teaspoon salt
¼ teaspoon curry powder
¼ teaspoon ground red pepper
6 large fresh spinach leaves
⅓ cup peeled, seeded, and chopped tomato
1 tablespoon minced fresh parsley

Slice eggs in half lengthwise; remove yolks. Chop egg whites and yolks separately. Set aside.

Coat a large nonstick skillet with cooking spray; place over medium-high heat until hot. Add green onions, and sauté until tender. Reduce heat to low. Add chopped egg whites, tuna, and next 4 ingredients; stir well. Cover and cook 5 minutes or until thoroughly heated.

Spoon mixture onto a spinach-lined serving platter. Sprinkle with chopped egg yolks, tomato, and parsley. Yield: 8 servings (148 calories per serving).

PROTEIN 14.1 / FAT 2.4 / CARBOHYDRATE 16.5 / CHOLESTEROL 67 / IRON 1.4 / SODIUM 256 / CALCIUM 24

TUNA NIÇOISE BROCHETTES

4 (8-ounce) tuna steaks (1-inch thick)
¾ cup dry sherry
1 tablespoon vegetable oil
1 tablespoon water
¼ cup reduced-sodium soy sauce
4 cloves garlic, minced
8 cherry tomatoes
2 large yellow squash, cut into ½-inch pieces
1 medium-size purple onion, cut into 8 wedges
1 (9-ounce) package frozen artichoke hearts, thawed
Vegetable cooking spray

Cut tuna into ¾-inch cubes. Place tuna in a large shallow dish; set aside.

Combine sherry and next 4 ingredients in a jar. Cover tightly, and shake vigorously. Pour sherry mixture over tuna; cover and marinate in refrigerator 8 hours.

Remove tuna from marinade, reserving marinade. Alternate tuna, tomatoes, squash, onion, and artichoke hearts on skewers. Coat grill rack with cooking spray; place on grill over medium-hot coals. Place kabobs on rack, and cook 10 to 12 minutes or until fish flakes easily when tested with a fork, turning and basting frequently with reserved marinade. Serve immediately. Yield: 8 servings (225 calories per serving).

PROTEIN 25.7 / FAT 7.1 / CARBOHYDRATE 8.6 / CHOLESTEROL 38 / IRON 1.9 / SODIUM 360 / CALCIUM 28

TUNA STEAKS CATALINA

¼ cup commercial reduced-calorie French dressing
2 tablespoons thinly sliced green onions
2 teaspoons grated lemon rind
¼ teaspoon freshly ground pepper
2 (12-ounce) tuna steaks (1-inch thick)
Vegetable cooking spray

Combine French dressing and next 3 ingredients. Place tuna steaks in a shallow dish; spread dressing mixture over steaks. Cover and marinate in refrigerator 1 hour.

Remove steaks from marinade; set aside. Bring marinade to a boil in a small saucepan; boil 2 minutes. Remove from heat.

Coat grill rack with cooking spray; place on grill over hot coals. Grill steaks 10 minutes on each side or until fish flakes easily when tested with a fork, basting frequently with marinade. Yield: 6 servings (178 calories per serving).

PROTEIN 28.6 / FAT 6.1 / CARBOHYDRATE 0.5 / CHOLESTEROL 47 / IRON 1.3 / SODIUM 155 / CALCIUM 3

LINGUINE WITH CLAM SAUCE

1 tablespoon olive oil
½ cup chopped onion
4 cloves garlic, minced
¼ cup finely chopped fresh parsley sprigs
¼ teaspoon crushed red pepper
½ cup Chablis or other dry white wine
1 cup water
2 (10-ounce) cans whole baby clams, drained
8 ounces linguine, uncooked

Place olive oil in a medium saucepan; place over medium heat until hot. Add onion and garlic; sauté until tender. Stir in parsley and crushed red pepper. Add wine; bring to a boil. Boil 6 minutes or until liquid is reduced to ¼ cup. Add water and simmer, uncovered, until thoroughly heated. Stir in clams, and cook until thoroughly heated.

Cook linguine according to package directions, omitting salt and fat; drain. Place linguine in a warm bowl. Add clam sauce, tossing well. Serve immediately. Yield: 6 servings (246 calories per 1-cup serving).

PROTEIN 18.4 / FAT 3.8 / CARBOHYDRATE 33.2 / CHOLESTEROL 35 / IRON 16.0 / SODIUM 62 / CALCIUM 70

CLAM-STUFFED PASTA SHELLS

12 jumbo macaroni shells, uncooked
Vegetable cooking spray
2 tablespoons minced onion
2 tablespoons shredded carrot
½ cup finely chopped fresh spinach
1 (7½-ounce) carton curd-style farmers cheese
¼ cup reduced-calorie mayonnaise
1 clove garlic, minced
¼ teaspoon hot sauce
2 (6½-ounce) cans minced clams, drained
1 (8-ounce) can no-salt-added tomato sauce
2 tablespoons reduced-calorie Italian dressing

Cook shells according to package directions, omitting salt and fat. Drain and set aside.

Coat a large nonstick skillet with cooking spray; place over medium-high heat until hot. Add onion and carrot, and sauté until tender.

Add spinach; cook 2 minutes. Remove from heat, and set aside.

Combine farmers cheese, mayonnaise, garlic, and hot sauce in a large bowl; stir well. Fold in reserved spinach mixture and clams. Spoon 2 tablespoons clam mixture into each shell.

Arrange shells in a 9-inch baking dish. Combine tomato sauce and dressing; pour over shells. Cover and bake at 350° for 15 minutes or until thoroughly heated. Yield: 6 servings (182 calories per serving).

PROTEIN 13.6 / FAT 7.3 / CARBOHYDRATE 16.9 / CHOLESTEROL 20 / IRON 7.1 / SODIUM 162 / 68

CRAB MANICOTTI

18 manicotti shells
1 (6-ounce) can lump crabmeat, drained
1½ cups part-skim ricotta cheese
¼ cup chopped fresh mushrooms
¼ cup chopped green onions
¼ cup Chablis or other dry white wine
1 tablespoon lemon juice
¼ teaspoon salt
Vegetable cooking spray
1 (15-ounce) can no-salt-added tomato sauce
1 (6-ounce) can no-salt-added tomato paste
½ teaspoon dried whole oregano
½ teaspoon dried whole basil
¼ teaspoon dried whole thyme
⅛ teaspoon garlic powder
1 tablespoon low-sodium Worcestershire sauce

Cook manicotti shells according to package directions, omitting salt and fat; drain shells, and set aside. Combine crabmeat and next 6 ingredients in a small bowl, stirring until blended. Divide crabmeat mixture evenly among manicotti shells. Place shells in a 13- x 9- x 2-inch baking dish that has been coated with cooking spray; set aside.

Combine tomato sauce and remaining ingredients in a medium saucepan; bring to a boil. Reduce heat, and simmer, uncovered, 5 minutes. Spoon tomato sauce mixture over manicotti; cover and bake at 350° for 40 minutes. Yield: 6 servings (207 calories per serving).

PROTEIN 16.9 / FAT 6.6 / CARBOHYDRATE 20.4 / CHOLESTEROL 49 / IRON 1.5 / SODIUM 385 / CALCIUM 313

SHERRIED LOBSTER TAILS

4 (6-ounce) frozen lobster tails, partially thawed
Vegetable cooking spray
⅓ cup dry sherry
1 tablespoon unsweetened orange juice
1 teaspoon grated orange rind
2 teaspoons vegetable oil
¼ teaspoon ground allspice

Split lobster tails lengthwise; cut through upper hard shell and meat to, but not through, bottom shell. Lift lobster meat through split shell to rest on outside of shell, leaving meat attached to far end of lobster shell.

Place lobster tails on rack of a broiler pan that has been coated with cooking spray. Combine sherry and remaining ingredients in a small bowl; stir well. Brush 2 tablespoons sherry mixture over each lobster tail. Broil 6 inches from heat 12 minutes, basting frequently with remaining sherry mixture. Yield: 4 servings (117 calories per serving).

PROTEIN 18.7 / FAT 3.0 / CARBOHYDRATE 2.6 / CHOLESTEROL 65 / IRON 0.4 / SODIUM 347 / CALCIUM 59

OYSTERS WITH SHERRY

Vegetable cooking spray
2 tablespoons margarine
2 (12-ounce) containers fresh Select oysters, drained
¼ cup dry sherry
1 teaspoon lemon juice
1 teaspoon minced fresh parsley
¼ teaspoon salt
¼ teaspoon ground white pepper
4 slices whole wheat bread, toasted

Coat a large nonstick skillet with cooking spray; add margarine, and place over medium-high heat until hot. Add next 6 ingredients. Cover, reduce heat, and simmer 5 minutes or until edges of oysters begin to curl.

Cut each slice of bread into 4 triangles. Transfer oysters to serving plates. Serve oysters with toast points. Yield: 4 servings (210 calories per serving).

PROTEIN 12.2 / FAT 10.0 / CARBOHYDRATE 18.1 / CHOLESTEROL 75 / IRON 9.7 / SODIUM 498 / CALCIUM 91

SHRIMP AND PASTA SHELLS WITH FETA CHEESE

Vegetable cooking spray
2 tablespoons olive oil
⅓ cup chopped onion
4 (14½-ounce) cans no-salt-added tomatoes, drained and coarsely chopped
4 cloves garlic, minced
½ cup clam juice
¼ cup Chablis or other dry white wine
1 tablespoon Pernod
¼ teaspoon salt
¼ teaspoon freshly ground pepper
1 teaspoon dried whole oregano
1 (8-ounce) package medium shell macaroni, uncooked
1¼ pounds large fresh shrimp, peeled and deveined
4 ounces feta cheese, crumbled
2 tablespoons chopped fresh parsley

Coat a medium skillet with cooking spray; add olive oil. Place over medium-high heat until hot. Add onion, and sauté until tender. Add tomatoes and garlic; cook 1 minute. Add clam juice, wine, and Pernod; cook over high heat 1 minute. Cover, reduce heat, and simmer an additional 15 minutes. Stir in salt, pepper, and oregano. Set aside.

Cook macaroni according to package directions, omitting salt and fat; drain.

Combine macaroni and reserved tomato mixture; stir gently. Pour into a 13- x 9- x 2-inch baking dish. Arrange shrimp over macaroni and tomato mixture. Top with crumbled feta cheese. Bake, uncovered, at 425° for 15 minutes or until cheese melts and shrimp turn pink. Remove from oven, and sprinkle with parsley. Yield: 6 servings (318 calories per serving).

PROTEIN 23.6 / FAT 7.3 / CARBOHYDRATE 38.0 / CHOLESTEROL 126 / IRON 2.9 / SODIUM 420 / CALCIUM 180

Ginger, curry, and a variety of fresh vegetables accent Shrimp Far-East Style with color and flavor.

SHRIMP FAR-EAST STYLE

2 tablespoons reduced-sodium soy sauce
2 teaspoons brown sugar
½ teaspoon ground ginger
½ teaspoon curry powder
½ teaspoon dry mustard
Vegetable cooking spray
1 tablespoon vegetable oil, divided
1½ cups broccoli flowerets
1 cup diagonally sliced carrots
1 medium-size sweet red pepper, seeded and cut into thin strips
½ cup sliced water chestnuts
1 clove garlic, minced
1½ pounds medium-size fresh shrimp, peeled and deveined
½ cup walnut halves

Combine first 5 ingredients, stirring well. Set soy sauce mixture aside.

Coat a wok with cooking spray. Add 1 teaspoon oil. Allow to heat at medium-high (325°) for 2 minutes. Add broccoli, carrots, red pepper, water chestnuts, and garlic; stir-fry 3 minutes. Remove vegetables from wok, and set aside. Add remaining 2 teaspoons oil, and allow to heat for 2 minutes. Add shrimp; stir-fry 3 minutes. Reduce heat to 225°; add vegetables and soy sauce mixture, tossing gently. Cook an additional 2 minutes. Sprinkle with walnut halves. Serve immediately. Yield: 6 servings (218 calories per serving).

PROTEIN 23.6 / FAT 8.8 / CARBOHYDRATE 11.1 / CHOLESTEROL 158 / IRON 3.5 / SODIUM 369 / CALCIUM 81

BAKED SCALLOPS

Vegetable cooking spray
2 tablespoons reduced-calorie margarine, divided
1 pound fresh bay scallops
½ cup sliced fresh mushrooms
½ cup diced sweet red pepper
2 green onions, sliced
1 tablespoon plus 2 teaspoons all-purpose flour
1¼ cups skim milk
1 tablespoon minced fresh parsley
¼ teaspoon salt
¼ teaspoon ground mace
⅛ teaspoon ground white pepper
3 tablespoons Chablis or other dry white wine
½ cup (2 ounces) shredded 40% less-fat Cheddar
    cheese
Dash of paprika

Coat a large nonstick skillet with cooking spray. Add 1 teaspoon margarine, and place over medium-high heat until hot. Add scallops, mushrooms, red pepper, and green onions; sauté 4 to 5 minutes. Remove scallops and vegetables from skillet, and set aside. Discard remaining liquid in skillet. Wipe skillet dry with a paper towel.

Melt remaining 1 tablespoon plus 2 teaspoons margarine in skillet over medium-low heat; add flour, stirring until smooth. Cook 1 minute, stirring constantly. Gradually add milk; cook over medium heat, stirring constantly, until mixture is thickened and bubbly. Stir in scallop-vegetable mixture, parsley, salt, mace, and white pepper. Remove from heat. Stir in wine.

Pour mixture into a 1½-quart casserole that has been coated with cooking spray. Bake, uncovered, at 350° for 20 minutes. Sprinkle with cheese. Bake an additional 3 to 5 minutes or until cheese melts. Sprinkle with paprika. Serve immediately. Yield: 4 servings (223 calories per serving).

PROTEIN 26.4 / FAT 7.7 / CARBOHYDRATE 11.5 / CHOLESTEROL 39 / IRON 1.1 / SODIUM 522 / CALCIUM 243

SCALLOP JAMBALAYA

Vegetable cooking spray
1 medium onion, sliced and separated into rings
1 cup chopped green pepper
½ cup sliced celery
1 clove garlic, minced
½ cup uncooked long-grain rice
1 (15-ounce) can no-salt-added tomato sauce
½ cup water
1 bay leaf
½ teaspoon dried whole basil
½ teaspoon chili powder
¼ teaspoon pepper
¼ teaspoon hot sauce
1 pound fresh bay scallops

Coat a large, deep nonstick skillet with cooking spray, and place over medium heat until hot. Add onion, green pepper, celery, and garlic; sauté until crisp-tender. Stir in rice, tomato sauce, water, bay leaf, basil, chili powder, pepper, and hot sauce. Bring mixture to a boil. Cover, reduce heat, and simmer 20 minutes or until rice is tender and liquid is absorbed. Remove and discard bay leaf. Add scallops; cover and cook 5 minutes or until scallops are opaque. Serve immediately. Yield: 4 servings (250 calories per 1¼-cups serving).

PROTEIN 22.6 / FAT 1.5 / CARBOHYDRATE 35.7 / CHOLESTEROL 37 / IRON 1.9 / SODIUM 228 / CALCIUM 58

For a grand entrée, impress friends by serving Artichoke-Cheese Soufflé (page 138).

ARTICHOKE-CHEESE SOUFFLÉ

6 large artichokes
Lemon wedge
2 tablespoons margarine
3 tablespoons all-purpose flour
1½ cups skim milk
1 cup (4 ounces) shredded 40% less-fat Cheddar
   cheese
¼ teaspoon salt
⅛ teaspoon ground white pepper
3 drops of hot sauce
4 eggs, separated
Vegetable cooking spray
1 tablespoon minced fresh parsley

Wash artichokes by plunging up and down in cold water. Cut off stem end, and trim about ½ inch from top of each artichoke. Remove any loose bottom leaves. With scissors, trim away about one-fourth of each outer leaf. Rub tops and edges of leaves with a lemon wedge.

Place artichokes in a large Dutch oven; add water to a depth of 1 inch. Bring to a boil; cover, reduce heat, and simmer 25 minutes or until almost tender. Spread leaves apart; scrape out the fuzzy thistle center (choke) with a spoon. Set artichokes aside.

Melt margarine in a heavy saucepan over low heat; add flour, stirring until smooth. Cook 1 minute, stirring constantly. Gradually add milk; cook over medium heat, stirring constantly, until mixture is thickened and bubbly. Add cheese, salt, pepper, and hot sauce, stirring until cheese melts. Remove from heat, and cool slightly.

Beat egg yolks at medium speed of an electric mixer until thick and lemon colored. Gradually stir about one-fourth of hot cheese mixture into beaten egg yolks; add to remaining hot mixture.

Beat egg whites (at room temperature) at high speed of an electric mixer until stiff but not dry; fold into cheese mixture. Spoon into artichoke cavities. Place artichokes in a 13- x 9- x 2-inch baking dish that has been coated with cooking spray. Bake at 350° for 20 minutes. Reduce temperature to 325°, and bake an additional 50 minutes or until puffed and golden. Sprinkle each soufflé with ½ teaspoon minced fresh parsley. Serve immediately. Yield: 6 servings (321 calories per serving).

PROTEIN 18.1 / FAT 10.6 / CARBOHYDRATE 46.8 / CHOLESTEROL 134 / IRON 5.7 / SODIUM 560 / CALCIUM 369

BAKED POTATOES WITH BROCCOLI AND CHEESE

6 (8-ounce) baking potatoes
½ cup plain nonfat yogurt
3 tablespoons minced onion
⅛ teaspoon salt
⅛ teaspoon ground white pepper
5 cups chopped fresh broccoli (about 1¾ pounds)
2 teaspoons reduced-calorie margarine
2 tablespoons cornstarch
1 tablespoon plus 1 teaspoon cold water
⅔ cup canned low-sodium chicken broth, undiluted
⅔ cup skim milk
¾ cup (3 ounces) 40% less-fat shredded Cheddar
   cheese
⅛ teaspoon paprika

Wash potatoes; bake at 475° for 45 minutes or until done. Let cool to touch. Cut a 1-inch lengthwise strip from top of each potato; carefully scoop out pulp, leaving shells intact.

Combine potato pulp, yogurt, and next 3 ingredients in a medium bowl. Beat at medium speed of an electric mixer until light and fluffy; spoon into shells. Bake at 475° for 20 minutes or until thoroughly heated.

Cook broccoli, covered, in a small amount of boiling water 10 minutes or until crisp-tender. Drain and pat dry with paper towels. Set aside.

Melt margarine in a heavy saucepan over low heat. Dissolve cornstarch in water, and add to margarine, stirring until smooth. Cook 1 minute, stirring constantly. Gradually add chicken broth and milk; cook over medium heat, stirring constantly, until mixture is thickened and bubbly. Add cheese; stir until cheese melts. Stir in broccoli, and cook over low heat until thoroughly heated. Spoon equal amounts of broccoli mixture over hot potatoes. Sprinkle with paprika. Yield: 6 servings (349 calories per serving).

PROTEIN 13.1 / FAT 4.0 / CARBOHYDRATE 67.1 / CHOLESTEROL 1 / IRON 3.9 / SODIUM 224 / CALCIUM 242

STUFFED EGGPLANT

2 large eggplants (about 2½ pounds)
Vegetable cooking spray
3¾ cups diced onion
1 (14½-ounce) can no-salt-added whole tomatoes, drained and chopped
½ pound fresh mushrooms, chopped
3 large cloves garlic, minced
1 tablespoon dried whole oregano
½ teaspoon salt, divided
1 tablespoon margarine
2 tablespoons all-purpose flour
1 cup skim milk
¼ teaspoon ground white pepper
¼ teaspoon ground cinnamon
⅛ teaspoon ground nutmeg
⅛ teaspoon ground red pepper
1½ cups (6 ounces) shredded part-skim mozzarella cheese, divided
¼ cup chopped fresh parsley

Wash eggplants and cut in half lengthwise, leaving stem intact. Remove pulp, leaving a ¼-inch-thick shell. Chop pulp and set pulp and shells aside.

Coat a large nonstick skillet with cooking spray; place over medium-high heat until hot. Add onion, and sauté until tender. Add reserved chopped eggplant, tomatoes, mushrooms, garlic, oregano, and ¼ teaspoon salt; stir well. Cover and cook over low heat 30 minutes.

Melt margarine in a small saucepan over low heat; add flour, stirring until smooth. Cook 1 minute, stirring constantly. Gradually add milk; cook over medium heat, stirring constantly, until mixture is thickened and bubbly. Stir in remaining ¼ teaspoon salt, white pepper and next 3 ingredients.

Combine eggplant mixture in a large bowl with ¾ cup white sauce and ¾ cup shredded mozzarella cheese; stir well. Place 2 cups mixture in each reserved eggplant shell, and place on a baking sheet. Cover with foil, and bake at 400° for 35 minutes.

Top with remaining white sauce and cheese. Bake, uncovered, 10 minutes or until cheese melts. Sprinkle with parsley. Yield: 4 servings (335 calories per serving).

PROTEIN 19.9 / FAT 11.1 / CARBOHYDRATE 44.3 / CHOLESTEROL 26 / IRON 4.2 / SODIUM 584 / CALCIUM 547

RATATOUILLE WITH PASTA

Vegetable cooking spray
1½ teaspoons olive oil
¾ cup cubed onion
2½ cups cubed eggplant
1 (16-ounce) can crushed tomatoes, undrained
1 (16-ounce) can red kidney beans, rinsed and drained
2½ cups cubed zucchini
2 cups cubed yellow squash
½ cup cubed sweet yellow pepper
½ cup cubed sweet red pepper
¼ cup water
1 clove garlic, minced
1 teaspoon dried Italian seasoning
¼ teaspoon salt
⅛ teaspoon pepper
2 cups peeled, seeded, and chopped tomatoes
¾ cup sliced fresh mushrooms
8 ripe olives, quartered
2 tablespoons minced fresh parsley
1 tablespoon red wine vinegar
6 ounces penne pasta, uncooked
4 ounces freshly grated Parmesan cheese

Coat a large saucepan with cooking spray; add olive oil. Place over medium heat until hot. Add onion and sauté until tender. Add eggplant, tomatoes, beans, zucchini, yellow squash, yellow pepper, red pepper, water, garlic, seasoning, salt, and pepper; bring to a boil. Reduce heat, and simmer 30 minutes or until mixture is thickened.

Coat a large nonstick skillet with cooking spray. Place over high heat until hot. Add tomatoes and mushrooms; sauté 4 minutes or until tender. Add sautéed vegetables, olives, parsley, and vinegar to eggplant mixture; stir well. Set aside, and keep warm.

Cook pasta according to package directions, omitting salt and fat; drain. Combine pasta and eggplant mixture in a large bowl; toss gently. Sprinkle with Parmesan cheese. Yield: 10 servings (194 calories per serving).

PROTEIN 10.7 / FAT 4.7 / CARBOHYDRATE 28.6 / CHOLESTEROL 8 / IRON 2.7 / SODIUM 324 / CALCIUM 195

LAYERED EGGPLANT CASSEROLE

1½ cups yellow squash, shredded (about ½ pound)
1½ cups zucchini, shredded (about ½ pound)
2 teaspoons salt
2 large eggplants (about 2½ pounds)
Vegetable cooking spray
6 ounces penne pasta, uncooked
2 eggs
1 egg yolk
½ cup part-skim ricotta cheese
3 tablespoons freshly grated Parmesan cheese
½ teaspoon freshly ground pepper
2 teaspoons olive oil
½ teaspoon dried whole oregano
½ teaspoon dried whole basil
2 (8-ounce) cans no-salt-added tomato sauce
2 cups peeled, seeded, and chopped
   tomatoes
¼ cup minced fresh parsley

Combine squash, zucchini, and salt; toss gently. Place in a colander; let stand 30 minutes. Rinse with cold water; pat dry between paper towels. Set aside.

Wash eggplants; chop ½ cup eggplant and set aside. Slice remaining eggplant into ¼-inch-thick slices.

Cover broiler pan with one layer of eggplant slices. Coat slices with cooking spray. Broil 3 inches from heat 1 minute or until golden brown. Turn slices; coat with cooking spray, and broil 1 minute or until slices are golden brown. Set aside. Repeat procedure with remaining eggplant slices.

Coat an 11- x 7- x 1½-inch baking dish with cooking spray. Arrange eggplant slices, overlapping slightly, to form a decorative pattern around sides and on bottom of baking dish. Set dish aside.

Cook pasta according to package directions, omitting salt and fat. Rinse with cold water; drain well. Arrange pasta in one direction on top of eggplant slices.

Combine eggs and next 4 ingredients in a small bowl, stirring well. Spoon cheese mixture over pasta.

Coat a medium nonstick skillet with cooking spray. Place over medium-high heat until hot; add olive oil. Add reserved squash and zucchini; sauté until vegetables are crisp-tender, stirring

gently. Add oregano and basil; cook an additional 4 minutes. Spoon vegetable mixture over pasta in baking dish.

Sprinkle reserved ½ cup chopped eggplant over vegetable mixture. Cover and bake at 375° for 1 hour. Remove from oven, and let stand 10 minutes before serving.

Combine tomato sauce and chopped tomatoes in a medium saucepan. Cook over medium heat until thoroughly heated.

Transfer eggplant casserole to individual warm serving plates. Serve each with ¾ cup tomato sauce. Top evenly with parsley. Yield: 6 servings (298 calories per serving).

PROTEIN 14.0 / FAT 7.8 / CARBOHYDRATE 46.0 / CHOLESTEROL 121 / IRON 3.3 / SODIUM 330 / CALCIUM 214

 SOLUBLE FIBER FACTS

Scientists now separate fiber into two distinct categories: insoluble and soluble. Water-insoluble fiber—wheat bran, corn bran, or rice bran—helps prevent constipation and may offer some protection against cancer. Soluble fiber, on the other hand, appears to help lower blood cholesterol levels.

The National Cancer Institute recommends that Americans aim for 20 to 35 grams of fiber a day. Currently, most Americans eat about 11 grams a day. Foods typically contain a mixture of both types of fiber, but often are more concentrated in one type. Health professionals recommend that about one-third of the total daily fiber allowance, roughly 7 to 10 grams, be of the soluble variety. For sources of cholesterol-lowering soluble fiber, refer to the chart.

FIBER CONTENT OF VARIOUS FOODS		
Food Item	Soluble Fiber (grams)	Total Fiber (grams)
Chick-peas, raw, ½ cup	2.5	5.0
Kidney beans, ½ cup cooked	2.5	5.8
Navy beans, ½ cup cooked	2.3	4.7
Oat bran, ⅓ cup dry	2.0	4.0
Barley, pearled, ¼ cup	1.6	6.0
Oatmeal, ¾ cup cooked	1.4	2.8
Prunes, 3 dried	1.0	3.7
Apple, raw with skin	0.9	2.8
Grapefruit, ½ medium	0.9	1.7

SPINACH-FILLED CRÊPES

1 cup skim milk
¾ cup whole wheat flour
¼ cup unbleached flour
¼ teaspoon salt
½ cup frozen egg substitute, thawed
Vegetable cooking spray
Spinach Filling

Combine first 5 ingredients in container of an electric blender. Top with cover, and blend at high speed for 30 seconds. Refrigerate batter 1 hour. (This allows flour particles to swell and soften so that crêpes are light in texture.)

Coat an 8-inch crêpe pan or nonstick skillet with cooking spray; place over medium-high heat until just hot, not smoking.

Pour 2 tablespoons batter into pan; quickly tilt pan in all directions so batter covers pan in a thin film. Cook 1 minute or until lightly browned.

Lift edge of crêpe to test for doneness. Crêpe is ready for flipping when it can be shaken loose from pan. Flip crêpe, and cook about 30 seconds on other side. (This side is usually spotty brown and is the side on which filling is placed.)

Place crêpes on a towel; keep warm. Stack between layers of wax paper to prevent sticking. Repeat until all batter is used.

Place ¼ cup Spinach Filling on each crêpe. Roll up, and place seam side down on a warm serving platter. Serve immediately. Yield: 6 servings (182 calories per 2-crêpe serving).

Spinach Filling:

1 (10-ounce) package frozen chopped spinach, thawed
1 tablespoon reduced-calorie margarine
2 tablespoons all-purpose flour
½ cup skim milk
2 (1-ounce) slices low-fat process American cheese
Vegetable cooking spray
2 tablespoons finely chopped shallots
½ cup sliced fresh mushrooms
½ cup diced firm tofu
1 cup frozen egg substitute, thawed
¼ teaspoon salt
⅛ teaspoon ground white pepper

Drain spinach; press between paper towels to remove excess moisture. Set aside.

Melt margarine in a small saucepan over low heat; add flour, stirring until smooth. Cook 1 minute, stirring constantly. Gradually add milk; cook over medium heat, stirring constantly, until thickened and bubbly. Add cheese slices and stir until cheese melts. Set aside.

Coat a nonstick skillet with cooking spray; place over medium heat until hot. Add shallots and mushrooms, and sauté until tender. Add reserved spinach, tofu, egg substitute, salt, and pepper. Cook over medium heat until mixture begins to set. Stir in cheese sauce; cook until mixture is set. Yield: 3 cups.

PROTEIN 16.0 / FAT 3.4 / CARBOHYDRATE 23.6 / CHOLESTEROL 1 / IRON 3.7 / SODIUM 509 / CALCIUM 239

CHEESE AND VEGETABLE QUICHE

¾ cup low-fat cottage cheese
1 (8-ounce) carton frozen egg substitute, thawed
⅓ cup skim milk
2 tablespoons chopped fresh basil
¼ teaspoon freshly ground pepper
1 tablespoon olive oil
1½ cups peeled, diced potatoes
½ cup sliced green onions
1 (10-ounce) package frozen chopped broccoli, thawed and well drained
½ cup chopped sweet red pepper
Vegetable cooking spray

Place cottage cheese in container of an electric blender or food processor; top with cover, and process until smooth. Add egg substitute, milk, basil, and pepper; process until smooth. Set aside.

Pour oil in a large nonstick skillet; place over medium heat until hot. Add potatoes and green onions; sauté 10 minutes. Add broccoli and red pepper; sauté an additional 4 minutes or until vegetables are crisp-tender.

Place vegetable mixture in 10-inch quiche dish that has been coated with cooking spray. Pour egg substitute mixture over vegetables. Bake at 350° for 50 minutes or until set. Let stand 10 minutes before slicing into wedges. Yield: 6 servings (112 calories per serving).

PROTEIN 10.1 / FAT 2.9 / CARBOHYDRATE 12.3 / CHOLESTEROL 1 / IRON 1.8 / SODIUM 193 / CALCIUM 83

Paper-thin layers of phyllo pastry surround Vegetable and Cheese Phyllo Pie.

VEGETABLE AND CHEESE PHYLLO PIE

1 (9-ounce) package frozen artichoke hearts,
   thawed and undrained
¼ cup water
2 cloves garlic, minced
1 (10-ounce) package frozen chopped spinach,
   thawed and drained
½ cup thinly sliced leeks (about 2 ounces)
1 teaspoon olive oil
1 (8-ounce) carton part-skim ricotta cheese
4 ounces goat cheese
¼ cup freshly grated Parmesan cheese
3 eggs, lightly beaten
1 teaspoon dried whole thyme
⅛ teaspoon ground white pepper
Butter-flavored vegetable cooking spray
13 sheets commercial frozen phyllo pastry, thawed

Combine artichoke hearts, water, and garlic in
a small saucepan. Cover and cook over medium
heat 6 minutes. Drain and coarsely chop artichokes. Combine artichoke mixture and spinach
in a large bowl; stir well, and set aside.

Sauté leeks in olive oil in a small skillet over
medium heat 2 minutes or just until tender. Add
leeks to artichoke mixture; stir in ricotta cheese
and next 5 ingredients.

Coat a 10-inch springform pan with cooking
spray; place 1 sheet of phyllo pastry in pan
(keep remaining phyllo pastry covered). Coat
phyllo with cooking spray. Layer 7 more sheets
phyllo pastry on first sheet, coating each layer
with cooking spray, and fanning each slightly to
the right. (The overhanging sheets of phyllo will

form a circle around the pan.) Gently press phyllo into pan forming a large shell; fill with vegetable-cheese mixture. Top with 5 more phyllo sheets, coating each layer with cooking spray and fanning each slightly to the right. Tuck top sheets down around filling. Fold edges over top to enclose filling. Bake, uncovered, at 400° for 25 minutes. Cover and bake an additional 35 minutes. Let stand 15 minutes. Remove from pan. Transfer to serving platter. Serve warm. Yield: 8 servings (217 calories per serving).

PROTEIN 12.7 / FAT 9.6 / CARBOHYDRATE 21.3 / CHOLESTEROL 99 / IRON 1.5 / SODIUM 306 / CALCIUM 235

ROLLED SOUFFLÉ OMELET

Vegetable cooking spray
2 tablespoons margarine, divided
¼ pound fresh crimini mushrooms, finely chopped
¼ pound fresh mushrooms, finely chopped
½ cup chopped green onions
2 tablespoons Madeira wine
½ teaspoon salt, divided
¼ teaspoon freshly ground pepper
2 tablespoons all-purpose flour
1 cup skim milk
⅛ teaspoon ground white pepper
5 eggs, separated
½ teaspoon cream of tartar
¼ cup freshly grated Parmesan cheese
1 tablespoon minced fresh chives
1 tablespoon minced fresh parsley
Tomato rose (optional)
Fresh parsley sprigs (optional)

Coat a 17- x 11- x 1-inch jellyroll pan with cooking spray; line with wax paper. Coat wax paper with cooking spray; set aside.

Coat a large nonstick skillet with cooking spray; add 1 tablespoon margarine. Place over medium heat until margarine melts. Add mushrooms, and sauté until tender. Add green onions, wine, ¼ teaspoon salt, and pepper; continue cooking until liquid has evaporated. Set mixture aside.

Melt remaining 1 tablespoon margarine in a heavy saucepan; add flour, stirring until smooth. Cook 1 minute, stirring constantly. Gradually add milk; cook over medium heat, stirring constantly, until mixture is thickened and bubbly. Stir in remaining ¼ teaspoon salt and ground white pepper.

Beat egg yolks until thick and lemon colored. Gradually stir about one-fourth of hot mixture into yolks; add to remaining hot mixture.

Beat egg whites (at room temperature) in a large bowl at high speed of an electric mixer until foamy. Add cream of tartar, and beat until stiff but not dry. Fold beaten egg whites, cheese, chives, and parsley into yolk mixture. Pour into prepared pan. Bake at 350° for 15 to 20 minutes or until lightly browned.

Loosen edges of soufflé with a metal spatula, but do not remove from pan; place pan on a wire rack. Let cool 15 minutes.

Carefully invert jellyroll pan onto wax paper; remove pan, and carefully peel wax paper from soufflé. Spoon reserved mushroom mixture over surface of soufflé, spreading to edges. Starting at short side, carefully roll up soufflé jellyroll fashion. If desired, garnish with a tomato rose and fresh parsley sprigs. Yield: 4 servings (228 calories per serving).

PROTEIN 14.3 / FAT 14.5 / CARBOHYDRATE 11.2 / CHOLESTEROL 255 / IRON 2.3 / SODIUM 615 / CALCIUM 208

SAY CHEESE, BUT MAKE IT LOW-FAT

For all its nutritional pluses (calcium, protein, riboflavin, and vitamin A), cheese does have one big minus—it can be high in fat. Of the 110 calories in an ounce of Cheddar cheese, almost 75 percent comes from fat, most of it the saturated variety. Other traditional hard cheeses—Swiss, Muenster, and Monterey Jack—are no different.

Cheese lovers do have a few alternatives. One option is to use less cheese in a recipe or on a cracker. Purchasing stronger flavored cheese, such as a sharp Cheddar instead of a mild one, often helps lower the quantity needed but heightens the pleasure. New to the market are a variety of low-fat cheeses with only 2 grams or less of fat per ounce.

Read cheese labels carefully before you buy. Some low-fat cheeses contain 3 to 5 grams of fat per ounce. To be sure, 5 grams of fat is a lot less than 8 or 9, but it still adds up to a hefty 40 percent of the calories.

VEGETABLE OMELET

Vegetable cooking spray
½ cup chopped onion
½ cup sliced fresh mushrooms
¼ cup finely chopped green pepper
¼ cup chopped sweet red pepper
½ cup peeled and chopped tomato
Dash of hot sauce
1 cup frozen egg substitute, thawed
3 tablespoons skim milk
Dash of pepper
¼ cup (1 ounce) 40% less-fat Cheddar cheese

Coat a small nonstick skillet with cooking spray; place over medium-high heat until hot. Add onion and next 3 ingredients; sauté until tender. Stir in tomato and hot sauce; cook until thoroughly heated. Set aside.

Combine egg substitute, milk, and pepper in a small bowl. Coat a 10-inch nonstick skillet or omelet pan with cooking spray; place over medium heat until hot enough to sizzle a drop of water. Pour egg substitute mixture into skillet. As mixture begins to cook, gently lift edges of omelet with a spatula, and tilt pan to allow uncooked portions to flow underneath. When egg mixture is set, spoon vegetable mixture over half of omelet; sprinkle with cheese. Loosen omelet with spatula, and carefully fold in half. Carefully slide omelet onto a warm serving platter. Cut omelet into 2 pieces. Serve immediately. Yield: 2 servings (146 calories per serving).

PROTEIN 17.0 / FAT 3.1 / CARBOHYDRATE 13.9 / CHOLESTEROL 0 / IRON 3.3 / SODIUM 273 / CALCIUM 184

VEGETARIAN COUSCOUS

Vegetable cooking spray
1 tablespoon margarine
1 tablespoon minced garlic
1 tablespoon minced fresh gingerroot
½ teaspoon ground cumin
½ teaspoon ground turmeric
¼ teaspoon ground cinnamon
⅛ teaspoon ground red pepper
7¾ cups water, divided
1 tablespoon chicken-flavored bouillon granules
1 cup chopped purple onion
2 (14½-ounce) cans no-salt-added whole tomatoes, drained and chopped
1 cup diagonally sliced celery
2 carrots, scraped and sliced diagonally
1 medium-size sweet potato, peeled and cubed
1 sweet red pepper, cut into ½-inch pieces
2 cups cubed turnips
2 cups cubed zucchini
2 tablespoons raisins
1 (15-ounce) can garbanzo beans, drained
10 ounces firm tofu, cubed
1¾ cups plus 2 tablespoons uncooked couscous
1 tablespoon plus 2 teaspoons sliced almonds, lightly toasted

Coat a large Dutch oven with cooking spray; add margarine. Place over medium-high heat until hot. Add garlic, gingerroot, cumin, turmeric, cinnamon, and ground red pepper. Cook 2 minutes, stirring constantly.

Stir in 4 cups water, bouillon granules, chopped onion, and tomatoes. Bring mixture to a boil; reduce heat and simmer, uncovered, 15 minutes. Stir in sliced celery, sliced carrot, and cubed sweet potato; cook 5 minutes. Add sweet red pepper pieces and cubed turnips; cook 4 minutes. Add cubed zucchini, raisins, garbanzo beans, and tofu. Cook 5 minutes. Remove mixture from heat.

Bring remaining 3¾ cups water to a boil in a medium saucepan. Remove from heat. Add couscous; cover and let stand 5 minutes or until couscous is tender and liquid is absorbed. To serve, place ½ cup cooked couscous in each individual serving bowl; spoon 1 cup vegetable mixture over each serving. Top evenly with toasted almonds. Yield: 10 servings (267 calories per serving).

PROTEIN 10.1 / FAT 4.2 / CARBOHYDRATE 49.3 / CHOLESTEROL 0 / IRON 3.7 / SODIUM 375 / CALCIUM 110

BARLEY RISOTTO WITH SPINACH AND CHEESE

Vegetable cooking spray
1 tablespoon margarine
¼ cup minced onion
¼ cup minced shallots
1 clove garlic, minced
½ cup Chablis or other dry white wine
1 cup pearl barley
5½ cups canned low-sodium chicken broth,
    undiluted and divided
1 pound fresh spinach
1⅓ cups freshly grated Parmesan cheese

Coat a Dutch oven with cooking spray; add margarine. Place over medium-high heat until hot. Add onion and shallots, and sauté until tender. Add garlic, and cook an additional 1 minute. Add wine, and cook until almost all liquid is absorbed, stirring frequently. Reduce heat to low, and stir in barley; cook 3 minutes, stirring constantly. Add ½ cup chicken broth; cook 8 minutes or until liquid is absorbed, stirring constantly. Repeat procedure using remaining chicken broth, stirring in ½ cup at a time.

Remove stems from spinach; wash leaves thoroughly, and tear into pieces. Stir spinach into barley mixture; cook just until spinach wilts. Stir in Parmesan cheese. Serve immediately. Yield: 4 servings (309 calories per 1-cup serving).

PROTEIN 11.9 / FAT 6.4 / CARBOHYDRATE 49.9 / CHOLESTEROL 6 / IRON 4.5 / SODIUM 288 / CALCIUM 245

ASIAN BURRITOS

1 ounce dried shiitake mushrooms
2 cups hot water
Vegetable cooking spray
1 tablespoon plus 1 teaspoon safflower oil, divided
4 eggs, lightly beaten
1 small onion, thinly sliced
1 teaspoon minced garlic
1 teaspoon minced fresh gingerroot
6 cups shredded Chinese cabbage
½ pound firm tofu, drained and cut into thin
    julienne strips
¼ pound zucchini, cut into thin julienne strips
1 medium carrot, scraped and cut into thin
    julienne strips
½ cup canned low-sodium chicken broth, undiluted
2 tablespoons reduced-sodium soy sauce
2 tablespoons water
1 tablespoon cornstarch
12 (6-inch) flour tortillas
3 tablespoons hoisin sauce
3 tablespoons water

Soak mushrooms in hot water 15 minutes; drain and cut into thin julienne strips. Set aside.

Coat a large nonstick skillet with cooking spray; add 2 teaspoons oil. Place over medium-high heat until hot. Add beaten eggs; spread quickly over surface of pan. As mixture begins to cook, gently lift edges of omelet with a spatula, and tilt pan to allow uncooked portions to flow underneath. Cook until eggs are set. Loosen edges with a spatula. Invert skillet onto a cutting surface; remove skillet. Roll up eggs jellyroll fashion, and cut into ⅛-inch-thick shreds. Set shreds aside.

Add remaining 2 teaspoons oil to skillet. Place over medium-high heat until hot. Add onion, garlic, and gingerroot; sauté 2 minutes. Add cabbage, tofu, zucchini strips, and carrot strips to skillet; sauté over high heat 2 minutes. Stir in chicken broth and soy sauce. Combine 2 tablespoons water and cornstarch; stir well. Gradually stir cornstarch mixture into vegetable mixture; cook until thickened, stirring constantly. Stir in reserved egg shreds.

Wrap tortillas in aluminum foil, and bake at 325° for 15 minutes. Combine hoisin sauce and 3 tablespoons water; stir well. Unwrap tortillas, and spread 1 tablespoon hoisin sauce mixture over each tortilla. Place 1 cup vegetable mixture evenly down center of each tortilla, and roll up. Yield: 6 servings (390 calories per serving).

PROTEIN 17.0 / FAT 14.2 / CARBOHYDRATE 53.9 / CHOLESTEROL 133 / IRON 6.9 / SODIUM 597 / CALCIUM 215

Savor Whole Wheat Calzones that are packed with garden-fresh vegetables and mozzarella cheese.

WHOLE WHEAT CALZONES WITH BROCCOLI AND MOZZARELLA CHEESE

1 package dry yeast
1 cup warm water (105° to 115°), divided
1 tablespoon honey
1¾ cups whole wheat flour
1 cup unbleached flour
½ teaspoon salt
3 tablespoons whole wheat flour, divided
Vegetable cooking spray
3 cups chopped fresh broccoli flowerets
½ cup chopped onion
⅓ cup shredded carrot
⅓ cup commercial oil-free Italian dressing
¼ teaspoon freshly ground pepper
1½ cups (6 ounces) shredded part-skim
  mozzarella cheese
1 egg
1 tablespoon water
2 tablespoons freshly grated Parmesan cheese

Dissolve yeast in ¼ cup warm water in a large mixing bowl; let stand 5 minutes.

Combine remaining ¾ cup warm water and honey; add to yeast mixture, stirring gently. Gradually stir in 1¾ cups whole wheat flour, unbleached flour, and salt to make a soft dough. Sprinkle 1 tablespoon whole wheat flour evenly over work surface. Turn dough out onto floured surface, and knead until smooth and elastic (about 8 to 10 minutes). Place dough in a large bowl that has been coated with cooking spray, turning to grease top. Cover and let rise in a warm place (85°), free from drafts, 45 minutes or until doubled in bulk.

Cook broccoli in boiling water 3 minutes or until crisp-tender. Drain; rinse with cold water, and drain again. Combine broccoli, onion, shredded carrot, and dressing in a small bowl.

Punch dough down, and divide into 6 equal portions. Shape each portion into a ball; cover and let rest 5 minutes. Sprinkle 1 teaspoon flour over work surface. Roll one portion into a 7-inch circle. Repeat with remaining portions, using 1 teaspoon whole wheat flour for each circle.

Divide broccoli mixture into 6 portions. Place one portion on half of each circle of dough. Sprinkle pepper and mozzarella cheese evenly over broccoli mixture. Combine egg and water; moisten edges of circles with egg mixture. Fold circles in half; crimp edges to seal. Sprinkle each with 1 teaspoon Parmesan cheese. Bake at 425° for 10 minutes or until golden brown. Yield: 6 servings (330 calories per serving).

PROTEIN 17.9 / FAT 7.2 / CARBOHYDRATE 51.6 / CHOLESTEROL 51 / IRON 2.9 / SODIUM 514 / CALCIUM 261

CORNMEAL PIE

2 cups yellow cornmeal
2 cups cold water
½ teaspoon salt
4½ cups boiling water
1 (4-ounce) can chopped green chiles, drained
2 tablespoons chopped jalapeño pepper
Vegetable cooking spray
1 cup diced onion
2 cloves garlic, minced
2 (14½-ounce) cans no-salt-added tomatoes, drained and chopped
1 (12-ounce) can no-salt-added corn, drained
1 medium-size sweet red pepper, cut into ¼-inch squares
18 pitted ripe olives, quartered
¾ cup diced celery
2 teaspoons chili powder
1 teaspoon dried whole oregano
½ teaspoon ground cumin
2 cups (8 ounces) shredded part-skim mozzarella cheese, divided

Combine cornmeal and cold water; stir well. Dissolve salt in boiling water in top of a large double boiler. Add cornmeal mixture; cook over boiling water 20 minutes, stirring occasionally. Remove from heat. Stir in chiles and jalapeño.

Coat a large nonstick skillet with cooking spray; place over medium heat until hot. Add onion and garlic; sauté until tender. Add tomatoes and next 7 ingredients; bring to a boil. Reduce heat, and simmer 15 minutes.

Coat an 8- x 8- x 2-inch baking dish with cooking spray. Pour in one-third of cornmeal mixture. Sprinkle with ¾ cup cheese. Spread half of vegetable mixture over cheese; repeat layers. Top with remaining cornmeal mixture. Cover; bake at 350° for 1½ hours. Uncover; sprinkle with remaining cheese. Bake at 450° for 10 minutes or until cheese is lightly browned. Yield: 8 servings (249 calories per serving).

PROTEIN 11.6 / FAT 6.5 / CARBOHYDRATE 36.4 / CHOLESTEROL 16 / IRON 2.2 / SODIUM 354 / CALCIUM 216

CHILES RELLENOS CASSEROLE

8 large Anahiem or long green chiles
1 (8-ounce) package part-skim mozzarella cheese
1 cup unbleached flour
¾ cup cornmeal
1 teaspoon baking powder
¼ teaspoon salt
1¼ cups skim milk
2 eggs, lightly beaten
Vegetable cooking spray
½ cup commercial salsa
Fresh cilantro sprigs (optional)

Wash and dry chiles; place on a baking sheet. Broil 3 to 4 inches from heat 8 to 10 minutes, turning often with tongs until blistered on all sides. Immediately place chiles in a paper sack. Close sack, and allow chiles to steam 15 minutes to loosen skins. Peel chiles; remove stems, cores, and seeds, keeping chiles intact.

Slice cheese lengthwise into 8 (1-inch) strips. Stuff each chile with a strip of cheese; set aside.

Combine flour, cornmeal, baking powder, and salt in a large bowl. Make a well in center of mixture. Combine milk and eggs; add to dry ingredients, stirring just until moistened.

Coat a 13- x 9- x 2-inch baking dish with cooking spray; place chiles in dish. Pour cornmeal mixture over chiles; bake at 375° for 25 minutes or until golden brown. Serve with salsa. Garnish with cilantro sprigs, if desired. Yield: 8 servings (208 calories per serving).

PROTEIN 12.4 / FAT 6.2 / CARBOHYDRATE 24.8 / CHOLESTEROL 67 / IRON 1.3 / SODIUM 321 / CALCIUM 263

TOFU STROGANOFF

1 (10½-ounce) package firm tofu
Vegetable cooking spray
2 teaspoons olive oil
2 cups sliced fresh mushrooms
½ cup shredded carrot
2 cloves garlic, crushed
2 tablespoons all-purpose flour
1 teaspoon chicken-flavored bouillon granules
¼ teaspoon pepper
¾ cup skim milk
¾ cup plain nonfat yogurt
3 cups hot cooked spinach egg noodles (cooked without salt or fat)
2 tablespoons minced fresh parsley

Wrap tofu in several layers of cheesecloth or paper towels; press lightly to remove excess moisture. Remove cheesecloth; cut tofu into ½-inch cubes. Set aside.

Coat a large nonstick skillet with cooking spray; add oil. Place over medium-high heat until hot. Add tofu; sauté 4 minutes. Remove from skillet; set aside. Add mushrooms, carrot, and garlic to skillet; sauté until vegetables are crisp-tender. Remove from skillet; set aside.

Combine flour, bouillon granules, and pepper, stirring until well blended. Gradually add milk, stirring until smooth. Add milk mixture to skillet; bring to a boil. Cook 1 minute, stirring constantly. Stir in yogurt, tofu, and vegetable mixture. Cook over low heat until thoroughly heated (do not boil). Serve over hot cooked noodles. Sprinkle with parsley. Yield: 6 servings (236 calories per serving).

PROTEIN 15.4 / FAT 7.3 / CARBOHYDRATE 29.5 / CHOLESTEROL 1 / IRON 7.6 / SODIUM 202 / CALCIUM 250

PASTA WITH LENTILS

Vegetable cooking spray
1 teaspoon olive oil
1 cup diced onion
1 cup diced carrot
⅔ cup diced celery
3 cups canned no-salt-added chicken broth, undiluted
1 cup dried lentils
1 bay leaf
¼ teaspoon salt
¼ teaspoon pepper
10 ounces fresh linguine, uncooked
¼ cup freshly grated Parmesan cheese
2 tablespoons minced fresh parsley
1 tablespoon chopped fresh basil

Coat a large nonstick skillet with cooking spray; add oil. Place over medium heat until hot. Add onion, carrot, and celery; cook until vegetables are crisp-tender. Stir in chicken broth, lentils, and bay leaf. Bring mixture to a boil; cover, reduce heat, and simmer 25 minutes or until lentils are tender. Remove and discard bay leaf. Stir in salt and pepper.

Cook pasta according to package directions, omitting salt and fat. Combine pasta, lentil mixture, and remaining ingredients, tossing well. Yield: 8 servings (229 calories per serving).

PROTEIN 12.7 / FAT 3.4 / CARBOHYDRATE 36.5 / CHOLESTEROL 18 / IRON 3.4 / SODIUM 286 / CALCIUM 91

EGG STORAGE TIPS

While putting all your eggs in one basket was never a good idea, neither is taking them out of the egg carton. Left uncovered in the refrigerator, eggs tend to absorb odors from the foods around them. And that can ruin their taste. In addition, uncovered egg shells tend to lose moisture faster than covered ones, making an egg old long before its time. If stored in the carton, an egg can stay fresh for as long as one full month.

When you want a unique but quick entrée, offer Veal and Asparagus Stir-Fry (page 158). Fennel, garlic, and a hint of lemon provide the perfect accent.

PASTA WITH BOLOGNESE SAUCE

2 cups boiling water
1 ounce dried porcini mushrooms
Vegetable cooking spray
1 tablespoon olive oil
1¼ cups chopped onion
¾ cup chopped carrot
½ cup chopped celery
3 cloves garlic, minced
½ pound ground chuck
½ pound fresh ground turkey
½ pound ground veal
½ cup Chablis or other dry white
   wine
4 (14½-ounce) cans no-salt-added whole
   tomatoes, undrained and chopped
2 bay leaves
½ teaspoon salt
¼ teaspoon freshly ground pepper
½ cup skim milk
1 teaspoon dried whole oregano
1 teaspoon dried whole thyme
⅛ teaspoon ground nutmeg
5 cups hot cooked pasta (cooked without
   salt or fat)

Pour 2 cups boiling water over mushrooms; let stand 30 minutes. Drain mushrooms through 2 layers of cheesecloth, reserving 1 cup liquid. Coarsely chop mushrooms, and set aside.

Coat a Dutch oven with cooking spray; add oil. Place over medium-high heat until hot. Add onion, carrot, celery, and garlic; sauté until tender. Add ground chuck, turkey, and veal; continue cooking until meat is browned, stirring to crumble. Drain and pat dry with paper towels. Wipe pan drippings from Dutch oven with a paper towel.

Return meat mixture to Dutch oven. Add wine. Bring mixture to a boil, and boil 2 minutes. Add reserved mushrooms and 1 cup liquid, tomatoes, bay leaves, salt, and pepper. Bring mixture to a boil; cover, reduce heat, and simmer 3 hours, stirring occasionally. Remove and discard bay leaves. Stir in milk, oregano, thyme, and nutmeg. Serve over hot cooked pasta. Yield: 10 servings (280 calories per 1 cup mixture and ½ cup pasta).

PROTEIN 20.1 / FAT 7.7 / CARBOHYDRATE 32.0 / CHOLESTEROL 77 / IRON 2.7 / SODIUM 194 / CALCIUM 102

SPINACH AND BEEF BAKE

1 (10-ounce) package frozen chopped spinach
Vegetable cooking spray
1 pound ground chuck
½ cup thinly sliced celery
½ cup chopped onion
½ cup cooked long-grain rice (cooked without salt
   or fat)
1 egg, beaten
½ teaspoon salt
½ teaspoon dried whole thyme
¼ teaspoon pepper
½ cup (2 ounces) shredded 40% less-fat Cheddar
   cheese
Sweet red pepper rings (optional)

Cook spinach according to package directions, omitting salt; drain well. Set aside. Coat a large nonstick skillet with cooking spray. Add ground chuck, celery, and onion. Cook over medium heat until browned, stirring to crumble meat. Drain well; pat dry with paper towels.

Combine spinach, meat mixture, rice, and next 4 ingredients in a medium bowl; mix well. Place mixture in a 1½-quart baking dish that has been coated with cooking spray. Bake, covered, at 350° for 20 minutes. Top with cheese and bake, uncovered, 5 minutes or until cheese melts. Garnish with red pepper rings, if desired. Yield: 6 servings (223 calories per serving).

PROTEIN 19.1 / FAT 11.8 / CARBOHYDRATE 10.6 / CHOLESTEROL 81 / IRON 2.9 / SODIUM 340 / CALCIUM 137

SUMMER SPAGHETTI SUPPER

1 (2-pound) spaghetti squash
1 pound ground chuck
½ cup chopped onion
1 clove garlic, minced
1½ cups sliced zucchini
1¼ cups peeled, seeded, and chopped tomato
1 tablespoon chopped fresh basil or 1 teaspoon
   dried whole basil
1 tablespoon chopped fresh parsley
½ teaspoon dried whole oregano
¼ teaspoon salt
¼ teaspoon pepper
¼ cup freshly grated Parmesan cheese

Wash squash; pierce with a fork several times. Place squash in a large baking dish. Bake at 350° for 1 hour or until squash yields to pressure. Let cool to touch. Cut squash in half lengthwise; remove and discard seeds. Using a fork, remove spaghetti-like strands from squash; transfer strands to a serving platter. Set aside, and keep warm. Discard shells.

Cook ground chuck, onion, and garlic in a large nonstick skillet over medium heat until browned, stirring to crumble. Drain well, and pat dry with paper towels. Wipe pan drippings from skillet with a paper towel. Return meat mixture to skillet. Add zucchini and next 6 ingredients. Cook over medium heat until thoroughly heated and zucchini is crisp-tender, stirring occasionally. Spoon meat mixture over spaghetti squash. Sprinkle with Parmesan cheese. Serve warm. Yield: 6 servings (228 calories per serving).

PROTEIN 18.1 / FAT 11.1 / CARBOHYDRATE 14.2 / CHOLESTEROL 51 / IRON 2.5 / SODIUM 243 / CALCIUM 114

BURGUNDY MEATBALLS

1 pound ground chuck
½ cup soft whole wheat breadcrumbs
¼ cup minced onion
1 tablespoon low-sodium Worcestershire sauce
2 teaspoons chopped fresh parsley
¼ teaspoon dried whole basil
¼ teaspoon pepper
Vegetable cooking spray
1 cup sliced fresh mushrooms
2 tablespoons all-purpose flour
½ cup hot water
½ teaspoon beef-flavored bouillon granules
½ cup white Burgundy

Combine first 7 ingredients in a medium bowl; stir well. Shape mixture into 1½-inch meatballs. Place meatballs on rack of a broiler pan that has been coated with cooking spray. Broil 6 inches from heat 5 minutes; turn meatballs, and broil an additional 5 minutes or until browned. Drain well on paper towels.

Coat a large nonstick skillet with cooking spray. Place over medium heat until hot; add mushrooms, and sauté until tender. Add flour, and cook 1 minute, stirring constantly. Combine hot water and bouillon granules, stirring until granules dissolve; stir bouillon mixture and wine into mushroom mixture. Continue cooking until mixture is thickened, stirring constantly. Add meatballs, and cook until thoroughly heated. Yield: 6 servings (195 calories per serving).

PROTEIN 16.9 / FAT 10.6 / CARBOHYDRATE 7.3 / CHOLESTEROL 52 / IRON 2.0 / SODIUM 171 / CALCIUM 17

BEEF BURGERS WITH SMOKY TEXAS SAUCE

1½ pounds ground chuck
2 tablespoons minced onion
¼ teaspoon salt
¼ teaspoon dried whole oregano
⅛ teaspoon pepper
Vegetable cooking spray
Smoky Texas Sauce

Combine first 5 ingredients in a medium bowl; stir well. Shape mixture into 6 patties. Place patties on rack of a broiler pan that has been coated with cooking spray. Broil 6 inches from heat 3 to 4 minutes. Turn patties, and broil an additional 3 to 4 minutes or to desired degree of doneness. Remove burgers; drain and pat dry with paper towels. Transfer to a serving platter. Spoon Smoky Texas Sauce evenly over burgers. Yield: 6 servings (244 calories per serving).

Smoky Texas Sauce:

1 (8-ounce) can no-salt-added tomato sauce
½ cup finely chopped onion
¼ cup finely chopped green pepper
1 tablespoon red wine vinegar
1 teaspoon Worcestershire sauce
2 teaspoons liquid smoke
1 teaspoon brown sugar
1 teaspoon chili powder
½ teaspoon dry mustard
¼ teaspoon ground red pepper
⅛ teaspoon garlic powder

Combine all ingredients in a medium saucepan. Bring to a boil; cover, reduce heat, and simmer 15 minutes, stirring occasionally. Yield: 1¼ cups.

PROTEIN 22.3 / FAT 14.2 / CARBOHYDRATE 5.6 / CHOLESTEROL 71 / IRON 2.3 / SODIUM 179 / CALCIUM 15

Presented differently but with the same great flavors as the traditional sandwich, Reuben Meat Roll is sure to please.

REUBEN MEAT ROLL

1 pound ground chuck
1 cup soft rye breadcrumbs
1 egg, beaten
¼ cup chopped onion
¼ cup finely chopped dill pickles
2 tablespoons commercial reduced-calorie Russian dressing
1 tablespoon low-sodium Worcestershire sauce
½ teaspoon pepper
Vegetable cooking spray
1 (10-ounce) can chopped sauerkraut, drained
½ cup (2 ounces) shredded Swiss cheese
1 (2-ounce) jar sliced pimiento, drained

Combine first 8 ingredients in a medium bowl; stir well. Shape mixture into a 12- x 10-inch rectangle on heavy-duty plastic wrap that has been coated with cooking spray.

Combine sauerkraut, Swiss cheese, and pimiento in a small bowl. Spread sauerkraut mixture over ground chuck mixture, leaving a 1-inch margin on all sides. Carefully roll meat jellyroll fashion, starting at narrow end, using plastic wrap to support meat. Pinch edges and seam of meat to seal. Remove from plastic wrap, and place roll, seam side down, on a rack in a roasting pan that has been coated with cooking spray. Cover and bake at 350° for 10 minutes. Uncover and bake an additional 35 to 40 minutes. Let stand 10 minutes before slicing. Yield: 6 servings (229 calories per serving).

PROTEIN 19.0 / FAT 13.1 / CARBOHYDRATE 7.9 / CHOLESTEROL 90 / IRON 1.9 / SODIUM 264 / CALCIUM 111

SPICED STEAK STRIPS

1½ pounds lean round steak (½-inch thick)
Vegetable cooking spray
½ cup chopped onion
1 clove garlic, minced
1 (8-ounce) can no-salt-added tomato
    sauce
¼ cup Burgundy or other dry red wine
1 tablespoon vinegar
1 teaspoon brown sugar
½ teaspoon ground cinnamon
¼ teaspoon salt
¼ teaspoon ground cloves
¼ teaspoon ground coriander
¼ teaspoon crushed red pepper flakes
3 cups hot cooked fine egg noodles (cooked
    without salt or fat)

Partially freeze steak; trim fat from steak. Slice steak diagonally across grain into ¼-inch strips. Coat a large nonstick skillet with cooking spray; place over medium-high heat until hot. Add steak strips, chopped onion, and garlic; cook until steak is browned. Drain and pat dry with paper towels. Wipe pan drippings from skillet with a paper towel.

Return steak mixture to skillet. Add tomato sauce and next 8 ingredients. Bring mixture to a boil; cover, reduce heat, and simmer 1 hour or until meat is tender, stirring occasionally. Serve over hot cooked noodles. Yield: 6 servings (291 calories per serving).

PROTEIN 28.4 / FAT 8.3 / CARBOHYDRATE 23.8 / CHOLESTEROL 95 / IRON 3.2 / SODIUM 165 / CALCIUM 23

BEEF WITH TOMATILLOS

1½ pounds lean round steak
Vegetable cooking spray
1⅓ cups chopped onion
2 cloves garlic, minced
1 cup husked and chopped tomatillos
½ cup water
1 tablespoon chopped jalapeño peppers
1 teaspoon dried coriander
½ teaspoon dried whole marjoram
¼ teaspoon salt
⅛ teaspoon crushed red pepper
½ cup low-fat sour cream
2 tablespoons minced fresh cilantro

Trim fat from steak; cut into 1-inch pieces. Coat a large nonstick skillet with cooking spray. Place over medium-high heat until hot. Add steak; cook until browned, stirring often. Remove steak; drain and pat dry with paper towels. Wipe pan drippings from skillet with a paper towel.

Coat skillet with cooking spray. Place over medium-high heat until hot. Add onion and garlic; sauté 5 minutes or until tender. Return steak to skillet; add tomatillos and next 6 ingredients, stirring well. Bring mixture to a boil; cover, reduce heat, and simmer 1 hour or until meat is tender. Place beef on 6 individual serving plates. Top each serving evenly with sour cream and fresh cilantro. Yield: 6 servings (216 calories per serving).

PROTEIN 26.0 / FAT 9.6 / CARBOHYDRATE 5.4 / CHOLESTEROL 78 / IRON 2.8 / SODIUM 166 / CALCIUM 42

LOSE WEIGHT TO LOWER BLOOD PRESSURE

Losing weight is another way to lower high blood pressure. When an overweight person loses as little as 5 to 10 pounds, blood pressure can be lowered. Researchers from Stanford University closely monitored a group of overweight men for a year. Some of the men dieted to lose weight while others exercised. In the end, it didn't seem to matter how the weight loss was achieved; both groups had similar drops in blood pressure. It is the actual weight loss itself that lowers blood pressure.

STEAK À LA ROMA

1½ pounds lean round steak
Vegetable cooking spray
2 teaspoons olive oil
½ cup chopped onion
½ cup chopped green pepper
1 clove garlic, minced
1 (8-ounce) can no-salt-added tomato sauce
¼ cup Burgundy or other dry red wine
1 tablespoon minced fresh parsley
½ teaspoon dried Italian seasoning
¼ teaspoon salt
⅛ teaspoon pepper
1 (9-ounce) package frozen artichoke hearts,
   thawed and quartered
¼ cup grated Parmesan cheese

Trim fat from steak; cut steak into 6 equal pieces. Coat a large nonstick skillet with cooking spray; add oil. Place over medium-high heat until hot. Add steak, and cook until browned on both sides. Remove steak from skillet; drain and pat dry with paper towels. Wipe pan drippings from skillet with a paper towel.

Add onion, green pepper, and garlic to skillet; sauté until tender. Add tomato sauce and next 5 ingredients; stir well. Return steak to skillet. Cover, reduce heat, and simmer 1½ to 2 hours or until steak is tender. Add artichoke hearts, and simmer 5 minutes or until thoroughly heated. Transfer steak to a serving platter. Spoon sauce over steak, and sprinkle with Parmesan cheese. Yield: 6 servings (236 calories per serving).

PROTEIN 27.8 / FAT 9.8 / CARBOHYDRATE 8.6 / CHOLESTEROL 73 / IRON 3.0 / SODIUM 245 / CALCIUM 69

FOOD SAFETY FOR MARINADES

Marinades that come in contact with raw meat, fish, or poultry can be a breeding ground for bacteria. Therefore, the U.S. Department of Agriculture recommends that care must be taken to ensure food safety. Marinade mixtures should be heated after the meat has been removed from it but before the marinade is used for basting or grilling. If not done, basting with the marinade towards the end of grilling may not provide enough cooking time to kill bacteria.

FLANK STEAK WITH SPICY MARINADE

1 (1½-pound) lean flank steak
⅓ cup Burgundy or other dry red wine
1 tablespoon lemon juice
1 tablespoon Worcestershire sauce
1 tablespoon water
1 teaspoon dried whole basil
½ teaspoon fennel seeds
½ teaspoon dried whole oregano
½ teaspoon dried whole thyme
¼ teaspoon salt
¼ teaspoon ground allspice
¼ teaspoon ground red pepper
Vegetable cooking spray

Trim fat from steak. Place steak in a large shallow dish. Combine wine and next 10 ingredients; pour over steak. Cover and marinate in refrigerator 24 hours, turning occasionally.

Remove steak from marinade. Place marinade in a small saucepan; bring to a boil, and cook 5 minutes. Coat grill rack with cooking spray; place on grill over hot coals. Place steak on rack, and cook 6 to 7 minutes on each side or to desired degree of doneness, basting frequently with marinade. Slice steak diagonally across grain into ¼-inch-thick slices, and serve immediately. Yield: 6 servings (218 calories per serving).

PROTEIN 22.4 / FAT 13.2 / CARBOHYDRATE 1.3 / CHOLESTEROL 61 / IRON 2.6 / SODIUM 196 / CALCIUM 20

TERIYAKI MARINATED FLANK STEAK

1 (1½-pound) lean flank steak
1 cup unsweetened pineapple juice
¼ cup dry sherry
¼ cup reduced-sodium soy sauce
2 cloves garlic, minced
1 teaspoon dry mustard
½ teaspoon ground ginger
¼ teaspoon curry powder
Vegetable cooking spray

Trim fat from steak. Place steak in a large shallow dish. Combine pineapple juice and next 6 ingredients; stir well. Divide mixture in half. Cover and chill half of mixture for use during grilling. Pour remaining half over steak. Cover and marinate in refrigerator 24 hours, turning occasionally.

Remove steak from marinade; discard marinade. Coat grill rack with cooking spray; place on grill over medium-hot coals. Place steak on rack, and cook 7 to 8 minutes on each side or to desired degree of doneness, turning and basting frequently with reserved pineapple juice mixture. Slice steak diagonally across grain into ¼-inch-thick slices. Yield: 6 servings (234 calories per serving).

PROTEIN 22.7 / FAT 13.3 / CARBOHYDRATE 4.4 / CHOLESTEROL 61 / IRON 2.5 / SODIUM 305 / CALCIUM 13

PEPPERED SIRLOIN WITH ZESTY SAUCE

1 (1-pound) lean boneless beef sirloin steak
2 tablespoons cracked pepper
Vegetable cooking spray
1 teaspoon margarine
2 tablespoons grated onion
¼ cup reduced-calorie mayonnaise
1 tablespoon prepared horseradish
½ teaspoon grated lemon rind
¼ teaspoon salt
¼ teaspoon freshly ground pepper
Paprika (optional)

Trim fat from steak. Press cracked pepper over entire surface of meat. Cover and refrigerate 30 minutes.

Coat a large nonstick skillet with cooking spray. Place over medium-high heat until hot. Add steak, and cook 6 minutes on each side or to desired degree of doneness. Remove steak from skillet; drain and pat dry with paper towels. Transfer steak to a serving platter, and keep warm. Wipe pan drippings from skillet with a paper towel.

Melt margarine in skillet over medium heat. Add onion, and sauté until tender. Add mayonnaise and next 4 ingredients. Cook over low heat until thoroughly heated, stirring constantly. Spoon sauce over warm steak. Sprinkle with paprika, if desired. Yield: 4 servings (239 calories per serving).

PROTEIN 26.5 / FAT 12.7 / CARBOHYDRATE 4.1 / CHOLESTEROL 81 / IRON 3.9 / SODIUM 330 / CALCIUM 30

BEEF ROAST WITH WILD MUSHROOM SAUCE

1 (3-pound) beef eye-of-round roast
½ cup brandy
¼ cup sherry wine vinegar
¼ cup minced shallots
1 clove garlic, minced
1 tablespoon minced fresh parsley
1 teaspoon dried whole thyme
½ teaspoon freshly ground pepper
¼ teaspoon salt
Vegetable cooking spray
2 cups water
2 tablespoons margarine
2 cups sliced fresh shiitake mushrooms
1 cup hot water
2 tablespoons all-purpose flour
1 teaspoon beef-flavored bouillon
  granules
Shiitake mushrooms (optional)

Trim fat from roast. Place roast in a large shallow dish. Combine brandy and next 7 ingredients in a small bowl, stirring well. Pour over roast. Cover and marinate in refrigerator 8 hours, turning occasionally.

Remove roast from marinade. Place marinade in a small saucepan; bring marinade to a boil, and cook 5 minutes. Place roast on rack of a broiler pan that has been coated with cooking spray. Insert meat thermometer into thickest part of roast. Pour 2 cups water into broiler pan. Cover roast with aluminum foil, and bake at 450° for 20 minutes. Uncover roast, and bake an additional 1½ hours or until meat reaches 140° (rare) or 160° (medium), basting roast frequently with marinade.

Let stand 15 minutes; cut diagonally across grain into thin slices. Transfer to a serving plate, and keep warm.

Melt margarine in a nonstick skillet over low heat. Add 2 cups mushrooms, and sauté until tender. Add 1 cup hot water, flour, and bouillon granules, stirring until smooth. Continue cooking until thickened. Spoon 2 tablespoons sauce over each serving of roast. Garnish with additional mushrooms, if desired. Yield: 12 servings (189 calories per serving).

PROTEIN 24.2 / FAT 7.5 / CARBOHYDRATE 3.6 / CHOLESTEROL 56 / IRON 2.0 / SODIUM 236 / CALCIUM 10

JALISCO-STYLE ROAST

1 (4-pound) lean boneless round roast
Vegetable cooking spray
¼ teaspoon garlic powder
⅛ teaspoon crushed red pepper
1 medium-size purple onion, sliced
1 tablespoon grated orange rind
1 cup unsweetened orange juice
1 tablespoon steak sauce
⅛ teaspoon ground cinnamon
⅛ teaspoon ground cloves

Trim fat from roast. Coat a Dutch oven with cooking spray; place over medium heat until hot. Add roast; cook until browned on all sides. Sprinkle with garlic powder and red pepper.

Combine onion and remaining ingredients; pour over roast. Cover, reduce heat, and simmer 2 to 2½ hours or until roast is tender. Transfer roast to serving plates. Spoon 3 tablespoons sauce over each serving. Yield: 14 servings (168 calories per serving).

PROTEIN 26.6 / FAT 4.7 / CARBOHYDRATE 3.2 / CHOLESTEROL 66 / IRON 2.5 / SODIUM 80 / CALCIUM 9

SWEDISH POT ROAST

1 (4-pound) lean boneless rump roast
Vegetable cooking spray
1 small onion, sliced
1 bay leaf
1 cup hot water
2 tablespoons low-sodium Worcestershire sauce
1 teaspoon beef-flavored bouillon granules
2 tablespoons all-purpose flour
½ teaspoon ground nutmeg
⅛ teaspoon pepper
¾ cup skim milk
¼ cup plain nonfat yogurt

Trim fat from roast. Coat a Dutch oven with cooking spray. Place over medium-high heat until hot. Add roast; cook until browned on all sides. Add onion and bay leaf. Combine water, Worcestershire sauce, and bouillon granules; stir well. Pour over roast. Cover, reduce heat, and simmer 2 to 2½ hours or until roast is tender.

Transfer roast to a serving platter, reserving ¼ cup liquid in Dutch oven. Discard bay leaf and remaining liquid. Combine flour, nutmeg, and pepper. Add to Dutch oven; stir until smooth. Gradually add milk, stirring constantly. Cook over medium heat until thickened, stirring constantly. Stir in yogurt just until blended. Spoon gravy over roast. Serve immediately. Yield: 14 servings (207 calories per serving).

PROTEIN 27.8 / FAT 8.4 / CARBOHYDRATE 3.1 / CHOLESTEROL 82 / IRON 3.0 / SODIUM 129 / CALCIUM 31

VEAL AND SPINACH MEATBALLS

1 (10-ounce) package frozen chopped spinach, thawed
1¼ pounds ground veal
¼ cup fine, dry breadcrumbs
1 egg, beaten
2 tablespoons minced onion
½ teaspoon dried whole marjoram
¼ teaspoon ground nutmeg
¼ teaspoon salt
⅛ teaspoon pepper
Vegetable cooking spray
1 (14½-ounce) can no-salt-added tomatoes, undrained and chopped
1 (6-ounce) can no-salt-added tomato paste
2 tablespoons minced fresh parsley
½ teaspoon dried whole chervil
¼ teaspoon garlic powder
¼ teaspoon pepper
3 cups hot cooked vermicelli (cooked without salt or fat)
3 tablespoons grated Parmesan cheese

Drain spinach; press between paper towels to remove excess moisture. Combine spinach and next 8 ingredients in a medium bowl; stir well. Shape into 60 meatballs, using 1 teaspoon mixture for each meatball.

Coat a large nonstick skillet with cooking spray; place over medium-high heat until hot. Add meatballs; cook, turning occasionally, until browned. Drain on paper towels. Wipe pan drippings from skillet with a paper towel.

Combine tomatoes and next 5 ingredients in skillet; stir well. Add meatballs to skillet; bring to a boil. Cover, reduce heat, and simmer 20 minutes. Serve over hot cooked vermicelli. Sprinkle with Parmesan cheese. Yield: 6 servings (316 calories per serving).

PROTEIN 31.2 / FAT 6.4 / CARBOHYDRATE 33.5 / CHOLESTEROL 142 / IRON 3.8 / SODIUM 310 / CALCIUM 140

Serve Veal and Spinach Meatballs over vermicelli for a flavorful Italian meal.

VEAL CACCIATORE

1 pound lean boneless veal
¼ cup Burgundy or other dry red wine
1 teaspoon low-sodium Worcestershire sauce
¼ teaspoon dried whole thyme
¼ teaspoon celery seeds
¼ teaspoon pepper
Vegetable cooking spray
½ cup chopped onion
½ cup chopped green pepper
½ cup sliced fresh mushrooms
½ cup shredded carrot
1 (14½-ounce) can no-salt-added tomatoes, undrained and chopped
1 teaspoon dried whole rosemary, crushed
½ teaspoon dried whole basil
¼ teaspoon garlic powder
¼ teaspoon dried whole oregano
¼ teaspoon beef-flavored bouillon granules
⅛ teaspoon ground red pepper

Trim fat from veal; cut into ½-inch cubes.

Combine wine, Worcestershire sauce, thyme, celery seeds, and ¼ teaspoon pepper in a large zip-top heavy-duty plastic bag; seal bag, and shake well. Add veal to bag; seal bag, and shake until veal is well coated. Marinate in refrigerator 2 hours.

Remove veal from marinade; discard marinade. Coat a large nonstick skillet with cooking spray; place over medium-high heat until hot. Add veal, and sauté until browned. Remove veal from skillet using a slotted spoon, and drain on paper towels. Wipe pan drippings from skillet with a paper towel. Add onion, green pepper, mushrooms, and carrot to skillet; sauté until crisp-tender. Return veal to skillet. Add tomatoes and remaining ingredients; bring to a boil. Cover, reduce heat, and simmer 15 minutes or until veal is tender. Yield: 4 servings (166 calories per serving).

PROTEIN 19.8 / FAT 5.1 / CARBOHYDRATE 9.4 / CHOLESTEROL 90 / IRON 1.9 / SODIUM 154 / CALCIUM 54

VEAL AND ASPARAGUS STIR-FRY

½ pound fresh asparagus spears
1 pound veal cutlets (¼-inch thick)
Vegetable cooking spray
1 teaspoon vegetable oil
1 small onion, thinly sliced
1 small sweet red pepper, seeded and cut into ¼-inch strips
¼ teaspoon salt
¼ teaspoon fennel seeds, crushed
⅛ teaspoon garlic powder
⅛ teaspoon crushed red pepper
2 tablespoons dry sherry
1 teaspoon lemon zest

Snap off tough ends of asparagus. Remove scales from stalks with a knife or vegetable peeler, if desired. Cut asparagus into 2-inch pieces. Set aside.

Trim fat from cutlets; cut into thin strips.

Coat a wok or large nonstick skillet with cooking spray; add oil. Place over medium-high heat until hot. Add veal; stir-fry 5 minutes or until browned. Remove veal from skillet with a slotted spoon; set aside.

Add reserved asparagus, onion, and next 5 ingredients to skillet; stir-fry 3 to 4 minutes or until vegetables are crisp-tender. Return veal to skillet. Add sherry and cook, stirring constantly, 1 minute or until thoroughly heated. Transfer to a serving platter, and sprinkle with lemon zest. Yield: 4 servings (245 calories per serving).

PROTEIN 23.4 / FAT 14.0 / CARBOHYDRATE 5.9 / CHOLESTEROL 116 / IRON 4.0 / SODIUM 252 / CALCIUM 34

 HOT WEATHER WORKOUTS

When exercising in hot, humid weather, be alert to early warning signs of heat exhaustion: rapid but weak pulse, nausea, faintness, profuse sweating, disorientation, confusion, or dry skin. Stop your workout immediately, find a cool area to rest, and drink plenty of fluids.

SUCCULENT VEAL CUTLETS

1 pound veal cutlets (¼-inch thick)
3 tablespoons all-purpose flour, divided
¼ teaspoon pepper
Vegetable cooking spray
1 tablespoon reduced-calorie margarine, divided
½ cup shredded zucchini
2 tablespoons sliced green onions
1 teaspoon minced fresh rosemary
½ teaspoon chicken-flavored bouillon granules
½ cup water
¼ cup skim milk
1 tablespoon dry vermouth

Trim fat from cutlets. Place between 2 sheets of wax paper; flatten to ⅛-inch thickness, using a meat mallet or rolling pin. Combine 2 tablespoons flour and pepper; stir well. Dredge cutlets in flour mixture.

Coat a large nonstick skillet with cooking spray; add 2 teaspoons margarine. Place over medium-high heat until hot. Add cutlets; cook 2 minutes on each side or until browned. Remove from skillet; drain on paper towels. Set aside. Wipe drippings from skillet with a paper towel.

Add remaining 1 teaspoon margarine to skillet; place over medium heat until hot. Add zucchini and green onions; sauté until crisp-tender. Stir in rosemary, remaining flour, bouillon granules, water, milk, and vermouth. Cook, stirring constantly, 2 minutes or until thickened. Add cutlets; simmer 5 minutes or until thoroughly heated. Transfer to a serving platter. Yield: 4 servings (250 calories per serving).

PROTEIN 23.9 / FAT 13.5 / CARBOHYDRATE 6.7 / CHOLESTEROL 86 / IRON 3.1 / SODIUM 207 / CALCIUM 35

VEAL IN MADEIRA ESPAGNOLE

1 pound veal cutlets (¼-inch thick)
3 tablespoons all-purpose flour, divided
Vegetable cooking spray
2 teaspoons margarine
½ cup water
2 tablespoons Madeira wine
½ teaspoon chicken-flavored bouillon granules
¼ teaspoon dried whole marjoram
¼ teaspoon dried whole thyme
⅛ teaspoon pepper
¼ cup sliced stuffed olives

Trim fat from cutlets. Place cutlets between 2 sheets of wax paper; flatten to ⅛-inch thickness, using a meat mallet or rolling pin. Dredge cutlets in 2 tablespoons flour. Coat a large nonstick skillet with cooking spray; add margarine. Place over medium-high heat until margarine melts. Add cutlets, and cook 4 minutes on each side or until browned. Remove cutlets from skillet; drain and pat dry with paper towels. Wipe pan drippings from skillet with a paper towel.

Combine remaining 1 tablespoon flour, water, and next 5 ingredients. Place in skillet, and cook over medium heat until thickened, stirring constantly. Add veal and olives; continue cooking until thoroughly heated. Yield: 4 servings (252 calories per serving).

PROTEIN 23.3 / FAT 14.3 / CARBOHYDRATE 6.0 / CHOLESTEROL 86 / IRON 3.4 / SODIUM 289 / CALCIUM 24

VEAL SHANKS MILANESE

4 (5-ounce) veal shanks
Vegetable cooking spray
1 (14½-ounce) can no-salt-added tomatoes, undrained and chopped
2 medium carrots, scraped and cut into ½-inch slices
1 small onion, sliced
¼ cup Chablis or other dry white wine
2 cloves garlic, minced
1 tablespoon minced fresh parsley
1 teaspoon grated lemon rind
½ teaspoon chicken-flavored bouillon granules
½ teaspoon dried whole thyme
¼ teaspoon dried whole rosemary, crushed
¼ teaspoon pepper

Trim fat from shanks. Coat a large skillet with cooking spray; place over medium-high heat until hot. Add shanks, and cook 3 minutes on each side or until browned. Transfer shanks to an ungreased 3-quart casserole. Combine tomatoes and remaining ingredients in a medium bowl; pour over shanks. Cover and bake at 325° for 1½ hours or until shanks are tender. Transfer to a serving platter with a slotted spoon. Yield: 4 servings (186 calories per serving).

PROTEIN 22.7 / FAT 5.7 / CARBOHYDRATE 10.9 / CHOLESTEROL 104 / IRON 1.9 / SODIUM 206 / CALCIUM 60

APPLE-STUFFED VEAL ROAST

1 (3½-pound) boneless rolled veal
  rump roast
1 cup soft light rye breadcrumbs
1 small apple, peeled, cored, and finely
  chopped
¼ cup finely chopped onion
2 tablespoons unsweetened apple
  juice
1 tablespoon golden raisins
1 teaspoon dried whole rosemary,
  crushed
¼ teaspoon garlic powder
¼ teaspoon pepper
Vegetable cooking spray
1 small onion, thinly sliced
½ cup unsweetened apple
  juice
¼ cup water
Fresh rosemary sprigs (optional)
Apple slices (optional)
Freshly ground pepper (optional)

Unroll roast, and trim excess fat from roast. Lay roast flat on wax paper. From center, slice horizontally through thickest part of each side of roast almost to outer edge; unfold cut pieces to enlarge roast.

Combine breadcrumbs, chopped apple, onion, 2 tablespoons apple juice, and raisins in a small bowl; stir well. Spoon breadcrumb mixture over roast, spreading to within 2 inches of edge. Roll up roast jellyroll fashion, enclosing stuffing completely. Tie securely with string.

Combine crushed rosemary, garlic powder, and pepper; stir well. Press mixture over entire surface of roast.

Coat a large ovenproof Dutch oven with cooking spray; place over medium-high heat until hot. Add roast, and cook until browned on all sides, turning occasionally. Add sliced onion, ½ cup apple juice, and water. Cover and bake at 325° for 1 hour and 15 minutes, basting frequently with pan juices. Remove roast from oven; let stand 5 minutes. Remove string before slicing. If desired, garnish with fresh rosemary sprigs, apple slices, and freshly ground pepper. Yield: 14 servings (213 calories per serving).

PROTEIN 28.8 / FAT 7.3 / CARBOHYDRATE 6.4 / CHOLESTEROL 138 / IRON 1.2 / SODIUM 99 / CALCIUM 9

TURKISH LAMB PATTIES

1 pound lean ground lamb
¼ cup finely chopped onion
2 tablespoons minced fresh parsley
2 tablespoons pine nuts, toasted
½ teaspoon dried whole oregano
¼ teaspoon garlic powder
¼ teaspoon freshly ground pepper
Vegetable cooking spray
1 (8-ounce) can no-salt-added tomato sauce
2 tablespoons Burgundy or other dry red wine
¼ teaspoon ground cumin
¼ teaspoon dry mustard
⅛ teaspoon ground red pepper

Combine first 7 ingredients in a medium bowl, stirring well. Shape mixture into 4 (1-inch-thick) patties. Coat a large nonstick skillet with cooking spray; place over medium-high heat until hot. Cook patties 5 minutes on each side or to desired degree of doneness. Remove from skillet, and drain well on paper towels. Set aside and keep warm. Wipe pan drippings from skillet with a paper towel.

Add tomato sauce, wine, cumin, mustard, and red pepper to skillet; stir well. Cook over medium heat 5 minutes. Add reserved patties, and cook until thoroughly heated. Yield: 4 servings (224 calories per serving).

PROTEIN 25.7 / FAT 10.5 / CARBOHYDRATE 7.3 / CHOLESTEROL 85 / IRON 2.3 / SODIUM 79 / CALCIUM 21

DILLY LAMB-STUFFED PEPPERS

6 medium-size sweet red peppers
1 pound lean ground lamb
½ cup chopped onion
½ cup finely chopped carrot
1 clove garlic, minced
1 (8-ounce) can no-salt-added tomato sauce
½ cup cooked long-grain rice (cooked without salt
  or fat)
1 tablespoon finely chopped dill pickle
1 teaspoon grated lemon rind
1 teaspoon Worcestershire sauce
½ teaspoon dried whole dillweed
¼ teaspoon salt
¼ teaspoon dried whole oregano
¼ teaspoon pepper

Cut tops off peppers; reserve tops. Remove and discard seeds. Cook peppers and tops 5 minutes in boiling water; drain. Set aside.

Combine lamb, onion, carrot, and garlic in a large nonstick skillet. Place over medium-high heat, and cook until meat is browned, stirring to crumble. Drain and pat dry with paper towels. Combine meat mixture with remaining ingredients; spoon evenly into reserved peppers. Top with reserved pepper tops. Place peppers in a shallow baking dish. Bake at 350° for 25 minutes or until thoroughly heated. Yield: 6 servings (194 calories per serving).

PROTEIN 18.5 / FAT 5.1 / CARBOHYDRATE 19.2 / CHOLESTEROL 57 / IRON 3.5 / SODIUM 198 / CALCIUM 31

MANDARIN LAMB STIR-FRY

4 (4-ounce) lamb cutlets (½-inch thick)
¼ cup water
3 tablespoons vinegar
2 tablespoons reduced-sodium soy sauce
2 teaspoons brown sugar
1 teaspoon cornstarch
¼ teaspoon ground coriander
¼ teaspoon ground red pepper
Vegetable cooking spray
1 teaspoon vegetable oil
1 medium-size sweet red pepper, seeded and cut into strips
1 cup sliced celery
1 cup cubed fresh pineapple, cut into 1-inch cubes
1 cup cauliflower flowerets
3 cups hot cooked long-grain rice (cooked without salt or fat)

Trim fat from cutlets; cut into thin strips.

Combine water and next 6 ingredients; stir until smooth. Set aside.

Coat a wok or large nonstick skillet with cooking spray; add oil. Heat at medium-high (325°) for 2 minutes. Add lamb; stir-fry 5 minutes. Remove strips from wok, and set aside. Add red pepper strips, celery, pineapple, and cauliflower to wok; stir-fry 1 minute. Add lamb and reserved vinegar mixture. Cook, stirring constantly, until thickened. Serve over hot cooked rice. Yield: 6 servings (287 calories per serving).

PROTEIN 18.5 / FAT 5.4 / CARBOHYDRATE 39.8 / CHOLESTEROL 53 / IRON 3.3 / SODIUM 280 / CALCIUM 37

 ## DANGERS OF SECOND-HAND SMOKE

The Surgeon General has confirmed that second-hand smoke (the term used to label the smoke that nonsmokers inhale involuntarily when exposed to smokers) is hazardous to health. Despite the ban on smoking in many public places, most Americans are still exposed to smoke fumes. In fact, the Environmental Protection Agency reports passive smoke to be one of the largest sources of indoor air pollution.

According to health professionals, children suffer the most. Youngsters who grow up with parents who smoke are at risk for a number of diseases, particularly heart disease. In addition, these children end up having more colds; more respiratory and ear infections; and more allergies than children of nonsmokers. Children whose parents smoke, says the Surgeon General, are twice as likely to become smokers themselves.

LAMB AEGEAN

Vegetable cooking spray
1 pound lean boneless lamb, cut into ½-inch cubes
1 leek, cut into 1-inch slices
1 cup Chablis or other dry white wine
1 teaspoon grated lemon rind
1 tablespoon lemon juice
½ teaspoon ground coriander
¼ teaspoon salt
¼ teaspoon ground cumin
⅛ teaspoon ground red pepper
6 cherry tomatoes, quartered
½ cup sliced ripe olives
3 cups hot cooked long-grain rice (cooked without salt or fat)

Coat a large nonstick skillet with cooking spray; place over medium-high heat until hot. Add lamb and leek, and cook until lamb is browned on all sides. Drain and pat dry with paper towels. Wipe pan drippings from skillet with a paper towel. Return lamb mixture to skillet. Add wine and next 6 ingredients. Bring mixture to a boil; cover, reduce heat, and simmer 20 minutes or until lamb is tender. Stir in tomatoes and olives. Serve over hot cooked rice. Yield: 6 servings (272 calories per serving).

PROTEIN 19.0 / FAT 5.8 / CARBOHYDRATE 34.5 / CHOLESTEROL 57 / IRON 3.2 / SODIUM 269 / CALCIUM 40

Serve Lamb Shashlik with Caraway Sauce over a bed of rice and garnish with sprigs of fresh thyme.

LAMB SHASHLIK WITH CARAWAY SAUCE

1½ pounds lean boneless lamb, cut into 1½-inch cubes
¾ cup Burgundy or other dry red wine
1 tablespoon chopped fresh parsley
1 clove garlic, minced
1 teaspoon Worcestershire sauce
½ teaspoon freshly ground pepper
¼ teaspoon dried whole thyme
1 bay leaf, crumbled
2 medium-size sweet red peppers, cut lengthwise into 1-inch strips
3 small yellow squash, cut into 1-inch pieces
½ pound fresh mushrooms
Vegetable cooking spray
3 cups hot cooked long-grain rice (optional)
Caraway Sauce

Trim excess fat from lamb; place lamb in a large shallow dish. Combine wine and next 6 ingredients; stir well. Pour marinade over lamb; cover and marinate in refrigerator 8 hours, turning occasionally.

Remove lamb from marinade, and set aside. Transfer marinade to a small saucepan; bring to a boil. Reduce heat, and simmer 5 minutes; set marinade aside.

Curl red pepper strips around squash pieces; arrange alternately with mushrooms and lamb on 6 (12-inch) skewers.

Coat grill rack with cooking spray; place on grill over medium-hot coals. Place kabobs on rack, and grill 12 to 14 minutes or to desired degree of doneness, turning and basting occasionally with reserved marinade. Serve over rice, if desired. Serve with Caraway Sauce. Yield: 6 servings (226 calories per serving).

Caraway Sauce:

Vegetable cooking spray
2 tablespoons finely chopped onion
½ teaspoon caraway seeds
⅓ cup plain nonfat yogurt
⅓ cup low-fat sour cream
1 tablespoon brandy
¼ teaspoon freshly ground pepper
⅛ teaspoon salt

Coat a nonstick skillet with cooking spray. Add onion and caraway seeds; sauté until onion is tender. Add yogurt and remaining ingredients, stirring well. Cook until thoroughly heated (do not boil). Yield: ¾ cup.

PROTEIN 27.2 / FAT 8.2 / CARBOHYDRATE 9.3 / CHOLESTEROL 90 / IRON 3.3 / SODIUM 138 / CALCIUM 76

 WHAT'S YOUR TRAINING HEART RATE?

If your fitness routine leaves you feeling overly winded, check your pulse rate. It may be that you are exercising above the level that's best for your heart. Not only is that dangerous, but there are also no extra health benefits from such a practice. To play it safe, know what fitness experts consider the training heart rate zone for your age group.

Use the chart below to determine your zone. If your age is not listed, calculate the zone using the following formula. First, start with the number 220. Subtract your current age from 220 to come up with the predicted maximum heart rate. If you are 25, for example, your maximum heart rate is 195 (220 - 25). Next, multiply that maximum number by 70 and 85 percent. This gives you a healthy range for your heart rate, with both an upper and a lower limit. Exercising is safe and effective when your training heart rate falls within this zone.

To determine your heart rate, locate your radial artery (on the thumb side of your wrist) and take your pulse during your exercise session. Take the pulse count for 10 seconds and then multiply that number by 6 to get your actual heart rate. If that number is above your training zone, slow down. If you're below the zone, step up the pace.

Age	Predicted Maximum Heart Rate	Number of Heartbeats in 10 Seconds		Training Zone	
		70%	85%	70%	85%
20	200	23	28	140	170
25	195	23	28	137	166
30	190	22	27	133	162
35	185	22	26	130	157
40	180	21	26	126	153
45	175	20	25	123	149
50	170	20	24	119	145
55	165	19	23	116	140
60	160	19	23	112	136

ROAST LAMB WITH MINT GLAZE

1 (3½-pound) lean boneless leg of lamb
2 cloves garlic, sliced
1 teaspoon dried whole rosemary
½ teaspoon freshly ground pepper
Vegetable cooking spray
½ cup water
¼ cup chopped fresh mint
2 tablespoons tarragon vinegar
1 tablespoon sugar
¼ teaspoon salt

Trim fat from leg of lamb. Make several small slits on outside of lamb, and insert garlic slices. Combine rosemary and pepper. Rub mixture over entire surface of lamb. Place on rack of a broiler pan that has been coated with cooking spray. Insert meat thermometer into thickest part of roast. Pour water into broiler pan. Bake, uncovered, at 325° for 2 hours or until meat thermometer registers 140° (rare) to 160° (medium). Transfer lamb to cutting board; reserve pan liquid. Let stand at room temperature 10 minutes before carving into ½-inch slices.

Skim fat off pan liquid. Place liquid in a small saucepan. Add mint and remaining ingredients. Cook over medium heat, stirring constantly, until sugar dissolves and mixture is thoroughly heated. Spoon over lamb, and serve warm. Yield: 12 servings (191 calories per serving).

PROTEIN 28.6 / FAT 7.0 / CARBOHYDRATE 1.4 / CHOLESTEROL 99 / IRON 2.3 / SODIUM 119 / CALCIUM 17

LAMB CHOPS WITH WINE SAUCE

6 (6-ounce) lean lamb loin chops (1-inch thick)
Vegetable cooking spray
½ cup Chablis or other dry white wine
2 tablespoons honey
¼ teaspoon salt
¼ teaspoon garlic powder
¼ teaspoon crushed red pepper
⅛ teaspoon ground ginger

Trim fat from chops. Coat a large nonstick skillet with cooking spray; place over medium-high heat until hot. Add chops; cook 4 minutes on each side or until browned. Remove from skillet; drain and pat dry with paper towels. Wipe pan

drippings from skillet with a paper towel.

Return chops to skillet. Combine wine and next 5 ingredients, stirring well. Pour wine mixture over chops; bring to a boil. Cover, reduce heat, and simmer 20 minutes or until chops are tender. Transfer chops to a serving platter, discarding wine mixture. Yield: 6 servings (184 calories per serving).

PROTEIN 24.1 / FAT 6.5 / CARBOHYDRATE 6.3 / CHOLESTEROL 85 / IRON 1.8 / SODIUM 159 / CALCIUM 13

GRILLED LAMB CHOPS CAPONATA

4 (6-ounce) lean lamb loin chops (1-inch thick)
¼ teaspoon salt
¼ teaspoon pepper
Vegetable cooking spray
Caponata

Trim fat from chops. Rub with salt and pepper. Cover; refrigerate 30 minutes. Coat grill rack with cooking spray; place on grill over medium-hot coals. Place chops on rack; grill 7 minutes on each side or to desired degree of doneness. Serve immediately with Caponata. Yield: 4 servings (202 calories per serving).

Caponata:

Vegetable cooking spray
1 teaspoon olive oil
1 small eggplant (about 10 ounces), peeled and diced
¼ cup finely chopped onion
¼ cup diced celery
1 clove garlic, minced
1 tablespoon sliced pimiento-stuffed olives
2 tablespoons chopped pimiento
1 tablespoon capers
2 teaspoons reduced-calorie catsup
1 teaspoon red wine vinegar
¼ teaspoon dried whole oregano
⅛ teaspoon ground red pepper

Coat a medium skillet with cooking spray; add oil. Place over medium heat until hot. Add eggplant, onion, celery, and garlic; sauté until tender, stirring often. Stir in remaining ingredients; cook until heated. Yield: 2 cups.

PROTEIN 25.1 / FAT 8.2 / CARBOHYDRATE 6.2 / CHOLESTEROL 85 / IRON 2.4 / SODIUM 486 / CALCIUM 43

Researchers have established a link between low levels of zinc in the blood and poor immune response. However, taking more zinc than necessary doesn't always bring about a better response from your immune system. Researchers caution that too much zinc can prove dangerous. In addition, excess zinc in the blood interferes with the body's absorption of copper and iron.

Most people fall below the RDA of 15 milligrams, but this isn't reason for undue concern. Zinc-rich foods are widely available. Oysters, wheat germ, bran, and red meats are excellent sources. Also notable for their zinc content are poultry, eggs, and dried beans. Researchers say that if people use these foods as part of a varied diet, their immune function will be enhanced.

ORIENTAL PORK QUICHE

1 (6-ounce) package frozen snow pea pods, thawed and drained
½ cup sliced fresh mushrooms
½ cup sliced water chestnuts
¼ cup chopped onion
¼ cup chopped sweet red pepper
¼ cup water
¾ cup diced lean cooked pork
1 (8-ounce) carton frozen egg substitute, thawed
½ cup (2 ounces) shredded Monterey Jack cheese
½ cup skim milk
2 tablespoons chopped fresh parsley
½ teaspoon salt
⅛ teaspoon ground red pepper
Vegetable cooking spray
Sliced fresh mushrooms (optional)

Combine first 6 ingredients in a medium saucepan. Cook over medium heat until vegetables are crisp-tender. Drain well.

Combine vegetable mixture, pork, and next 6 ingredients in a large bowl, stirring well. Pour mixture into a 9-inch quiche dish that has been coated with cooking spray. Bake at 350° for 35 to 40 minutes or until set. Let stand 10 minutes before serving. Garnish with sliced fresh mushrooms, if desired. Yield: 6 servings (137 calories per serving).

PROTEIN 12.8 / FAT 5.9 / CARBOHYDRATE 7.5 / CHOLESTEROL 26 / IRON 1.9 / SODIUM 331 / CALCIUM 128

SESAME-MUSTARD BAKED PORK CHOPS

4 (6-ounce) lean center-loin pork chops (½-inch thick)
3 tablespoons Dijon mustard
¼ cup fine, dry breadcrumbs
¼ cup grated Parmesan cheese
2 tablespoons sesame seeds
1 tablespoon minced fresh parsley
¼ teaspoon garlic powder
Vegetable cooking spray

Trim fat from chops. Spread mustard on both sides of each chop. Combine breadcrumbs and next 4 ingredients; dredge chops in breadcrumb mixture. Place chops in a 13- x 9- x 2-inch baking dish that has been coated with cooking spray. Bake at 350° for 45 minutes or until pork chops are tender. Yield: 4 servings (287 calories per serving).

PROTEIN 31.1 / FAT 13.9 / CARBOHYDRATE 6.8 / CHOLESTEROL 82 / IRON 2.0 / SODIUM 556 / CALCIUM 130

GRILLED PORK CHOPS ROSÉ

4 (6-ounce) lean center-loin pork chops (½-inch thick)
¾ cup rosé wine
2 tablespoons reduced-sodium soy sauce
1 tablespoon brown sugar
1 clove garlic, minced
¼ teaspoon dried whole oregano
Vegetable cooking spray

Trim fat from chops. Place chops in an 11- x 7- x 1½-inch baking dish. Combine wine and next 4 ingredients, stirring well; pour over chops. Cover and marinate in refrigerator 8 hours, turning occasionally.

Remove chops from marinade, and set aside. Place marinade in a small saucepan. Bring to a boil, and cook 5 minutes. Coat grill rack with cooking spray; place on grill over medium-hot coals. Place chops on rack, and cook 15 to 20 minutes or until tender, turning and basting frequently with marinade. Yield: 4 servings (232 calories per serving).

PROTEIN 24.7 / FAT 11.2 / CARBOHYDRATE 6.2 / CHOLESTEROL 77 / IRON 1.4 / SODIUM 364 / CALCIUM 16

Carrots, leeks, and fresh parsley adorn Vegetable Pork Chop Skillet with flavor.

VEGETABLE PORK CHOP SKILLET

4 (6-ounce) lean center-loin pork chops (½-inch thick)
½ teaspoon ground allspice
¼ teaspoon pepper
Vegetable cooking spray
1 teaspoon chicken-flavored bouillon granules
1 cup hot water
¾ cup sliced carrots
2 leeks, cut into 1-inch pieces

Trim fat from chops. Combine allspice and pepper; rub chops with allspice mixture. Coat a large nonstick skillet with cooking spray, and place over medium-high heat until hot. Add chops, and cook 3 minutes on each side or until browned. Drain chops on paper towels. Wipe pan drippings from skillet with a paper towel.

Return chops to skillet. Combine bouillon granules and hot water, stirring until granules dissolve; pour over chops. Bring bouillon mixture to a boil; cover and simmer 25 minutes. Add carrots and leeks to skillet; cover and simmer 20 minutes. Transfer to a serving platter. Yield: 4 servings (251 calories per serving).

PROTEIN 25.2 / FAT 11.5 / CARBOHYDRATE 10.8 / CHOLESTEROL 77 / IRON 2.3 / SODIUM 147 / CALCIUM 47

VINTAGE-STUFFED PORK TENDERLOINS

Vegetable cooking spray
½ cup finely chopped onion
3 (⅜-inch-thick) slices cracked wheat bread, cut into
   ½-inch cubes
¾ cup quartered, seedless red grapes
3 tablespoons cream sherry
2 teaspoons grated orange rind
¼ teaspoon ground allspice
¼ teaspoon ground mace
¼ teaspoon ground white pepper
2 (¾-pound) pork tenderloins
¼ cup frozen unsweetened orange juice
   concentrate, thawed and undiluted
2¼ cups water, divided
1 teaspoon prepared mustard
Grape clusters (optional)

Coat a large nonstick skillet with cooking spray; place over medium heat until hot. Add onion, and sauté until tender. Remove from heat, and stir in bread cubes and next 6 ingredients; set aside.

Trim fat from pork. Cut a pocket lengthwise, almost to, but not through the base of each tenderloin. Spoon grape mixture evenly into pockets. Bring sides of meat together, and secure at 1-inch intervals, using heavy string. Place on rack of a broiler pan that has been coated with cooking spray. Insert meat thermometer into thickest part of roast, if desired. Combine orange juice, ¼ cup water, and mustard; brush tenderloins with orange juice mixture. Pour remaining 2 cups water into broiler pan. Loosely cover tenderloins with aluminum foil. Bake at 350° for 45 minutes, basting occasionally. Uncover, and bake an additional 30 minutes or until meat thermometer registers 170°, basting occasionally.

Transfer tenderloins to a serving platter. Let stand 5 minutes; remove string. Garnish with grape clusters, if desired. Yield: 6 servings (237 calories per serving).

PROTEIN 27.7 / FAT 5.0 / CARBOHYDRATE 17.3 / CHOLESTEROL 83 / IRON 1.8 / SODIUM 148 / CALCIUM 33

PORK PICCATA

¼ cup all-purpose flour
¼ teaspoon salt
¼ teaspoon dried whole rosemary, crushed
⅛ teaspoon garlic powder
⅛ teaspoon pepper
1 pound pork medallions
Vegetable cooking spray
1 teaspoon vegetable oil
1 tablespoon margarine
1 tablespoon all-purpose flour
½ cup canned no-salt-added chicken broth,
   undiluted
1 tablespoon lemon juice
2 teaspoons grated lemon rind

Combine first 5 ingredients in a small bowl; stir well. Dredge pork in flour mixture.

Coat a large nonstick skillet with cooking spray; add oil. Place over medium-high heat until hot. Add medallions, and cook 4 to 5 minutes on each side or until browned. Transfer to a serving platter, and keep warm.

Melt margarine in a small heavy saucepan over low heat; add 1 tablespoon flour, stirring until smooth. Cook 1 minute, stirring constantly. Gradually add chicken broth and lemon juice; cook over medium heat, stirring constantly, until mixture is thickened and bubbly. Remove from heat, and stir in lemon rind. Spoon sauce over pork, and serve immediately. Yield: 4 servings (230 calories per serving).

PROTEIN 27.2 / FAT 8.8 / CARBOHYDRATE 8.8 / CHOLESTEROL 83 / IRON 1.7 / SODIUM 257 / CALCIUM 15

PINEAPPLE PORK CARIBE

1½ pounds lean boneless pork loin
Vegetable cooking spray
1 (8-ounce) can unsweetened pineapple
    tidbits, undrained
2 tablespoons lime juice
2 tablespoons raisins
2 teaspoons brown sugar
½ teaspoon ground coriander
¼ teaspoon salt
¼ teaspoon ground cardamom
⅛ teaspoon ground red pepper
¾ cup peeled, seeded, and chopped
    tomatoes
1 small onion, thinly sliced
1 tablespoon cornstarch
2 tablespoons rum
4 cups hot cooked long-grain rice (cooked
    without salt or fat)

Trim fat from pork; cut pork into ½-inch cubes. Coat a large nonstick skillet with cooking spray; place over medium-high heat until hot. Add pork cubes, and cook 10 minutes or until browned, stirring frequently. Remove pork cubes from skillet. Drain and pat dry with paper towels. Wipe pan drippings from skillet with a paper towel.

Drain pineapple, reserving juice; set pineapple aside. Combine pork, pineapple juice, and next 7 ingredients in skillet; stir well. Bring to a boil; cover, reduce heat, and simmer 20 to 25 minutes or until pork is tender. Add reserved pineapple, tomato, and onion; cover and simmer 10 minutes.

Combine cornstarch and rum, stirring until blended; pour over pork mixture. Cook, stirring constantly, until thickened and bubbly. Serve over hot cooked rice. Yield: 8 servings (290 calories per serving).

PROTEIN 22.4 / FAT 3.5 / CARBOHYDRATE 40.4 / CHOLESTEROL 62 / IRON 2.4 / SODIUM 121 / CALCIUM 28

PORK ROAST WITH PEARS AND SWEET POTATOES

1 (2½-pound) lean boneless pork loin roast, rolled
    and tied
1 (6-ounce) can frozen unsweetened orange juice
    concentrate, thawed and undiluted
¼ cup water
2 tablespoons dry vermouth
2 teaspoons grated orange rind
½ teaspoon ground allspice
Vegetable cooking spray
3 medium-size fresh pears, cored and cut into
    wedges
2 cups peeled, cubed, and cooked sweet potatoes

Untie roast, and trim fat. Retie roast and place in a shallow baking dish. Combine orange juice concentrate and next 4 ingredients; stir well and pour over roast. Cover and marinate in refrigerator at least 8 hours, turning occasionally.

Drain marinade from roast; set roast aside. Place marinade in a small saucepan; bring to a boil. Reduce heat and simmer 5 minutes. Set marinade aside.

Place roast on a rack in a roasting pan that has been coated with cooking spray. Insert meat thermometer into thickest part of roast, if desired. Place roast in a 450° oven. Reduce heat to 350°, and bake 1 hour and 30 minutes, basting frequently with reserved marinade. Remove from oven, and arrange pears and sweet potatoes around roast. Pour remaining marinade over pears and sweet potatoes. Return to oven, and bake 15 minutes or until meat thermometer registers 170°.

Let roast stand 10 minutes. Remove string; cut roast diagonally across grain into ½-inch slices. Arrange roast, pears, and sweet potatoes on a serving platter. Yield: 10 servings (277 calories per serving).

PROTEIN 27.2 / FAT 8.9 / CARBOHYDRATE 21.5 / CHOLESTEROL 80 / IRON 1.0 / SODIUM 69 / CALCIUM 23

Enjoy fresh-from-the-garden goodness in Chicken Thighs au Poivre (page 170).

CHICKEN THIGHS AU POIVRE

2 teaspoons cracked pepper
1½ pounds chicken thighs, skinned
Vegetable cooking spray
1 cup water
½ cup sliced green onions
1 teaspoon chicken-flavored bouillon granules
¼ teaspoon garlic powder
2 cups diced yellow squash
1 cup Sugar Snap peas, trimmed
½ cup diced sweet red pepper
Fresh parsley sprigs (optional)

Press cracked pepper into each side of chicken. Set aside.

Coat a large nonstick skillet with cooking spray. Place over medium-high heat until hot. Add chicken, and cook 2 minutes on each side or until browned. Remove from skillet. Drain and pat dry with paper towels. Wipe pan drippings from skillet with a paper towel. Return chicken to skillet. Add water, onions, bouillon granules, and garlic powder. Bring to a boil; cover, reduce heat, and simmer 30 minutes or until chicken is tender.

Add squash, peas, and sweet red pepper; cover and cook 3 to 5 minutes or until vegetables are crisp-tender. Transfer chicken and vegetables to a serving platter, and garnish with parsley sprigs, if desired. Yield: 4 servings (189 calories per serving).

PROTEIN 21.0 / FAT 8.6 / CARBOHYDRATE 6.8 / CHOLESTEROL 70 / IRON 2.4 / SODIUM 178 / CALCIUM 43

SPICY CHICKEN STRIPS

4 (4-ounce) skinned, boned chicken breast halves
1 (8-ounce) carton plain nonfat yogurt
2 tablespoons lemon juice
½ teaspoon chili powder
½ teaspoon garlic powder
¼ teaspoon ground cumin
1 cup crushed unsalted tortilla rounds
Vegetable cooking spray
2 cups finely shredded iceberg lettuce

Cut chicken into 1-inch strips; set aside. Combine yogurt and next 4 ingredients in a medium bowl; stir well. Add chicken strips, and toss to coat. Cover and marinate in refrigerator 8 hours, stirring occasionally.

Remove chicken from marinade, and roll in tortilla crumbs to coat. Place on a baking sheet that has been coated with cooking spray. Bake at 350° for 35 minutes, or until lightly browned and crisp. Line serving platter with shredded lettuce. Arrange chicken strips over lettuce, and serve immediately. Yield: 4 servings (269 calories per serving).

PROTEIN 31.5 / FAT 7.3 / CARBOHYDRATE 18.3 / CHOLESTEROL 67 / IRON 1.7 / SODIUM 141 / CALCIUM 137

PESTO 'N' PASTA CHICKEN

4 (4-ounce) skinned, boned chicken breast halves
6 ounces penne pasta, uncooked
1 cup firmly packed fresh spinach leaves
2 tablespoons grated Parmesan cheese
1 tablespoon chopped fresh basil
1 tablespoon pine nuts, toasted
½ teaspoon garlic powder
¼ teaspoon red pepper flakes
½ cup plain nonfat yogurt
Vegetable cooking spray

Partially freeze chicken breast halves; slice diagonally across grain into ¼-inch strips, and set aside.

Cook noodles according to package directions, omitting salt and fat. Drain well; set aside and keep warm.

Combine spinach and next 5 ingredients in container of an electric blender or food processor. Top with cover, and process until smooth. Pour into a small bowl, and stir in yogurt. Set mixture aside.

Coat a large skillet with cooking spray; place over medium-high heat until hot. Add chicken and sauté until browned; stir in reserved spinach mixture. Cover and simmer 5 minutes or until thoroughly heated and chicken is tender (do not boil).

Add reserved noodles to skillet. Toss gently to combine. Serve immediately. Yield: 6 servings (228 calories per serving).

PROTEIN 23.8 / FAT 4.1 / CARBOHYDRATE 22.9 / CHOLESTEROL 72 / IRON 1.9 / SODIUM 104 / CALCIUM 91

EXOTIC CHICKEN KABOBS

⅔ cup lemon juice
¼ cup minced fresh mint
2 tablespoons olive oil
2 tablespoons honey
6 (4-ounce) skinned, boned chicken breast halves,
 cut into 1-inch-wide strips
1 small cantaloupe, peeled, seeded and cut into
 2-inch cubes
Vegetable cooking spray

Combine lemon juice, mint, oil, and honey in a small bowl; stir well. Place chicken and cantaloupe in a shallow dish. Pour half of lemon juice mixture over chicken and cantaloupe, reserving remaining lemon juice mixture. Cover and marinate in refrigerator at least 8 hours, stirring occasionally. Cover and refrigerate remaining lemon juice mixture.

Remove chicken and cantaloupe from marinade; discard marinade. Thread chicken and cantaloupe alternately on 6 (12-inch) skewers. Coat grill rack with cooking spray; place on grill over medium-hot coals. Place kabobs on rack, and cook about 12 minutes, turning and basting frequently with remaining lemon juice mixture. Yield: 6 servings (208 calories per serving).

PROTEIN 26.4 / FAT 6.2 / CARBOHYDRATE 11.4 / CHOLESTEROL 70 / IRON 1.1 / SODIUM 69 / CALCIUM 24

CHICKEN FRIED RICE

3 (4-ounce) skinned, boned chicken breast halves
2 cups water
2 tablespoons reduced-sodium soy sauce
1 egg, lightly beaten
½ teaspoon pepper
Vegetable cooking spray
2 teaspoons peanut oil
½ cup finely chopped fresh mushrooms
¼ cup thinly sliced green onions
2 cups hot cooked long-grain rice (cooked without
 salt or fat)

Combine chicken and water in a large saucepan. Bring to a boil; cover, reduce heat, and simmer 30 minutes or until chicken is tender. Remove chicken, reserving broth. Cut chicken into ¾-inch pieces, and set aside.

Skim and discard fat from broth, reserving ⅓ cup broth; save remaining broth for other uses. Combine ⅓ cup reserved broth, soy sauce, egg, and pepper; stir well. Set aside.

Coat a wok with cooking spray; add oil. Heat at medium-high (375°) until hot. Add mushrooms and onions; stir-fry 3 minutes. Stir in rice and chicken. Cook, stirring frequently, 6 to 8 minutes or until thoroughly heated. Drizzle egg mixture over rice and chicken mixture, stirring constantly, until egg is soft-cooked. Serve warm. Yield: 4 servings (292 calories per serving).

PROTEIN 24.3 / FAT 6.1 / CARBOHYDRATE 32.6 / CHOLESTEROL 103 / IRON 2.4 / SODIUM 375 / CALCIUM 32

GRILLED CHICKEN WITH SOUR CREAM SAUCE

1 cup chopped tomato
1 (8-ounce) carton low-fat sour cream
½ cup diced, peeled cucumber
1 tablespoon red wine vinegar
¼ teaspoon garlic powder
¼ teaspoon dried whole oregano
4 (4-ounce) skinned, boned chicken
 breast halves
2 tablespoons lemon juice
¼ teaspoon dried whole oregano
¼ teaspoon cracked pepper
Vegetable cooking spray

Combine first 6 ingredients in a small bowl, stirring well. Cover and chill 2 hours.

Sprinkle chicken with lemon juice, oregano, and pepper. Coat grill rack with cooking spray; place on grill over medium-hot coals. Place chicken on rack, and cook 20 minutes or until chicken is tender, turning frequently. Transfer chicken to a serving platter; serve with sour cream sauce. Yield: 4 servings (232 calories per serving).

PROTEIN 28.1 / FAT 10.1 / CARBOHYDRATE 6.6 / CHOLESTEROL 92 / IRON 1.3 / SODIUM 90 / CALCIUM 83

LEMON-ALMOND CHICKEN

4 (4-ounce) skinned, boned chicken breast halves
¼ cup all-purpose flour
½ teaspoon ground ginger
¼ teaspoon pepper
Vegetable cooking spray
1 tablespoon vegetable oil
½ cup water
1 teaspoon grated lemon rind
3 tablespoons lemon juice
1 teaspoon cornstarch
2 teaspoons water
1 red-skinned Bartlett pear, cored and finely
  chopped
2 tablespoons slivered almonds, toasted
2 tablespoons minced fresh parsley

Place chicken between 2 sheets of wax paper; flatten to ¼-inch thickness, using a meat mallet or rolling pin.
Combine flour, ginger, and pepper; stir well.

Dredge chicken in flour mixture.
Coat a large nonstick skillet with cooking spray; add oil, and place over medium-high heat until hot. Add chicken, and cook 3 minutes on each side or until browned. Remove from skillet. Drain and pat dry with paper towels. Transfer chicken to a serving platter, and keep warm. Wipe pan drippings from skillet with a paper towel.
Add ½ cup water, lemon rind, and juice to skillet; stir well. Dissolve cornstarch in 2 teaspoons water; add to skillet, stirring well. Stir in pear; cook over medium-high heat, stirring constantly, until slightly thickened. Remove from heat, and spoon over chicken. Sprinkle with almonds and parsley. Serve immediately. Yield: 4 servings (260 calories per serving).

PROTEIN 27.9 / FAT 9.5 / CARBOHYDRATE 15.5 / CHOLESTEROL 70 / IRON 1.6 / SODIUM 63 / CALCIUM 37

CHICKEN WITH ARTICHOKES

6 (4-ounce) skinned, boned chicken breast halves
½ teaspoon garlic powder
Vegetable cooking spray
1½ cups sliced fresh mushrooms
½ cup chopped onion
1 (14½-ounce) can no-salt-added stewed tomatoes,
  undrained
⅔ cup uncooked brown rice
1 cup water
½ cup Chablis or other dry white wine
1 teaspoon chicken-flavored bouillon granules
1 (14-ounce) can artichoke hearts, drained and cut
  into quarters
2 tablespoons minced fresh parsley

Sprinkle chicken with garlic powder. Place in

a large Dutch oven that has been coated with cooking spray. Cook over medium heat until browned. Remove chicken. Drain and pat dry with paper towels; set aside. Wipe pan drippings from Dutch oven with a paper towel.
Coat Dutch oven with cooking spray, and place over medium-high heat until hot. Add mushrooms and onion; sauté until tender. Add chicken, tomatoes, and next 4 ingredients. Bring to a boil. Cover, reduce heat, and simmer 20 minutes. Stir in artichoke hearts and parsley. Cover and cook 25 minutes or until chicken and rice are tender. Yield: 6 servings (260 calories per serving).

PROTEIN 29.3 / FAT 3.5 / CARBOHYDRATE 27.2 / CHOLESTEROL 70 / IRON 2.8 / SODIUM 237 / CALCIUM 59

NUTRITION GUIDELINES REAFFIRMED

In 1988, the National Research Council recommended nutrition guidelines that include eating less fat and fewer cholesterol-rich foods and increasing the amount of complex carbohydrates in the diet. In addition, Americans need to pay attention to the amount of protein consumed, mainly because meats are a source of saturated fat, and most Americans consume well above the RDA for protein.

Slice Apple-Stuffed Chicken Rolls and arrange them to show off the spiral apple filling.

APPLE-STUFFED CHICKEN ROLLS

Vegetable cooking spray
¼ cup finely chopped green onions
1 cup unsweetened apple juice, divided
½ cup finely chopped, peeled apple
½ cup soft rye breadcrumbs
2 tablespoons minced fresh parsley
⅛ teaspoon salt
⅛ teaspoon caraway seeds
4 (4-ounce) skinned, boned chicken breast halves
2 teaspoons reduced-calorie margarine
2 tablespoons brandy
1 tablespoon cornstarch
Apple slices (optional)

Coat a large nonstick skillet with cooking spray; place over medium-high heat until hot. Add onions, and sauté until tender. Remove from heat. Stir in 2 tablespoons apple juice and next 5 ingredients. Remove from skillet, and set aside. Wipe pan drippings from skillet with a paper towel.

Place chicken between 2 sheets of wax paper; flatten to ¼-inch thickness, using a meat mallet or rolling pin. Divide breadcrumb mixture evenly among chicken breast halves, spooning mixture into center of each half. Roll breast up lengthwise, tucking ends under. Secure with wooden picks.

Coat skillet with cooking spray; add margarine, and place over medium-high heat until hot. Add chicken rolls, and cook until browned on all sides. Add 2 tablespoons apple juice and brandy. Cover, reduce heat, and simmer 45 minutes, or until chicken is tender. Transfer chicken to a serving platter; remove wooden picks, and keep warm.

Add cornstarch to pan juices in skillet; stir until smooth. Stir in remaining ¾ cup apple juice. Bring to a boil; cook 1 minute or until thickened and bubbly. Spoon sauce over chicken rolls. Garnish with apple slices, if desired. Yield: 4 servings (202 calories per serving).

PROTEIN 27.1 / FAT 3.0 / CARBOHYDRATE 15.6 / CHOLESTEROL 66 / IRON 1.4 / SODIUM 208 / CALCIUM 30

For an easy entrée that pleases the entire family, try Quick Sesame Chicken.

QUICK SESAME CHICKEN

1 (8-ounce) can unsweetened pineapple slices, undrained
1 tablespoon sesame seeds, toasted
3 tablespoons honey
¼ teaspoon rubbed sage
4 (6-ounce) skinned chicken breast halves
Vegetable cooking spray

Drain pineapple, reserving 3 tablespoons juice. Set pineapple aside. Combine reserved pineapple juice, sesame seeds, honey, and sage in a small bowl; stir well.

Place chicken, skinned side down, on rack of a broiler pan that has been coated with cooking spray. Brush chicken with honey mixture. Broil 8 inches from heat 25 minutes, basting often with honey mixture. Turn chicken; broil an additional 15 minutes or until tender.

Baste reserved pineapple slices with honey mixture, and broil 5 minutes, turning once. Transfer chicken to a serving platter. Cut pineapple slices in half, and arrange on each chicken breast half. Yield: 4 servings (240 calories per serving).

PROTEIN 29.2 / FAT 4.8 / CARBOHYDRATE 19.9 / CHOLESTEROL 78 / IRON 1.5 / SODIUM 70 / CALCIUM 43

CRUNCHY OVEN-FRIED CHICKEN

¼ cup reduced-calorie mayonnaise
¼ teaspoon ground cinnamon
¼ teaspoon pepper
⅔ cup nutlike cereal nuggets
2 tablespoons minced fresh parsley
4 (6-ounce) skinned chicken breast halves
Vegetable cooking spray

Combine first 3 ingredients in a small bowl, stirring well. Combine cereal and parsley, stirring well. Brush each chicken breast half with mayonnaise mixture; dredge in cereal mixture.

Place chicken on rack of a broiler pan that has been coated with cooking spray. Bake, uncovered, at 400° for 45 minutes or until chicken is tender. Serve warm. Yield: 4 servings (262 calories per serving).

PROTEIN 31.0 / FAT 7.5 / CARBOHYDRATE 16.8 / CHOLESTEROL 83 / IRON 2.0 / SODIUM 311 / CALCIUM 26

TEXAS VEGETABLE CHICKEN

1 (3-pound) broiler-fryer, cut up and skinned
Vegetable cooking spray
1 teaspoon vegetable oil
1 cup chopped zucchini
½ cup chopped onion
1 (14-ounce) can no-salt-added stewed tomatoes, undrained and chopped
1 (4-ounce) can chopped green chiles, undrained
½ cup frozen whole kernel corn
2 teaspoons chicken-flavored bouillon granules
½ teaspoon ground cumin
¼ teaspoon garlic powder

Trim excess fat from chicken. Rinse chicken under cold, running water, and pat dry.

Coat a large nonstick skillet with cooking spray; add oil and place over medium-high heat until hot. Add chicken, and cook until lightly browned on all sides. Remove chicken; drain on paper towels. Wipe pan drippings from skillet with a paper towel.

Coat skillet with cooking spray. Add zucchini and onion; sauté until crisp-tender. Return chicken to skillet. Add tomatoes and remaining ingredients; stir gently. Cover; cook over medium heat 30 minutes or until chicken is tender. Yield: 6 servings (210 calories per serving).

PROTEIN 25.4 / FAT 7.6 / CARBOHYDRATE 9.6 / CHOLESTEROL 73 / IRON 1.7 / SODIUM 503 / CALCIUM 41

LEMON-MUSHROOM CHICKEN

1 (3-pound) broiler-fryer, skinned
Vegetable cooking spray
½ pound fresh mushrooms, thinly sliced
1½ teaspoons minced fresh tarragon, divided
2 tablespoons minced fresh parsley
1 teaspoon grated lemon rind
¼ cup lemon juice, divided
1 cup soft whole wheat breadcrumbs, toasted
1 tablespoon olive oil

Remove giblets and neck from chicken, and reserve for other uses. Rinse chicken under cold, running water, and pat dry. Set aside.

Coat a large nonstick skillet with cooking spray, and place over medium-high heat until hot. Add mushrooms, and sauté until tender.

Remove from heat and drain. Stir in 1 teaspoon tarragon, parsley, lemon rind, 2 tablespoons lemon juice, and breadcrumbs; mix well.

Place chicken, breast side up, on a rack in a roasting pan that has been coated with cooking spray. Stuff with mushroom mixture. Truss chicken. Combine remaining ½ teaspoon tarragon, 2 tablespoons lemon juice, and oil, and brush over chicken. Insert meat thermometer in meaty part of thigh, making sure it does not touch bone. Bake at 350° for 1½ to 2 hours or until meat thermometer registers 185°, basting with remaining lemon juice mixture. Yield: 6 servings (212 calories per serving).

PROTEIN 25.5 / FAT 8.9 / CARBOHYDRATE 7.3 / CHOLESTEROL 73 / IRON 1.8 / SODIUM 122 / CALCIUM 28

RASPBERRY-ORANGE CHICKEN

1 (3-pound) broiler-fryer, skinned
Vegetable cooking spray
2 tablespoons reduced-calorie margarine, melted
1 (10¼-ounce) jar low-sugar orange marmalade
¼ cup raspberry vinegar
½ teaspoon dried whole thyme

Remove giblets and neck from chicken, and reserve for other uses. Rinse chicken under cold, running water, and pat dry. Place chicken, breast side up, on a rack in a roasting pan that has been coated with cooking spray. Truss chicken. Brush chicken with margarine. Insert meat thermometer in meaty part of thigh, making sure it does not touch bone. Bake, uncovered, at 375° for 45 minutes.

Combine marmalade, vinegar, and thyme in a small saucepan. Cook over medium heat until heated and smooth, stirring occasionally. Divide marmalade mixture in half. Set aside half to serve with chicken.

Brush chicken with remaining half of marmalade mixture. Bake 45 minutes or until meat thermometer registers 185°, basting frequently with marmalade mixture. Transfer chicken to a serving platter. Cook reserved marmalade mixture over medium heat until warm, stirring occasionally. Spoon over chicken. Yield: 6 servings (244 calories per serving).

PROTEIN 23.6 / FAT 8.6 / CARBOHYDRATE 17.2 / CHOLESTEROL 73 / IRON 1.1 / SODIUM 107 / CALCIUM 14

Serve Tropical Cornish Hens when you want an unusual entrée. Fresh mango, banana, pineapple, and orange juice add to the tropical flair.

TROPICAL CORNISH HENS

2 (1-pound) Cornish hens, skinned
½ teaspoon coarsely ground pepper
Vegetable cooking spray
2 tablespoons plus 2 teaspoons frozen orange juice
   concentrate, thawed and undiluted
1 tablespoon bourbon
⅛ teaspoon garlic powder
1 firm, ripe banana, peeled and coarsely chopped
½ cup peeled, diced fresh mango
½ cup unsweetened pineapple chunks
Orange slices (optional)
Orange curls (optional)

Remove giblets from hens; reserve for other uses. Rinse hens under cold, running water, and pat dry. Split each hen in half lengthwise using an electric knife. Sprinkle with pepper.

Place hens, cut side down, in a roasting pan that has been coated with cooking spray.

Combine orange juice concentrate, bourbon, and garlic powder in a small bowl. Brush hens with orange juice mixture. Bake at 350° for 45 minutes, basting frequently with orange juice mixture. Add banana, mango, and pineapple to pan. Drizzle with remaining orange juice mixture. Bake 20 minutes or until fruit is thoroughly heated and hens are done. If desired, garnish with oranges slices and orange curls. Yield: 4 servings (264 calories per serving).

PROTEIN 27.8 / FAT 7.3 / CARBOHYDRATE 21.2 / CHOLESTEROL 83 / IRON 1.5 / SODIUM 82 / CALCIUM 27

GRILLED BASIL HENS

4 (1-pound) Cornish hens, skinned
2 cups Chablis or other dry white wine
½ cup minced fresh basil
1 teaspoon garlic powder
½ teaspoon hot sauce
Vegetable cooking spray

Remove giblets from hens; reserve for other uses. Rinse hens under cold, running water, and pat dry. Split each hen in half lengthwise using an electric knife. Place in a large shallow dish.

Combine wine, basil, garlic powder, and hot

sauce; stir well. Divide wine mixture in half; set aside half for basting during cooking. Cover and chill. Pour remaining half of wine mixture over hens. Cover and marinate in refrigerator at least 8 hours, turning occasionally.

Remove hens from marinade; discard marinade. Coat grill rack with cooking spray; place on grill over medium-hot coals. Place hens on rack, and cook 40 to 50 minutes or until done, turning and basting frequently with reserved wine mixture. Yield: 8 servings (176 calories per serving).

PROTEIN 25.9 / FAT 6.7 / CARBOHYDRATE 0.9 / CHOLESTEROL 79 / IRON 1.4 / SODIUM 80 / CALCIUM 26

TURKEY-BROCCOLI PATTIES

1 (10-ounce) package frozen chopped broccoli, thawed
1 pound fresh raw ground turkey
½ cup soft whole wheat breadcrumbs
1 egg, beaten
½ teaspoon ground nutmeg
¼ teaspoon ground white pepper
Vegetable cooking spray
Mustard Sauce

Drain thawed broccoli, and pat dry with paper towels. Finely chop broccoli, and set aside.

Combine broccoli, turkey, and next 4 ingredients; stir well. Shape turkey mixture into 6 patties. Place patties on rack of a broiler pan that has been coated with cooking spray. Bake, uncovered, at 425° for 12 to 13 minutes on each side or until done. Transfer patties to a serving platter. Spread 1 tablespoon Mustard Sauce over each patty. Yield: 6 servings (154 calories per serving).

Mustard Sauce:

1 (8-ounce) carton plain nonfat yogurt
1 tablespoon Dijon mustard
½ teaspoon Worcestershire sauce

Line a colander or sieve with a double layer of cheesecloth that has been rinsed out and squeezed dry; allow cheesecloth to extend over outside edges of colander. Stir yogurt until smooth; pour into colander and fold edges of cheesecloth over to cover yogurt. Place colander over a large bowl to drain; refrigerate 12 to 24 hours. Remove yogurt from colander and discard liquid in bowl.

Combine strained yogurt, mustard, and Worcestershire sauce in a small bowl; stir well. Yield: ¼ cup plus 2 tablespoons.

PROTEIN 21.4 / FAT 4.2 / CARBOHYDRATE 7.1 / CHOLESTEROL 77 / IRON 1.6 / SODIUM 186 / CALCIUM 122

FESTIVE TURKEY POLENTA

Vegetable cooking spray
1 teaspoon vegetable oil
½ pound fresh raw ground turkey
1 clove garlic, minced
1 (15-ounce) can stewed tomatoes, undrained and chopped
1 teaspoon dried Italian seasoning
¼ teaspoon ground red pepper
1 cup yellow cornmeal
3 cups water, divided
¼ teaspoon dried whole tarragon
3 tablespoons grated Romano cheese, divided

Coat a medium skillet with cooking spray; add oil. Place over medium-high heat until hot. Add ground turkey and garlic, and cook over medium heat until turkey is browned, stirring to crumble. Drain and pat dry with paper towels. Wipe pan drippings from skillet with a paper towel.

Add turkey mixture, stewed tomatoes, Italian seasoning, and red pepper to skillet. Bring to a boil; cover, reduce heat, and simmer 10 minutes. Set aside.

Combine cornmeal, 1 cup water, and tarragon in a small bowl. Bring 2 cups water to a boil in top of a double boiler over boiling water; add cornmeal mixture, stirring constantly. Reduce heat to low; cook until thickened and bubbly, stirring frequently. Cover and cook an additional 30 minutes, stirring occasionally; remove from heat. Spread half of cornmeal mixture in an ungreased shallow 2-quart casserole. Top with half of turkey mixture, and sprinkle with 1 tablespoon plus 1½ teaspoons Romano cheese. Repeat layers. Serve immediately. Yield: 6 servings (168 calories per serving).

PROTEIN 12.0 / FAT 3.7 / CARBOHYDRATE 21.1 / CHOLESTEROL 25 / IRON 1.8 / SODIUM 244 / CALCIUM 77

EASY TURKEY-MOZZARELLA BAKE

½ cup unprocessed oat bran
½ teaspoon garlic powder
2 egg whites, lightly beaten
2 tablespoons water
4 (4-ounce) turkey breast cutlets
Vegetable cooking spray
1 (8-ounce) can no-salt-added tomato sauce
½ cup (2 ounces) shredded part-skim mozzarella
    cheese

Combine oat bran and garlic powder; set aside. Combine egg whites and water; dip turkey cutlets in egg white mixture, and dredge in oat bran mixture. Cover and chill 1 hour.

Coat a large nonstick skillet with cooking spray; place over medium-high heat until hot. Add cutlets, and cook 3 minutes on each side or until lightly browned. Remove cutlets from skillet. Drain and pat dry with paper towels.

Arrange cutlets in a 10- x 6- x 2-inch baking dish that has been coated with cooking spray. Pour tomato sauce over cutlets; sprinkle with cheese. Bake at 375° for 20 minutes or until thoroughly heated. Yield: 4 servings (258 calories per serving).

PROTEIN 33.8 / FAT 7.1 / CARBOHYDRATE 12.6 / CHOLESTEROL 72 / IRON 2.0 / SODIUM 148 / CALCIUM 102

GRILLED TURKEY TERIYAKI

½ cup water
⅓ cup low-sodium soy sauce
¼ cup dry sherry
2 teaspoons dry mustard
2 teaspoons ground ginger
¼ teaspoon garlic powder
4 (4-ounce) turkey breast cutlets
Vegetable cooking spray

Combine first 6 ingredients in a shallow dish. Add turkey cutlets, turning to coat. Cover and marinate in refrigerator at least 2 hours, turning occasionally.

Remove cutlets from marinade, reserving marinade. Place marinade in a small saucepan; bring to a boil. Boil 5 minutes.

Coat grill rack with cooking spray; place on grill over medium coals. Place cutlets on rack,

and cook 4 minutes on each side or until done, basting frequently with reserved marinade. Yield: 4 servings (159 calories per serving).

PROTEIN 26.7 / FAT 3.3 / CARBOHYDRATE 1.5 / CHOLESTEROL 61 / IRON 1.4 / SODIUM 578 / CALCIUM 26

TOMATO TURKEY STIR-FRY

1 pound boneless fresh turkey breast slices
½ teaspoon dried whole rosemary, crushed
¼ teaspoon cracked pepper
¼ cup Chablis or other dry white wine
1 teaspoon cornstarch
Vegetable cooking spray
2 teaspoons peanut oil
1½ cups broccoli flowerets
½ cup chopped onion
2 firm, ripe tomatoes, cut into 16 wedges
2 tablespoons pine nuts, toasted

Cut turkey into thin strips. Sprinkle with rosemary and pepper. Combine wine and cornstarch. Stir well, and set aside.

Coat a wok or large nonstick skillet with cooking spray. Add peanut oil; place over medium-high heat (325°) until hot. Add turkey strips, and stir-fry 2 minutes or until browned. Add broccoli and onion; stir-fry 2 minutes. Add tomatoes. Pour reserved wine mixture over vegetable mixture. Cook, stirring constantly, 2 minutes or until slightly thickened and thoroughly heated. Transfer to a serving bowl; sprinkle with pine nuts, and serve immediately. Yield: 6 servings (152 calories per serving).

PROTEIN 20.3 / FAT 5.4 / CARBOHYDRATE 6.4 / CHOLESTEROL 45 / IRON 1.9 / SODIUM 60 / CALCIUM 30

Orange, Kiwifruit, and Purple Onion Salad (page 181) offers an unusual blend of flavors with fresh basil and raspberry vinegar.

Salads & Salad Dressings

Pear and Arugula Salad is topped with a creamy yogurt dressing and garnished with fresh blueberries.

PEAR AND ARUGULA SALAD

2 cups water
2 tablespoons lemon juice
2 medium-size fresh pears
¼ cup plain nonfat yogurt
3 tablespoons reduced-calorie mayonnaise
1 tablespoon white wine vinegar
2 teaspoons sugar
¼ teaspoon ground white pepper
1 bunch fresh arugula
Fresh blueberries (optional)

Combine water and lemon juice in a medium bowl, stirring well.

Peel and core pears; quarter lengthwise. Slice quarters lengthwise into ¼-inch-thick slices, leaving slices attached ½-inch from stem end. Dip pears in lemon juice mixture, and drain well. Set aside.

Combine yogurt and next 4 ingredients in a small bowl; stir well with a wire whisk.

Remove stems from arugula, and arrange leaves on 4 salad plates. Arrange pears over arugula, letting slices fan out slightly. Drizzle each salad with 2 tablespoons yogurt mixture. Garnish with fresh blueberries, if desired. Serve immediately. Yield: 4 servings (111 calories per serving).

PROTEIN 1.5 / FAT 3.5 / CARBOHYDRATE 20.5 / CHOLESTEROL 4 / IRON 0.4 / SODIUM 95 / CALCIUM 62

ORANGE, KIWIFRUIT, AND PURPLE ONION SALAD

1 small purple onion, thinly sliced
6 ounces fresh spinach
6 medium kiwifruit, peeled and cut into ¼-inch slices
3 large oranges, peeled and cut into ¼-inch slices
1 tablespoon julienne-cut fresh basil
2 tablespoons raspberry vinegar
2 tablespoons olive oil
1 tablespoon water

Soak onion slices in cold water 30 minutes; drain. Arrange spinach leaves on serving plates. Arrange kiwifruit, orange slices, and onion on spinach leaves. Sprinkle with fresh basil.

Combine vinegar, oil, and water; stir with a wire whisk until well-blended. Pour evenly over salads. Serve immediately. Yield: 6 servings (122 calories per serving).

PROTEIN 2.6 / FAT 5.1 / CARBOHYDRATE 18.2 / CHOLESTEROL 0 / IRON 1.3 / SODIUM 24 / CALCIUM 81

PAPAYA AND AVOCADO SALAD

3 tablespoons water
2 tablespoons balsamic vinegar
1 tablespoon plus 1½ teaspoons reduced-sodium soy sauce
1 teaspoon grated fresh gingerroot
1 teaspoon sesame oil
1 teaspoon hoisin sauce
½ teaspoon dry mustard
1 medium papaya (about 1 pound)
1 large Hass avocado (about ¾ pound)
Fresh basil leaves (optional)

Combine first 7 ingredients in a jar; cover tightly, and shake vigorously. Set aside.

Peel papaya; cut in half lengthwise. Scoop out seeds. Slice papaya into 16 slices. Set aside.

Cut avocado in half lengthwise. Carefully remove pit. Peel avocado, and slice into 12 slices.

Arrange 4 papaya slices and 3 avocado slices on individual salad plates. Drizzle dressing evenly over fruit slices. Garnish with fresh basil leaves, if desired. Serve immediately. Yield: 4 servings (117 calories per serving).

PROTEIN 1.8 / FAT 7.9 / CARBOHYDRATE 12.4 / CHOLESTEROL 0 / IRON 0.6 / SODIUM 284 / CALCIUM 26

SPROUT SALAD

2 cups fresh bean sprouts
2 tablespoons reduced-sodium soy sauce
2 tablespoons rice vinegar
2 teaspoons sesame oil
3 cups shredded jicama
¼ cup plus 2 tablespoons ¼-inch diagonally sliced green onions
2 tablespoons minced fresh cilantro
1½ teaspoons crushed red pepper
Fresh cilantro sprigs (optional)

Place bean sprouts in a colander. Pour 1 quart boiling water over sprouts. Rinse in cold water; drain and set aside.

Combine soy sauce, vinegar, and oil in a medium bowl; stir well with a wire whisk. Add bean sprouts, jicama, green onions, cilantro, and red pepper; stir well. Cover; chill at least 1 hour. Garnish with cilantro sprigs, if desired. Yield: 5 cups (33 calories per ½-cup serving).

PROTEIN 1.4 / FAT 1.1 / CARBOHYDRATE 5.2 / CHOLESTEROL 0 / IRON 0.6 / SODIUM 125 / CALCIUM 12

MOROCCAN CARROT SALAD

1 pound carrots, shredded
¼ cup minced green onions
2 tablespoons lemon juice
1 tablespoon unsweetened orange juice
1 teaspoon olive oil
½ teaspoon salt
½ teaspoon ground cumin
⅛ teaspoon ground white pepper
⅛ teaspoon ground red pepper
¼ cup minced fresh parsley
1 tablespoon grated orange rind
¾ teaspoon grated lemon rind
Tomato shells (optional)

Blanch carrots in boiling water 30 seconds or until crisp-tender. Drain; rinse under cold water until cool. Drain; place in a medium bowl.

Combine green onions and next 7 ingredients; pour over carrots. Add parsley, orange rind, and lemon rind; stir well. Spoon into tomato shells, if desired. Cover; chill thoroughly. Yield: 6 servings (38 calories per ½-cup serving).

PROTEIN 0.8 / FAT 0.9 / CARBOHYDRATE 7.8 / CHOLESTEROL 0 / IRON 0.7 / SODIUM 218 / CALCIUM 28

CELERIAC REMOULADE

4 cups water
¼ cup lemon juice
1 (¾-pound) celeriac
4 cups shredded cabbage
½ cup shredded carrot
3 tablespoons white wine vinegar with tarragon
1 tablespoon safflower oil
⅛ teaspoon salt
¼ cup reduced-calorie mayonnaise
2 tablespoons Dijon mustard
2 tablespoons minced fresh parsley
1 teaspoon dried whole tarragon

Combine water and ¼ cup lemon juice in a large bowl; set mixture aside. Peel celeriac thoroughly, cutting away any pitted areas. Shred celeriac in a food processor or by hand. Immediately place celeriac in lemon juice mixture to prevent discoloration.

Drain celeriac, and return to bowl; add cabbage and carrot. Combine vinegar, oil, and salt in a small bowl, stirring well with a wire whisk. Pour over celeriac mixture, tossing well. Cover and marinate at room temperature for up to 3 hours, stirring occasionally.

Combine mayonnaise and mustard; add to celeriac mixture, tossing to coat. Stir in minced parsley and tarragon. Yield: 6 servings (78 calories per 1-cup serving).

PROTEIN 1.1 / FAT 5.4 / CARBOHYDRATE 7.1 / CHOLESTEROL 3 / IRON 0.7 / SODIUM 323 / CALCIUM 46

CELERIAC ADDS FLAVOR

Celeriac is popular for flavoring soups and stews, but it also adds crisp texture when shredded or chopped for use in salads and side dishes. To prepare celeriac, start by peeling it thoroughly, cutting away any pitted areas. For salads such as Celeriac Remoulade, celeriac can be shredded in a food processor or by hand. Immediately place shredded celeriac in lemon juice to prevent discoloration. Drain the celeriac and add it to your favorite salad or side dish.

MARINATED CUCUMBER SALAD

⅓ cup white wine vinegar
1 tablespoon Dijon mustard
2 teaspoons vegetable oil
1 teaspoon reduced-sodium soy sauce
1 clove garlic, crushed
¼ teaspoon dried whole basil
¼ teaspoon dried whole tarragon
⅛ teaspoon dried whole thyme
2 medium cucumbers, thinly sliced
1 medium-size purple onion, thinly sliced
1 (4-ounce) can sliced ripe olives, drained
Lettuce leaves (optional)

Combine first 8 ingredients in container of an electric blender or food processor; top with cover, and process until well blended. Combine vinegar mixture, cucumber slices, onion slices, and olives, tossing gently to coat. Cover and refrigerate 2 hours. Serve on lettuce-lined salad plates, if desired. Yield: 6 servings (55 calories per 1-cup serving).

PROTEIN 1.0 / FAT 3.1 / CARBOHYDRATE 6.0 / CHOLESTEROL 0 / IRON 0.8 / SODIUM 214 / CALCIUM 33

EGGPLANT SALAD ORIENTAL

1 pound Asian eggplant
Vegetable cooking spray
2 tablespoons reduced-sodium soy sauce
2 tablespoons hot water
1 tablespoon brown sugar
1 teaspoon sesame oil
½ teaspoon minced fresh gingerroot
1 tablespoon sesame seeds, toasted

Wash eggplant; pierce skins in several places. Place eggplant on a baking sheet that has been coated with cooking spray. Bake at 400° for 20 minutes, turning once. Remove from oven, and let cool. Cut into quarters, and arrange on a serving platter.

Combine soy sauce and next 4 ingredients; stir well with a wire whisk. Pour over eggplant, and sprinkle with sesame seeds. Cover and chill 1 hour. Serve immediately. Yield: 6 servings (45 calories per serving).

PROTEIN 1.6 / FAT 1.8 / CARBOHYDRATE 6.9 / CHOLESTEROL 0 / IRON 0.7 / SODIUM 204 / CALCIUM 32

POTATO SALAD PICCATA

1 pound small new potatoes
¼ cup Chablis or other dry white wine
3 tablespoons canned no-salt-added chicken
    broth, undiluted
2 tablespoons water
1 tablespoon olive oil
2 teaspoons tarragon vinegar
2 teaspoons freshly squeezed lemon juice
1 teaspoon Dijon mustard
¼ teaspoon salt
¼ teaspoon freshly ground pepper
3 tablespoons minced green onions
3 tablespoons minced fresh parsley
1 tablespoon capers, chopped

Wash potatoes. Cook in boiling water to cover 15 minutes or until tender; drain and cool slightly. Cut into ¼-inch slices, and place in a medium bowl. Add wine; toss gently. Let stand 15 minutes, tossing occasionally.

Combine chicken broth and next 7 ingredients, stirring well with a wire whisk. Pour over potato mixture. Add green onions, parsley, and chopped capers; toss gently. Cover and chill at least 1 hour. Yield: 6 servings (88 calories per ½-cup serving).

PROTEIN 2.1 / FAT 2.5 / CARBOHYDRATE 13.5 / CHOLESTEROL 0 / IRON 1.3 / SODIUM 431 / CALCIUM 17

MIXED GREENS, MUSHROOM, AND HAZELNUT SALAD

¼ cup plus 2 tablespoons hazelnuts
1 tablespoon plus 1 teaspoon lemon juice
1 tablespoon plus 1 teaspoon coarse-grained
    mustard
1 teaspoon olive oil
½ pound fresh mushrooms, sliced
2 cups torn red leaf lettuce
1 cup torn romaine lettuce
1 cup torn arugula
1 cup torn radicchio
1 cup torn curly endive
⅓ cup canned low-sodium chicken broth, undiluted
1 tablespoon plus 1 teaspoon raspberry vinegar
1 teaspoon hazelnut oil
¼ teaspoon salt
⅛ teaspoon freshly ground pepper

Toast hazelnuts on a baking sheet at 350° for 10 minutes. Rub briskly with a towel to remove skins. Coarsely chop hazelnuts, and set aside.

Combine lemon juice, mustard, and olive oil in a medium bowl; stir well. Add mushrooms, and toss gently to coat. Set aside.

Combine salad greens in a large bowl, and toss well. Combine chicken broth and remaining ingredients in a small bowl; stir with a wire whisk until blended. Pour over salad greens, and toss well. Add mushroom mixture and hazelnuts; toss gently. Place mixture on individual salad plates. Yield: 8 servings (60 calories per 1-cup serving).

PROTEIN 1.7 / FAT 4.8 / CARBOHYDRATE 3.5 / CHOLESTEROL 0 / IRON 0.8 / SODIUM 151 / CALCIUM 48

WARM SPINACH SALAD WITH FETA CHEESE

½ pound fresh spinach
½ cup diced purple onion
2 tablespoons sherry vinegar
1 clove garlic, minced
¼ teaspoon salt
⅛ teaspoon freshly ground pepper
½ cup canned low-sodium chicken broth,
    undiluted
1 tablespoon olive oil
Dash of ground red pepper
¼ cup crumbled feta cheese

Remove stems from spinach; wash leaves, and pat dry thoroughly with paper towels. Combine spinach and diced purple onion in a large bowl; set aside.

Combine sherry vinegar, garlic, salt, and freshly ground pepper in a small bowl; stir with a wire whisk until well blended. Pour over reserved spinach mixture, and toss gently.

Combine chicken broth, olive oil, and red pepper in a small saucepan. Place over medium heat until thoroughly heated. Pour over spinach mixture, tossing gently.

Arrange spinach mixture on individual serving plates. Top each serving with 1½ teaspoons feta cheese. Serve immediately. Yield: 8 servings (51 calories per 1-cup serving).

PROTEIN 3.1 / FAT 2.8 / CARBOHYDRATE 4.1 / CHOLESTEROL 3 / IRON 2.4 / SODIUM 202 / CALCIUM 104

GREEK SALAD

2¼ cups diced tomato
1 large cucumber, peeled, seeded, and coarsely chopped
½ cup diced purple onion
8 Greek olives, pitted and chopped
¼ cup chopped fresh parsley
¼ cup crumbled feta cheese
½ teaspoon dried whole oregano
⅛ teaspoon freshly ground pepper
3 tablespoons canned no-salt-added chicken broth, undiluted
3 tablespoons water
1 tablespoon red wine vinegar
2 teaspoons lemon juice
1 teaspoon olive oil
⅛ teaspoon salt
Dash of freshly ground pepper
Dash of ground red pepper
Fresh radicchio leaves (optional)
Fresh arugula leaves (optional)

Combine first 8 ingredients in a medium bowl. Combine chicken broth, water, vinegar, lemon juice, olive oil, salt, pepper, and red pepper in a small bowl, stirring well.

Pour chicken broth over tomato mixture, tossing well. Cover and chill 1 hour before serving. If desired, serve on fresh radicchio leaves and garnish with fresh arugula leaves. Yield: 10 servings (38 calories per ½-cup serving).

PROTEIN 1.5 / FAT 2.1 / CARBOHYDRATE 3.8 / CHOLESTEROL 5 / IRON 0.6 / SODIUM 125 / CALCIUM 43

WARM RED CABBAGE SALAD WITH BAKED GOAT CHEESE

3 tablespoons fine, dry breadcrumbs
1 tablespoon sesame seeds
5 ounces goat cheese
1 tablespoon olive oil
Vegetable cooking spray
8 cups finely shredded red cabbage (about 2 pounds)
½ cup canned low-sodium chicken broth, undiluted
3 tablespoons sherry vinegar
2 tablespoons minced shallots
2 teaspoons sesame oil
⅛ teaspoon freshly ground pepper
2 tablespoons minced fresh parsley

Combine breadcrumbs and sesame seeds in a small bowl; set aside. Cut cheese into 8 equal rounds. Brush cheese with olive oil, and dredge in breadcrumb mixture, coating well. Place cheese rounds on a baking sheet that has been coated with cooking spray; set aside.

Place cabbage in a large bowl; set aside. Combine chicken broth and next 3 ingredients in a small saucepan; bring to a boil over medium heat. Remove from heat, and pour over cabbage. Add pepper, and toss gently. Place mixture on individual salad plates; set aside.

Broil cheese rounds 6 inches from heat 5 minutes or until golden brown. Top each salad with a warm round of cheese. Sprinkle with parsley, and serve immediately. Yield: 8 servings (118 calories per 1-cup serving).

PROTEIN 4.1 / FAT 7.5 / CARBOHYDRATE 8.0 / CHOLESTEROL 16 / IRON 0.8 / SODIUM 257 / CALCIUM 140

 TRENDY SALAD FARE

Looking for ways to add zip to your salad? Both of these salad ingredients pack a lot of flavor and pizazz in just a small size portion. Arugula is a tender, mustard-flavored green that resembles the leaves of the radish in flavor and appearance. To store, wrap the roots in damp toweling, enclose the bunch in plastic, and refrigerate for no more than a few days. It is an excellent

source of calcium, iron, and vitamins A and C.

Radicchio is closely related to Belgian endive and escarole and it resembles baby red cabbage. Its firm, red leaves hold up to cooking, making it useful when shredded and lightly sautéed with other vegetables. For optimum crispness, store radicchio, unwashed and loosely wrapped, in the refrigerator for up to a week.

LENTIL SALAD

1 (12-ounce) package dried lentils
3½ cups water
1 cup finely chopped onion
2 cloves garlic, crushed
2 bay leaves
1 teaspoon Herbes de Provence
⅓ cup canned no-salt-added chicken broth, undiluted
3 tablespoons lemon juice
3 tablespoons red wine vinegar
1 clove garlic, minced
1 teaspoon olive oil
½ teaspoon salt
¼ teaspoon pepper
¼ teaspoon ground cumin
3 drops of hot sauce
½ cup scraped and diced carrot
1½ cups peeled, seeded, and diced tomato
1 cup seeded and diced sweet red pepper
½ cup diced purple onion
½ cup diced celery
2 tablespoons chopped fresh parsley

Combine lentils and water in a large saucepan. Place saucepan over medium heat. Stir in chopped onion, crushed garlic, bay leaves, and Herbes de Provence. Bring lentil mixture to a boil. Cover, reduce heat, and simmer 20 minutes or until lentils are tender. Remove and discard bay leaves. Set lentil mixture aside, and keep warm.

Combine chicken broth, lemon juice, red wine vinegar, garlic, oil, salt, pepper, cumin, and hot sauce in a small bowl; stir with a wire whisk until well blended. Pour over lentils, and toss gently. Set aside.

Blanch carrot in boiling water 1 minute. Drain and rinse under cold water until cool; drain again, and place in a small bowl. Add tomato, diced sweet red pepper, purple onion, celery, and chopped parsley; stir into lentil mixture. Serve warm. Yield: 16 servings (94 calories per ½-cup serving).

PROTEIN 6.7 / FAT 0.7 / CARBOHYDRATE 16.3 / CHOLESTEROL 0 / IRON 2.5 / SODIUM 85 / CALCIUM 25

POLENTA, MOZZARELLA, AND TOMATO SALAD

2 cups water
½ teaspoon salt
½ cup instant polenta
Vegetable cooking spray
1 tablespoon freshly grated Parmesan cheese
2 tablespoons red wine vinegar
1 tablespoon canned low-sodium chicken broth, undiluted
1½ teaspoons olive oil
1½ cups ripe tomatoes, peeled, seeded, and cut into ½-inch cubes
6 ounces mozzarella cheese, cut into ½-inch cubes
1 tablespoon chopped fresh basil
1 tablespoon chopped purple onion
Fresh basil leaves (optional)

Bring water and salt to a boil in a medium saucepan. Slowly add polenta to boiling water, stirring constantly. Reduce heat to medium-low, and cook 5 minutes, stirring constantly. Pour polenta onto a baking sheet that has been coated with cooking spray. Shape into a 10-inch square. Allow to cool completely.

Cut cooled polenta into ½-inch cubes. Toss cubes with grated Parmesan cheese, and return to baking sheet. Bake at 350° for 20 minutes. Remove from oven, and let cool.

Combine vinegar, chicken broth, and olive oil in a small bowl; stir well with a wire whisk, and set mixture aside.

Combine tomatoes and next 3 ingredients in a medium bowl, tossing well. Add polenta cubes, and toss gently. Pour reserved dressing over salad, and toss lightly. Garnish with fresh basil leaves, if desired. Serve immediately. Yield: 8 servings (109 calories per ½-cup serving).

PROTEIN 5.7 / FAT 6.2 / CARBOHYDRATE 7.6 / CHOLESTEROL 18 / IRON 0.4 / SODIUM 256 / CALCIUM 138

Fresh tomatoes, cilantro, and colorful peppers make Southwestern Pasta Salad a bright delight.

SOUTHWESTERN PASTA SALAD

¼ (16-ounce) package ditalini macaroni, uncooked
½ cup diced sweet red pepper
½ cup diced sweet yellow pepper
1 cup peeled, seeded, and chopped tomato
¼ cup diced purple onion
1 tablespoon plus 1½ teaspoons minced fresh cilantro
1 clove garlic, minced
1 small jalapeño pepper, seeded and minced
1½ teaspoons olive oil
1½ teaspoons red wine vinegar
¼ cup crumbled feta cheese
2 tablespoons pine nuts, toasted

Cook macaroni according to package directions, omitting salt and fat. Drain and set aside. Combine sweet red pepper and next 8 ingredients in a large bowl. Stir in macaroni. Cover and chill at least 2 hours. Top with cheese and pine nuts. Yield: 8 servings (114 calories per ½-cup serving).

PROTEIN 3.8 / FAT 4.9 / CARBOHYDRATE 15.1 / CHOLESTEROL 6 / IRON 1.1 / SODIUM 86 / CALCIUM 46

WILD RICE, FENNEL, AND ORANGE SALAD

¾ pound fennel, washed
½ cup uncooked wild rice
1 tablespoon grated orange rind
1 large navel orange, peeled, seeded, and sectioned (about ½ cup)
¼ cup green onions, diagonally sliced
2 tablespoons chopped fresh parsley
⅛ teaspoon salt
Dash of freshly ground pepper
Champagne Vinaigrette

Trim leaves off fennel and mince, reserving 1½ teaspoons. Trim off tough outer stalks and discard. Cut bulb in half lengthwise; remove core. Cut crosswise into ⅛-inch slices.

Cook wild rice according to package directions, omitting salt and fat; drain well. Combine reserved sliced fennel, minced leaves, rice, and next 6 ingredients in a medium bowl; toss gently. Pour Champagne Vinaigrette over salad, and toss gently. Cover; chill thoroughly. Yield: 8 servings (67 calories per ½-cup serving).

Champagne Vinaigrette:

¼ cup canned low-sodium chicken broth, undiluted
2 tablespoons champagne vinegar
1 tablespoon minced shallot
1 tablespoon olive oil
½ teaspoon salt

Combine all ingredients in a small bowl, stirring well. Yield: ½ cup.

PROTEIN 2.4 / FAT 1.9 / CARBOHYDRATE 11.4 / CHOLESTEROL 0 /
IRON 1.2 / SODIUM 187 / CALCIUM 39

COUSCOUS SALAD

1¼ cups water
1 cup uncooked couscous
3 cups chopped tomato
1¾ cups chopped English cucumber
⅓ cup minced fresh parsley
¼ cup diagonally sliced green onions
1 (14-ounce) can hearts of palm, rinsed, drained,
  and sliced
½ teaspoon salt
¼ teaspoon freshly ground pepper
Red Wine Vinaigrette

Place water in a medium saucepan, and bring to a boil. Stir in couscous. Cover, remove from heat, and let stand 5 minutes.

Combine couscous and next 7 ingredients, stirring well. Pour vinaigrette over salad, and toss gently. Cover and chill thoroughly. Yield: 16 servings (66 calories per ½-cup serving).

Red Wine Vinaigrette:

⅓ cup hot water
¾ teaspoon chicken-flavored bouillon granules
2 tablespoons red wine vinegar
1 tablespoon lemon juice
1 teaspoon olive oil
1 teaspoon mustard
¼ teaspoon salt
⅛ teaspoon freshly ground pepper

Combine water and bouillon granules in a medium bowl; stir until granules dissolve. Add vinegar and remaining ingredients; stir well. Yield: ½ cup plus 1 tablespoon.

PROTEIN 2.2 / FAT 0.5 / CARBOHYDRATE 14.1 / CHOLESTEROL 0 /
IRON 0.5 / SODIUM 154 / CALCIUM 12

ORIENTAL BEEF SALAD

1 (¾-pound) lean flank steak
½ cup reduced-sodium soy sauce
3 cloves garlic, minced
1 tablespoon grated fresh gingerroot
2½ teaspoons sesame oil, divided
3 cups torn red leaf lettuce
2 cups torn romaine lettuce
2 cups torn curly endive
1½ cups finely shredded red cabbage
1½ cups scored, sliced English cucumber
1 small sweet red pepper, cut into thin
  julienne strips
1 medium carrot, scraped and cut into thin
  julienne strips
1 small purple onion, thinly sliced
¼ cup canned low-sodium chicken broth,
  undiluted
2 tablespoons reduced-sodium soy sauce
1 tablespoon rice vinegar
1 teaspoon lemon juice
½ teaspoon crushed red pepper
1 teaspoon sesame seeds, toasted
Fresh cilantro sprigs (optional)

Trim fat from steak, and place in an 11- x 7- x 2-inch baking dish. Combine ½ cup soy sauce, garlic, gingerroot, and 1½ teaspoons sesame oil; stir well. Pour over steak. Cover and marinate in refrigerator at least 8 hours, turning steak occasionally.

Combine red leaf lettuce and next 7 ingredients in a large bowl. Combine remaining 1 teaspoon sesame oil, chicken broth, 2 tablespoons soy sauce, vinegar, lemon juice, and crushed red pepper in a small bowl; stir with a wire whisk until blended, and pour over vegetable mixture. Toss gently, and set aside.

Remove steak from marinade; discard marinade. Place steak on rack of a broiler pan. Broil steak 4 inches from heat 12 minutes or to desired degree of doneness, turning once. Cut steak diagonally across grain into thin slices. Divide vegetable mixture evenly among 6 serving plates. Arrange steak over vegetable mixture; sprinkle with sesame seeds, and garnish with fresh cilantro sprigs, if desired. Yield: 6 servings (169 calories per serving).

PROTEIN 14.6 / FAT 8.8 / CARBOHYDRATE 8.1 / CHOLESTEROL 35 /
IRON 2.4 / SODIUM 319 / CALCIUM 56

Fresh cilantro adds south-of-the-border taste to Ensalada Tostada, a satisfying Mexican salad.

ENSALADA TOSTADA

4 (4-ounce) skinned, boned chicken breast halves
2 bay leaves
¼ teaspoon salt
¼ teaspoon cracked pepper
6 (6-inch) corn tortillas
Vegetable cooking spray
2 heads romaine lettuce, torn into bite-size pieces
1 large avocado, cut into ½-inch cubes
1 large green pepper, diced
¾ cup chopped tomato
1 small purple onion, thinly sliced
⅓ cup chopped fresh cilantro
Dressing (recipe follows)
Fresh cilantro sprigs (optional)

Place chicken in a large nonstick skillet; cover

with cold water. Add bay leaves, salt, and cracked pepper. Bring to a boil over high heat; cover, reduce heat, and simmer 15 minutes or until done. Remove and discard bay leaves. Drain chicken and set aside.

Cut each tortilla into 8 wedges; place on a baking sheet that has been coated with cooking spray. Bake at 350° for 15 minutes or until crisp, turning once. Set aside.

Shred chicken into bite-size pieces. Combine chicken, lettuce, and next 5 ingredients in a large bowl. Pour ½ cup dressing over salad, and toss well. Garnish with cilantro sprigs, if desired. Serve with tortilla wedges and remaining ¾ cup dressing. Yield: 6 servings (241 calories per 3-cup serving).

Dressing:

⅓ cup hot water
¾ teaspoon chicken-flavored bouillon granules
⅓ cup water
¼ cup cider vinegar
2 tablespoons tarragon vinegar
1 tablespoon olive oil
1 teaspoon sugar
½ teaspoon Kosher salt
1 teaspoon mustard seeds
1 teaspoon dry mustard
1 teaspoon paprika
¼ teaspoon pepper

Combine hot water and bouillon granules, stirring until granules dissolve. Combine bouillon mixture, ⅓ cup water, and remaining ingredients in a small bowl, stirring well with a wire whisk. Yield: 1¼ cups.

PROTEIN 21.7 / FAT 10.1 / CARBOHYDRATE 17.5 / CHOLESTEROL 47 / IRON 3.9 / SODIUM 482 / CALCIUM 94

SMOKED CHICKEN AND PASTA SALAD

8 ounces penne pasta, uncooked
1 (2½-pound) smoked chicken, skinned
2½ cups peeled, seeded, and chopped tomato
½ cup diced purple onion
¼ cup chopped fresh parsley
2 tablespoons balsamic vinegar
2 tablespoons red wine vinegar
1 tablespoon olive oil
1 teaspoon sugar
½ teaspoon salt
¼ teaspoon freshly ground pepper
4 ounces Fontina cheese thinly sliced
½ cup pine nuts, toasted

Cook pasta according to package directions, omitting salt and fat; drain. Debone chicken; discard bones. Shred meat, and place in a large bowl. Add pasta, tomato, and next 8 ingredients, stirring well. Place in a 3-quart casserole; top with cheese. Bake at 450° for 15 minutes or until cheese melts. Place salad on individual serving plates. Sprinkle each serving with pine nuts. Yield: 10 servings (269 calories per 1-cup serving).

PROTEIN 20.8 / FAT 11.5 / CARBOHYDRATE 21.0 / CHOLESTEROL 54 / IRON 2.1 / SODIUM 159 / CALCIUM 87

CHICKEN SALAD IN ORANGE CUPS

2 medium oranges
1½ cups diced, cooked chicken breast (skinned before cooking and cooked without salt)
¼ cup chopped green pepper
¼ cup sliced green onions
3 tablespoons reduced-calorie mayonnaise
2 teaspoons unsweetened orange juice
2 teaspoons honey
½ teaspoon ground coriander
¼ teaspoon ground ginger
Fresh parsley sprigs (optional)

Cut oranges in half crosswise. Clip membranes, being careful not to puncture bottom. Remove pulp; set aside. Using kitchen shears, cut edges of orange cups into scallops. Set aside.

Dice reserved orange pulp. Combine pulp, chicken, pepper, and onions in a medium bowl. Combine mayonnaise, orange juice, honey, coriander, and ginger in a small bowl; stir well. Pour over chicken mixture; toss gently.

Divide chicken mixture evenly among orange cups. Cover and chill thoroughly. Garnish with parsley sprigs, if desired. Yield: 4 servings (144 calories per serving).

PROTEIN 16.8 / FAT 4.9 / CARBOHYDRATE 7.5 / CHOLESTEROL 48 / IRON 0.8 / SODIUM 123 / CALCIUM 22

 SUBSTITUTES FOR SULFITES

Not too long ago, restaurant and supermarket personnel liberally sprinkled sulfite, a preservative, on fruits and vegetables to keep the produce fresh. But when researchers discovered that sulfites can cause severe, even fatal, allergic reactions in a small number of people, the FDA eventually banned their use in many foods. Manufacturers scrambled to find new alternatives.

Today, harmless powdered compounds such as ascorbic acid (vitamin C) and citric acid are used to keep produce fresh. The powders mix easily with water. Dipping produce, especially salad bar items, into these "freshener" liquids prevents the discoloration that normally occurs when a cut surface is exposed to air. At home, you can get the same effect by sprinkling cut-up fruits or other vegetables with lemon juice, which is high in citric acid.

SPICY ASIAN PEANUT SALAD

4½ cups finely shredded red cabbage
3 cups fresh bean sprouts
2½ cups shredded carrots
½ pound snow peas, cut into julienne strips
1 medium-size sweet red pepper, cut into julienne strips
¼ cup diagonally sliced green onions
Peanut Sauce
2 pounds medium-size shrimp, peeled and deveined
Fresh cilantro sprigs (optional)

Combine first 6 ingredients, and stir well. Spoon Peanut Sauce over cabbage mixture, and toss gently. Set cabbage mixture aside.

Bring 1½ quarts water to a boil; add shrimp, and cook 3 to 5 minutes. Drain well; rinse with cold water, and drain again. Cut shrimp in half lengthwise.

Place 1 cup salad mixture on each of 12 individual serving plates. Top with equal amounts of shrimp, and garnish with cilantro sprigs, if desired. Yield: 12 servings (135 calories per 1-cup serving).

Peanut Sauce:

½ cup soft tofu
⅓ cup canned low-sodium chicken broth, undiluted
¼ cup reduced-sodium soy sauce
3 tablespoons balsamic vinegar
3 tablespoons dry sherry
3 tablespoons creamy peanut butter
2 cloves garlic, chopped
1 tablespoon plus 1½ teaspoons sugar
1 tablespoon chopped fresh gingerroot
1 teaspoon sesame oil
½ teaspoon crushed red pepper

Combine all ingredients in container of an electric blender or food processor; top with cover, and process until mixture is smooth. Yield: 1⅔ cups).

PROTEIN 14.6 / FAT 3.6 / CARBOHYDRATE 11.4 / CHOLESTEROL 98 / IRON 3.0 / SODIUM 348 / CALCIUM 75

SEAFOOD PAELLA SALAD

3 cups water
½ teaspoon salt
1½ cups uncooked long grain rice
½ teaspoon dried whole saffron
¾ cup water
¼ cup lemon juice
1 tablespoon olive oil
½ teaspoon chicken-flavored bouillon granules
¼ teaspoon salt
⅛ teaspoon pepper
Dash of ground red pepper
4 cups water
¾ pound unpeeled small fresh shrimp
1 (9-ounce) package frozen artichoke hearts, thawed
¾ cup diced green pepper
½ cup frozen English peas, thawed
½ cup peeled, seeded, and chopped tomato
1 (4-ounce) jar diced pimiento, drained
1 tablespoon minced fresh parsley

Bring 3 cups water and ½ teaspoon salt to a boil in a medium saucepan; stir in rice and saffron. Cover, reduce heat, and simmer 20 minutes or until rice is tender and liquid is absorbed.

Combine ¾ cup water and next 6 ingredients. Stir with a wire whisk until well blended. Add ½ cup dressing mixture to warm rice; stir well to separate grains. Transfer rice to a large bowl, and cool completely.

Bring 4 cups water to a boil; add shrimp, and cook 3 to 5 minutes. Drain well; rinse with cold water, and drain again. Peel and devein shrimp.

Add shrimp, artichoke hearts, green pepper, peas, tomato, and pimiento to cooled rice mixture; toss gently. Pour remaining dressing over rice mixture, and toss gently to coat. Cover and refrigerate at least 1 hour, stirring occasionally. Sprinkle with parsley. Yield: 8 servings (209 calories per 1-cup serving).

PROTEIN 11.2 / FAT 2.9 / CARBOHYDRATE 34.5 / CHOLESTEROL 54 / IRON 2.6 / SODIUM 405 / CALCIUM 41

SCALLOP AND PASTA SALAD

1½ pounds fresh bay scallops, halved
½ cup lemon juice
½ cup lime juice
¾ pound small shell macaroni, uncooked
1 teaspoon vegetable oil
1 cup diced sweet red pepper
1 cup diced green pepper
¼ cup chopped fresh cilantro
2 tablespoons diced purple onion
1 jalapeño pepper, seeded and minced
¼ cup water
2 tablespoons rice vinegar
1 teaspoon olive oil
1 teaspoon Dijon mustard
¼ teaspoon salt
⅛ teaspoon pepper
Fresh cilantro sprigs (optional)

Place scallops in boiling water to cover; reduce heat and simmer 4 minutes. Drain. Transfer scallops to a glass bowl. Pour lemon juice and lime juice over scallops. Cover and marinate in refrigerator at least 4 hours.

Cook macaroni according to package directions, omitting salt and fat; drain. Rinse with cold water, and drain well. Place macaroni in a large bowl. Add vegetable oil, and toss gently.

Drain scallops; add scallops, sweet red pepper, and next 4 ingredients to macaroni. Combine water, vinegar, olive oil, mustard, salt, and pepper; stir with a wire whisk until blended. Pour over macaroni mixture, and toss gently. Garnish with fresh cilantro sprigs, if desired. Serve immediately. Yield: 12 servings (175 calories per 1-cup serving).

PROTEIN 13.4 / FAT 1.8 / CARBOHYDRATE 25.4 / CHOLESTEROL 19 / IRON 0.6 / SODIUM 154 / CALCIUM 19

SMOKED TURKEY, POTATO, AND GREEN BEAN SALAD

1 pound small red potatoes
½ cup canned low-sodium chicken broth, undiluted
½ cup water
2 tablespoons lemon juice
2 tablespoons white wine vinegar
1 tablespoon Dijon mustard
1 tablespoon olive oil
½ teaspoon salt
¼ teaspoon freshly ground pepper
3 cups sliced fresh mushrooms
½ pound green beans, sliced into ¾-inch pieces
¾ pound smoked turkey, sliced into 1- x ¼- x ¼-inch strips
1 cup sweet red pepper, sliced into 1- x ¼- x ¼-inch strips
¾ cup diagonally sliced celery
½ cup diced purple onion
¼ cup minced fresh parsley

Cook potatoes in boiling water to cover until almost tender (about 12 minutes); drain, reserving water, and set aside. Combine chicken broth and next 7 ingredients in a small bowl; stir well. Place mushrooms in a large bowl; add chicken broth mixture, and toss to combine.

Bring reserved water to a boil; add green beans, and cook 3 minutes or until crisp-tender. Drain and set aside.

Cut potatoes into quarters, and add to mushroom mixture. Stir in beans, turkey, sweet red pepper, celery, and onion. Transfer to individual serving plates. Sprinkle with parsley. Yield: 10 servings (124 calories per 1-cup serving).

PROTEIN 10.1 / FAT 3.7 / CARBOHYDRATE 13.4 / CHOLESTEROL 19 / IRON 1.8 / SODIUM 409 / CALCIUM 22

GRADING SCHOOL LUNCHES

One recent study found that some school foods pack nearly 30 percent more fat and 100 times more sodium than is recommended. This unhealthy balance can damage long-term eating habits for a child.

The good news is that many school systems are eager to tackle these nutrition concerns. Menus are being revised to reduce fat and salt. Furthermore, some teachers and lunchroom workers are working together to plan nutrition education strategies. The goal is to offer lunchroom choices that reinforce what's taught in health classes. Since school lunches provide one-third of the RDA for nutrients, this is one strategy that health professionals applaud.

CAESAR SALAD DRESSING

1 egg
2 tablespoons red wine vinegar
1 clove garlic, crushed
1 teaspoon Dijon mustard
1 teaspoon anchovy paste
¼ teaspoon salt
⅛ teaspoon freshly ground pepper
¼ cup plus 2 tablespoons hot water
1 teaspoon chicken-flavored bouillon granules
¼ cup olive oil

Pour water to a depth of 2 inches in a medium saucepan; bring to a boil, and turn off heat. Carefully lower egg into water using a slotted spoon; let stand 1 minute. Remove egg from water, and let cool.

Combine egg, vinegar, and next 5 ingredients in container of an electric blender; top with cover, and process 10 seconds. Combine hot water and bouillon granules, stirring until granules are dissolved. With blender running, gradually add bouillon mixture and olive oil in a slow, steady stream. Cover and chill thoroughly. Serve with salad greens. Yield: 1 cup (37 calories per tablespoon).

PROTEIN 0.5 / FAT 3.8 / CARBOHYDRATE 0.2 / CHOLESTEROL 12 / IRON 0.1 / SODIUM 144 / CALCIUM 2

ORIENTAL DRESSING

¼ cup reduced-sodium soy sauce
3 tablespoons rice vinegar
2 green onions, chopped
1 tablespoon chopped fresh gingerroot
2 teaspoons honey
¼ teaspoon hot sauce
¼ cup dark sesame oil

Combine first 6 ingredients in container of an electric blender; top with cover, and blend at high speed 30 seconds. With blender running, gradually add oil in a slow, steady stream. Blend 15 seconds. Cover and chill thoroughly. Stir well before serving. Serve with salad greens or use to prepare chicken salad. Yield: 1 cup (36 calories per tablespoon).

PROTEIN 0.3 / FAT 3.4 / CARBOHYDRATE 1.4 / CHOLESTEROL 0 / IRON 0.1 / SODIUM 151 / CALCIUM 2

CREAMY VINAIGRETTE

¾ cup soft tofu
3 tablespoons plain nonfat yogurt
2 egg yolks
2 tablespoons sherry wine vinegar
1 teaspoon Dijon mustard
½ teaspoon salt
⅛ teaspoon ground white pepper
3 tablespoons extra virgin olive oil

Position knife blade in food processor bowl; add first 7 ingredients. Top with cover, and process 1 minute. With processor running, gradually add olive oil through food chute in a slow, steady stream; process until smooth. Cover and chill thoroughly. Serve with salad greens. Yield: 1⅓ cups (30 calories per tablespoon).

PROTEIN 0.9 / FAT 2.7 / CARBOHYDRATE 0.3 / CHOLESTEROL 27 / IRON 0.3 / SODIUM 72 / CALCIUM 21

CURRY DRESSING

Vegetable cooking spray
¼ cup finely chopped onion
2 tablespoons water
2 teaspoons curry powder
¼ cup reduced-calorie mayonnaise
¼ cup plain nonfat yogurt
2 tablespoons chutney
1 tablespoon lemon juice
1 clove garlic, crushed
1 teaspoon reduced-sodium soy sauce
¼ teaspoon salt

Coat a small nonstick skillet with cooking spray; place over low heat until hot. Add chopped onion, and sauté 2 minutes. Add water; cook 3 minutes or until onion is transparent. Stir in curry powder; cook 1 minute, stirring constantly. Set aside and cool slightly.

Combine onion mixture, mayonnaise, and remaining ingredients in container of an electric blender or food processor; top with cover, and process until smooth. Serve with salad greens, raw vegetables, ham, or chicken. Yield: ¾ cup (26 calories per tablespoon).

PROTEIN 0.5 / FAT 1.4 / CARBOHYDRATE 3.1 / CHOLESTEROL 2 / IRON 0.2 / SODIUM 112 / CALCIUM 14

MONOUNSATURATES MAKE HEADLINES

Monounsaturated fats, once regarded as neutral participants in the battle against cholesterol, are now regarded as fighters against heart disease. These fats lower cholesterol as well as polyunsaturated fats do. In studies in which monounsaturated fats were used to replace saturated fats in the diet, total cholesterol levels dropped dramatically. Even more advantageous is that monounsaturated fats, unlike their polyunsaturated counterparts, lower only the harmful LDL cholesterol. Helpful HDL cholesterol, the variety that aids in removing fat and cholesterol from the blood, is left intact.

You need not give up polyunsaturates for mono-unsaturate-rich fats, however. Clearly, both varieties are healthful alternatives. Most foods have a mixture of three types of fat. For the healthiest alternative, choose foods that contain primarily unsaturated fat, either polyunsaturated or monounsaturated. Following is a chart that gives a few types of vegetable oils and their fat content. Notice that three oils in particular are high in monounsaturates: olive, canola, and peanut.

FAT PROFILE OF VARIOUS OILS			
OIL	% SATURATED	% MONO-UNSATURATED	% POLY-UNSATURATED
CANOLA (RAPESEED)	7	55	33
SAFFLOWER	9	12	75
CORN	13	24	59
SOYBEAN	14	23	58
OLIVE	14	72	9
PEANUT	19	46	30
PALM	49	37	9
PALM KERNEL	81	11	2
COCONUT	86	6	2

GARLIC-DILL BUTTERMILK DRESSING

½ cup nonfat buttermilk
¼ cup instant nonfat dry milk powder
2 tablespoons reduced-calorie mayonnaise
2 tablespoons champagne vinegar
1 small clove garlic, crushed
2 teaspoons minced fresh dillweed
½ teaspoon salt
Dash of ground red pepper

Combine buttermilk, milk powder, and mayonnaise in a small bowl; chill 30 minutes or until slightly thickened. Add vinegar and remaining ingredients; stir with a wire whisk until well blended. Cover and chill thoroughly. Serve with salad greens. Yield: 1 cup (15 calories per tablespoon).

PROTEIN 1.0 / FAT 0.6 / CARBOHYDRATE 1.6 / CHOLESTEROL 1 / IRON 0.0 / SODIUM 105 / CALCIUM 25

SPICY YOGURT DRESSING

1 cup plain nonfat yogurt
¼ cup reduced-calorie mayonnaise
1 teaspoon sugar
½ teaspoon ground cumin
¼ teaspoon salt
⅛ teaspoon ground white pepper
Dash of ground red pepper
Dash of ground cardamom
1 tablespoon finely chopped cilantro

Position knife blade in food processor bowl; add first 8 ingredients. Top with cover, and process until smooth. Pour mixture into a small bowl; stir in cilantro. Serve over thinly sliced cucumbers, avocados, or tomatoes. Yield: 1⅓ cups (15 calories per tablespoon).

PROTEIN 0.6 / FAT 0.9 / CARBOHYDRATE 1.2 / CHOLESTEROL 0 / IRON 0.0 / SODIUM 57 / CALCIUM 21

HORSERADISH SLAW DRESSING

¼ cup reduced-calorie mayonnaise
¼ cup soft tofu
¼ cup low-fat sour cream
1 tablespoon grated fresh horseradish
1 tablespoon cider vinegar
2 teaspoons sugar
¼ teaspoon salt

Combine all ingredients in container of an electric blender or food processor; top with cover, and process until smooth. Cover and chill. Serve with salad greens. Yield: ¾ cup (27 calories per tablespoon).

PROTEIN 0.5 / FAT 2.1 / CARBOHYDRATE 1.5 / CHOLESTEROL 4 / IRON 0.1 / SODIUM 88 / CALCIUM 16

SWEET 'N' SOUR SALAD DRESSING

¾ cup plain low-fat yogurt
¼ cup reduced-calorie mayonnaise
3 tablespoons cider vinegar
2 tablespoons sugar
½ teaspoon paprika
¼ teaspoon dry mustard

Combine all ingredients in a small bowl; stir with a wire whisk until well blended. Cover and chill thoroughly. Serve with salad greens. Yield: 1 cup (23 calories per tablespoon).

PROTEIN 0.6 / FAT 1.2 / CARBOHYDRATE 2.8 / CHOLESTEROL 2 / IRON 0.0 / SODIUM 35 / CALCIUM 20

HONEY-LIME CREAM DRESSING

½ cup plus 2 tablespoons low-fat sour cream
½ cup low-fat cottage cheese
⅓ cup lime juice
3 tablespoons honey
⅛ teaspoon ground white pepper

Combine all ingredients in container of an electric blender or food processor; top with cover, and process until smooth. Cover and chill thoroughly. Serve with fresh fruit salad. Yield: 1¾ cups (18 calories per tablespoon).

PROTEIN 0.7 / FAT 0.7 / CARBOHYDRATE 2.5 / CHOLESTEROL 2 / IRON 0.0 / SODIUM 19 / CALCIUM 8

ANCHO CHILE MAYONNAISE

½ cup reduced-calorie mayonnaise
½ cup soft tofu
1 tablespoon plus 1½ teaspoons Ancho Chile Paste
1 clove garlic, minced
2 teaspoons lime juice
¼ teaspoon salt

Combine all ingredients in container of an electric blender or food processor; top with cover, and process until smooth. Serve with Mexican or chicken salads. Yield: 1 cup (27 calories per tablespoon).

Ancho Chile Paste:

3 dried ancho chiles
6 cups water
2 tablespoons lime juice
1 tablespoon olive oil

Wash chiles, and place in a large saucepan; add 6 cups water. Place a bowl or plate over chiles to keep them submerged. Cover and bring to a boil. Remove from heat, and let chiles stand, covered, 2 hours or until chiles are softened. Drain chiles. Remove and discard stems and seeds.

Place chiles in container of an electric blender or food processor; top with cover, and process until smooth, scraping sides of container occasionally with a spatula. Add lime juice and olive oil; process until mixture is combined. Store in refrigerator or freezer. Use Ancho Chile Paste as a flavoring in Southwestern dishes, stews, or chili. Yield: 1 cup.

PROTEIN 0.6 / FAT 2.4 / CARBOHYDRATE 1.1 / CHOLESTEROL 3 / IRON 0.1 / SODIUM 94 / CALCIUM 14

For a change from the everyday salad, make a sandwich instead by filling pita bread with fresh vegetables as in Garden Patch Pitas (page 196).

Sandwiches & Snacks

PEAR WALDORF PITAS

1 small fresh pear, chopped (about 1 cup)
½ cup thinly sliced celery
½ cup seedless red grapes, halved
2 tablespoons finely chopped walnuts
2 tablespoons lemon low-fat yogurt
2 tablespoons reduced-calorie mayonnaise
⅛ teaspoon poppy seeds
2 (6-inch) whole wheat pita bread rounds, cut in half crosswise
4 leaf lettuce leaves

Combine first 4 ingredients in a medium bowl. Combine yogurt, mayonnaise, and poppy seeds, stirring well. Add yogurt mixture to fruit mixture, stirring gently. Cover and chill.

Line pita halves with lettuce. Spoon ½ cup fruit mixture into each pita half. Yield: 4 servings (123 calories per serving).

PROTEIN 2.5 / FAT 4.7 / CARBOHYDRATE 18.5 / CHOLESTEROL 3 / IRON 0.8 / SODIUM 78 / CALCIUM 41

GARDEN PATCH PITAS

½ cup chopped cauliflower
½ cup finely chopped zucchini
½ cup finely chopped cucumber
½ cup finely chopped tomato
½ cup thinly sliced mushrooms
½ cup thinly sliced carrots
⅓ cup white wine vinegar
1 tablespoon sugar
1 tablespoon vegetable oil
¼ teaspoon pepper
⅛ teaspoon salt
2 (6-inch) whole wheat pita bread rounds, cut in half crosswise
4 red leaf lettuce leaves

Combine first 6 ingredients in a medium bowl. Combine vinegar, sugar, oil, pepper, and salt in a jar; cover tightly, and shake vigorously. Pour over vegetable mixture; toss well. Cover and chill 6 to 8 hours.

Line pita halves with lettuce. Spoon ¾ cup vegetable mixture into each pita half using a slotted spoon. Serve immediately. Yield: 4 servings (170 calories per serving).

PROTEIN 3.9 / FAT 4.4 / CARBOHYDRATE 28.1 / CHOLESTEROL 0 / IRON 2.2 / SODIUM 94 / CALCIUM 63

COBB SANDWICHES

2 (4-ounce) skinned, boned chicken breast halves
¼ teaspoon pepper
⅛ teaspoon salt
¼ cup commercial reduced-calorie blue cheese dressing
8 thin slices whole wheat bread
4 leaves romaine lettuce
4 (½-inch-thick) tomato slices
8 thin slices avocado, peeled

Place chicken in a small skillet; sprinkle with pepper and salt. Add water to cover; bring to a boil. Reduce heat, cover, and simmer 5 to 7 minutes or until chicken is tender. Drain on paper towels. Slice chicken into thin strips. Set chicken aside.

Divide ¼ cup dressing among 4 slices of bread. Top each with lettuce leaf, tomato slice, chicken strips, and 2 avocado slices. Top with remaining bread slices. Yield: 4 servings (257 calories per serving).

PROTEIN 20.6 / FAT 7.1 / CARBOHYDRATE 30.8 / CHOLESTEROL 41 / IRON 2.1 / SODIUM 715 / CALCIUM 88

TURKEY SANDWICHES

3 tablespoons light process cream cheese product, softened
1 tablespoon skim milk
1 teaspoon coarse-grained mustard
¼ teaspoon dried whole dillweed
¾ cup minced cooked turkey
¼ cup plus 2 tablespoons (1½ ounces) shredded 40% less-fat Cheddar cheese
2 tablespoons chopped ripe olives
2 tablespoons chopped jicama
8 slices pumpernickel bread

Combine first 4 ingredients in a medium bowl, stirring well. Add turkey, cheese, ripe olives, and jicama; stir well.

Spread turkey mixture evenly over 4 slices of bread; top with remaining bread slices. Yield: 4 servings (243 calories per serving).

PROTEIN 16.0 / FAT 6.0 / CARBOHYDRATE 34.3 / CHOLESTEROL 20 / IRON 2.1 / SODIUM 522 / CALCIUM 154

Dillweed and cucumber enhance the sophistication of Gourmet Lobster Sandwich.

GOURMET LOBSTER SANDWICH

2 (6-ounce) lobster tails, fresh or frozen, thawed
1 tablespoon grated cucumber, well drained
3 tablespoons reduced-calorie mayonnaise
½ teaspoon vinegar
⅛ teaspoon onion powder
⅛ teaspoon dried whole dillweed
Dash of crushed red pepper
2 slices sourdough bread
2 red leaf lettuce leaves
4 thin slices tomato

Cook lobster tails in boiling water 6 to 8 minutes or until done. Drain. Rinse with cold water. Split and clean tails. Cut lobster tail meat into 16

(¼-inch-thick) slices. Cover and chill.

Press cucumber between paper towels to remove excess moisture. Combine cucumber, mayonnaise, vinegar, onion powder, dillweed, and crushed red pepper; stir well. Cover and chill at least 1 hour.

Arrange bread on individual serving plates. Spread 2 teaspoons cucumber mixture on each slice of bread. Top each with a lettuce leaf, 2 tomato slices, and 8 slices of lobster. Top with remaining cucumber mixture. Yield: 2 servings (271 calories per serving).

PROTEIN 29.7 / FAT 7.5 / CARBOHYDRATE 20.4 / CHOLESTEROL 99 / IRON 1.8 / SODIUM 814 / CALCIUM 123

HAM SANDWICHES WITH APPLE SLAW

½ cup shredded cabbage
½ cup shredded red cabbage
⅓ cup shredded Granny Smith apple
3 tablespoons commercial reduced-calorie blue cheese dressing
1 teaspoon skim milk
1 teaspoon cider vinegar
¼ teaspoon sugar
¼ teaspoon poppy seeds
8 (1-ounce) slices lean cooked ham
4 slices rye bread

Combine first 8 ingredients in a small bowl; stir well. Cover and chill at least 2 hours. Place 2 slices of ham on each slice of bread. Spoon ⅓ cup slaw mixture over ham on each sandwich. Serve immediately. Yield: 4 servings (141 calories per serving).

PROTEIN 13.5 / FAT 4.0 / CARBOHYDRATE 14.4 / CHOLESTEROL 37 / IRON 0.9 / SODIUM 1144 / CALCIUM 47

SCRAMBLED EGG SANDWICHES

Vegetable cooking spray
1 teaspoon vegetable oil
¼ cup thinly sliced fresh mushrooms
2 tablespoons minced zucchini
1 tablespoon minced sweet red pepper
4 eggs, beaten
2 tablespoons (½ ounce) shredded part-skim mozzarella cheese
2 tablespoons skim milk
¼ teaspoon salt
¼ teaspoon pepper
4 slices oatmeal bread, toasted

Coat a medium nonstick skillet with cooking spray; add oil. Place over medium-high heat until hot. Add mushrooms, zucchini, and red pepper; sauté until tender.

Combine eggs and next 4 ingredients; beat well with a wire whisk. Pour over mushroom mixture in skillet, and cook over medium heat, stirring often, until eggs are firm but still moist. Top each slice of bread with ¼ cup scrambled egg mixture. Serve immediately. Yield: 4 servings (167 calories per serving).

PROTEIN 9.3 / FAT 8.4 / CARBOHYDRATE 13.6 / CHOLESTEROL 211 / IRON 1.9 / SODIUM 358 / CALCIUM 83

CREOLE EGGPLANT SANDWICHES

Vegetable cooking spray
¼ cup chopped onion
¼ cup chopped green pepper
1 (16-ounce) can no-salt-added stewed tomatoes, undrained
½ teaspoon dried whole basil
½ teaspoon dried whole thyme
¼ teaspoon garlic powder
¼ teaspoon crushed red pepper
1 medium eggplant (about 1 pound)
1 egg, lightly beaten
2 tablespoons skim milk
¼ cup all-purpose flour
2 teaspoons vegetable oil
6 (½-inch-thick) slices Italian bread, toasted
2 tablespoons grated Parmesan cheese

Coat a large nonstick skillet with cooking spray; place over medium heat until hot. Add onion and green pepper; sauté until tender. Add tomatoes and next 4 ingredients. Reduce heat, and simmer 15 minutes or until thickened. Set aside and keep warm.

Peel eggplant, and cut crosswise into 6 (¼-inch-thick) slices. (Reserve remaining eggplant for other uses.) Combine egg and milk; stir well. Dip eggplant in egg mixture; dredge in flour.

Coat a large nonstick skillet with cooking spray; add oil. Place over medium heat until hot. Add eggplant, and cook until browned on both sides. Remove from skillet, and drain on paper towels. Place an eggplant slice on each slice of bread. Spoon tomato mixture over eggplant. Sprinkle each sandwich with 1 teaspoon Parmesan cheese. Serve immediately. Yield: 6 servings (194 calories per serving).

PROTEIN 7.2 / FAT 3.5 / CARBOHYDRATE 33.5 / CHOLESTEROL 35 / IRON 2.0 / SODIUM 281 / CALCIUM 77

GRILLED CHEESE WITH PINEAPPLE

2 teaspoons reduced-calorie mayonnaise
Dash of ground nutmeg
4 thin slices whole wheat bread
2 (1-ounce) slices 40% less-fat Cheddar cheese
2 (½-inch-thick) slices fresh pineapple, peeled and cored
Vegetable cooking spray

Combine mayonnaise and nutmeg; blend well. Spread ½ teaspoon mayonnaise mixture on each slice of bread. Place a cheese slice on two slices of bread; top with pineapple and remaining slices of bread.

Transfer sandwiches to a sandwich press or hot griddle that has been coated with cooking spray. Cook until bread is lightly browned and cheese is slightly melted. Yield: 2 servings (204 calories per serving).

PROTEIN 8.4 / FAT 6.9 / CARBOHYDRATE 32.2 / CHOLESTEROL 2 / IRON 1.1 / SODIUM 338 / CALCIUM 228

MIXED GRILLS

½ cup ground cooked turkey breast (skinned before cooking and cooked without salt)
½ cup ground lean cooked ham
2 tablespoons low-sugar orange marmalade
1 tablespoon plus 1½ teaspoons coarse-grained mustard
8 thin slices whole wheat bread
Vegetable cooking spray

Combine turkey, ham, marmalade, and mustard in a small bowl; stir well. Spread meat mixture evenly over 4 slices of bread; top with remaining bread slices.

Transfer sandwiches to a sandwich press or hot griddle that has been coated with cooking spray. Cook until bread is lightly browned. Yield: 4 servings (263 calories per serving).

PROTEIN 22.7 / FAT 6.2 / CARBOHYDRATE 30.4 / CHOLESTEROL 48 / IRON 2.0 / SODIUM 412 / CALCIUM 71

TERIYAKI SLOPPY JOES

1¼ pounds ground chuck
¼ cup chopped green onions
⅓ cup chopped celery
⅓ cup chopped water chestnuts
¼ teaspoon minced fresh gingerroot
1 clove garlic, minced
3 tablespoons low-sodium teriyaki sauce
⅓ cup tomato paste
¼ cup reduced-calorie catsup
2 teaspoons cider vinegar
½ cup water
4 hamburger buns, split and toasted

Combine first 6 ingredients in a large nonstick skillet; cook over medium heat, stirring occasionally, until meat is browned and vegetables are tender. Drain well and pat dry with paper towels. Wipe pan drippings from skillet with a paper towel.

Return meat mixture to skillet; add teriyaki sauce, tomato paste, catsup, and vinegar, stirring well. Reduce heat to low, and simmer 15 minutes, stirring frequently. Add water, stirring well; cook an additional 5 minutes.

Spoon ⅓ cup meat mixture over each bun half. Yield: 8 servings (224 calories per serving).

PROTEIN 16.4 / FAT 10.4 / CARBOHYDRATE 16.2 / CHOLESTEROL 50 / IRON 2.3 / SODIUM 160 / CALCIUM 23

LAMB BURGERS

3 tablespoons plain nonfat yogurt
1 tablespoon reduced-calorie mayonnaise
½ teaspoon prepared mustard
¼ teaspoon paprika
1 pound lean ground lamb
½ teaspoon garlic powder
½ teaspoon dried whole oregano
½ teaspoon low-sodium Worcestershire sauce
¼ teaspoon paprika
¼ teaspoon pepper
Vegetable cooking spray
4 lettuce leaves
4 tomato slices
2 onion rolls, split and toasted

Combine yogurt, mayonnaise, mustard, and paprika in a small bowl; stir well. Cover and chill at least 2 hours.

Combine lamb and next 5 ingredients, stirring well. Shape lamb mixture into 4 (¼-inch-thick) patties. Place patties on rack of a broiler pan that has been coated with cooking spray. Broil 3 inches from heat 3 to 4 minutes on each side or to desired degree of doneness. Drain patties on paper towels.

Place a lettuce leaf, tomato slice, and lamb patty on each bun half. Top each patty with 1 tablespoon yogurt mixture. Serve immediately. Yield: 4 servings (249 calories per serving).

PROTEIN 24.7 / FAT 7.9 / CARBOHYDRATE 18.5 / CHOLESTEROL 76 / IRON 2.4 / SODIUM 193 / CALCIUM 51

BARBECUE PORK SANDWICHES

1 (1-pound) pork tenderloin
Vegetable cooking spray
1 teaspoon vegetable oil
½ cup no-salt-added tomato sauce
¼ cup light beer
2 tablespoons brown sugar
1 tablespoon lemon juice
1 tablespoon low-sodium Worcestershire sauce
¼ teaspoon garlic powder
Dash of hot sauce
2 whole wheat hamburger buns, split
   and toasted

Trim fat from pork. Butterfly pork, and place between 2 sheets of wax paper. Pound to ¼-inch thickness using a meat mallet or rolling pin. Cut into 4 cutlets.

Coat a large nonstick skillet with cooking spray; add oil. Place over medium-high heat until hot. Add cutlets, and cook 3 minutes on each side or until browned. Remove cutlets from skillet. Drain and pat dry with paper towels. Wipe pan drippings from skillet with a paper towel.

Add tomato sauce and next 6 ingredients to skillet; stir well. Bring sauce to a boil; add cutlets. Cover, reduce heat, and simmer 30 minutes, turning cutlets often.

Spread 1½ teaspoons sauce on each bun half; top with cutlets and 2 tablespoons sauce. Yield: 4 servings (250 calories per serving).

PROTEIN 27.9 / FAT 6.9 / CARBOHYDRATE 17.2 / CHOLESTEROL 90 / IRON 1.9 / SODIUM 195 / CALCIUM 25

BLACK BEAN QUESADILLA SANDWICHES

1 (15-ounce) can black beans, rinsed,
   drained, and mashed
1 (4-ounce) can chopped green chiles, drained
2 tablespoons chopped tomato
1 tablespoon chopped fresh cilantro
8 (6-inch) whole wheat tortillas
4 ounces crumbled goat cheese
1 tablespoon plus 1 teaspoon chopped tomato
2 teaspoons chopped fresh cilantro

Combine beans, green chiles, 2 tablespoons tomato, and 1 tablespoon cilantro; stir well. Spread bean mixture evenly onto 4 tortillas. Top each evenly with goat cheese. Top with remaining tortillas. Place sandwiches on an ungreased baking sheet. Bake at 350° for 12 minutes or until cheese softens. Top each sandwich with 1 teaspoon chopped tomato and ½ teaspoon cilantro. To serve, cut into wedges. Yield: 4 servings (268 calories per serving).

PROTEIN 13.2 / FAT 7.5 / CARBOHYDRATE 40.2 / CHOLESTEROL 25 / IRON 2.8 / SODIUM 345 / CALCIUM 175

CHICKEN PICADILLO TACOS

Vegetable cooking spray
½ pound ground chicken
¼ cup chopped onion
¼ cup chopped sweet red pepper
1 clove garlic, minced
⅓ cup peeled, chopped tomato
2 tablespoons canned low-sodium chicken broth,
   undiluted
¼ cup peeled, diced apple
1 tablespoon chopped pickled jalapeño pepper
1½ teaspoons cider vinegar
¼ teaspoon ground cumin
¼ teaspoon ground cinnamon
⅛ teaspoon salt
2 tablespoons raisins
4 taco shells
1 cup shredded iceberg lettuce
½ cup (2 ounces) shredded Monterey Jack cheese

Coat a large nonstick skillet with cooking spray. Place over medium heat until hot. Add chicken, onion, sweet red pepper, and garlic; cook until chicken is browned, stirring frequently. Add tomato and next 7 ingredients. Bring to a boil; reduce heat, and simmer 8 minutes or until thickened. Stir in raisins.

Heat taco shells according to package directions. Spoon ½ cup chicken mixture into each shell. Top each taco with ¼ cup shredded lettuce and 2 tablespoons cheese. Serve immediately. Yield: 4 servings (203 calories per serving).

PROTEIN 18.2 / FAT 8.2 / CARBOHYDRATE 13.8 / CHOLESTEROL 44 / IRON 1.5 / SODIUM 310 / CALCIUM 129

After work or after school, Brontosaurus Bites can be enjoyed by all.

APPLE-PEANUT BUTTER SPREAD

¼ cup part-skim ricotta cheese
3 tablespoons creamy peanut butter
2 tablespoons unsweetened apple juice
½ teaspoon vanilla extract
¼ teaspoon lemon juice
⅛ teaspoon ground cardamom
1 small apple, shredded (about 1 cup)

Combine ricotta cheese, peanut butter, apple juice, vanilla, lemon juice, and cardamom in a small bowl; beat at low speed of an electric mixer until smooth.

Add shredded apple, stirring until thoroughly combined. Serve spread at room temperature with sliced apples, sliced pears, rice cakes, or graham crackers. Yield: 1¼ cups (25 calories per tablespoon).

PROTEIN 1.1 / FAT 1.5 / CARBOHYDRATE 2.0 / CHOLESTEROL 1 / IRON 0.1 / SODIUM 16 / CALCIUM 10

BRONTOSAURUS BITES

4 slices light whole wheat bread
3 tablespoons Neufchâtel cheese spread with strawberries
1 tablespoon wheat germ
1 tablespoon cranberry juice cocktail
36 champagne grapes, halved lengthwise
2 strawberries, cut into small slivers
4 currants (optional)

Cut bread with a 3-inch dinosaur cutter. (Reserve leftover bread for other uses.)

Combine Neufchâtel cheese, wheat germ, and juice; stir well. Spread 1 tablespoon on each bread cutout. Press grape halves and strawberry slivers into cheese mixture. Garnish with currants, if desired. Yield: 4 servings (73 calories per serving).

PROTEIN 2.5 / FAT 3.1 / CARBOHYDRATE 10 / CHOLESTEROL 8 / IRON 0.4 / SODIUM 81 / CALCIUM 19

GRAHAMY BANANAS

½ cup graham cracker crumbs
1 tablespoon brown sugar
2 teaspoons unsweetened cocoa
4 medium bananas, peeled and cut into ½-inch pieces
2 tablespoons unsweetened orange juice

Combine cracker crumbs, sugar, and cocoa; mix well. Dip banana pieces in orange juice; dredge in crumb mixture.

Arrange banana slices in a single layer on a baking sheet. Freeze until firm. Remove from freezer, and let stand at room temperature for 10 minutes to soften slightly. Yield: 4 dozen (13 calories each).

PROTEIN 0.2 / FAT 0.1 / CARBOHYDRATE 2.9 / CHOLESTEROL 0 / IRON 0.1 / SODIUM 7 / CALCIUM 1

STRAWBERRY-BANANA MUFFIN BITES

1 cup whole wheat flour
¾ cup unprocessed oat bran
¼ cup crunchy nutlike cereal nuggets
¼ cup sugar
2 teaspoons baking powder
½ teaspoon ground cinnamon
¼ teaspoon salt
1 (8-ounce) carton strawberry-banana low-fat yogurt
¼ cup reduced-calorie margarine, melted
2 eggs, beaten
½ cup sliced fresh strawberries, slightly mashed
½ cup mashed ripe banana
Vegetable cooking spray

Combine first 7 ingredients in a large bowl; stir well.

Combine yogurt, margarine, and eggs, blending well. Add to dry ingredients, stirring just until moistened. Gently fold in mashed strawberries and banana.

Spoon batter into miniature muffin pans that have been coated with cooking spray, filling three-fourths full. Bake at 400° for 18 minutes or until golden. Remove from pans immediately. Yield: 4 dozen (36 calories each).

PROTEIN 1.2 / FAT 1.1 / CARBOHYDRATE 5.8 / CHOLESTEROL 9 / IRON 0.3 / SODIUM 43 / CALCIUM 19

KIWIFRUIT COLADA POPSICLES

1 cup unsweetened pineapple juice
1 (8-ounce) carton piña colada low-fat yogurt
2 kiwifruit, peeled
1 tablespoon powdered sugar
¼ teaspoon coconut extract
8 (3-ounce) paper cups
8 wooden sticks

Combine first 5 ingredients in container of an electric blender; top with cover, and process until smooth. Pour into paper cups. Cover tops of cups with aluminum foil, and insert a wooden stick through foil into center of each cup. Freeze until firm. To serve, remove foil, and peel paper cup away from popsicle. Yield: 8 servings (58 calories per serving).

PROTEIN 1.4 / FAT 0.4 / CARBOHYDRATE 12.3 / CHOLESTEROL 1 / IRON 0.2 / SODIUM 15 / CALCIUM 48

TORTILLA ROLL-UPS

¼ cup light process cream cheese product
2 tablespoons no-sugar-added apricot spread
1 tablespoon crunchy peanut butter
2 teaspoons skim milk
6 (6-inch) flour tortillas, softened

Combine first 4 ingredients; stir well. Spread 1 tablespoon plus 1½ teaspoons cream cheese mixture evenly over each tortilla. Roll up jellyroll fashion. Wrap each tortilla roll in plastic wrap, and chill at least 2 hours. To serve, slice into 1-inch pieces. Yield: 3 dozen (22 calories each).

PROTEIN 0.6 / FAT 0.8 / CARBOHYDRATE 3.5 / CHOLESTEROL 0 / IRON 0.1 / SODIUM 12 / CALCIUM 6

Top garden-fresh vegetables with the surprising flavor of Spinach-Parmesan Sauce (page 206).

Sauces & Condiments

(Clockwise from top): Amaretto-Almond Sauce, Plum Sauce, and Mississippi Mud Sauce can be served over angel food cake, ice milk, or fresh fruit.

CRANBERRY DESSERT SAUCE

½ cup fresh cranberries
½ cup chopped fresh pineapple
½ cup peeled, sliced banana
1 medium orange, peeled, sectioned, and seeded
2 tablespoons cranberry juice cocktail
¼ teaspoon ground cinnamon
¼ teaspoon brandy flavoring

Combine all ingredients in container of an electric blender or food processor; top with cover, and process until coarsely chopped. Cover and chill at least 3 hours. Serve over ice milk. Yield: 2 cups (8 calories per tablespoon).

PROTEIN 0.1 / FAT 0.0 / CARBOHYDRATE 1.9 / CHOLESTEROL 0 / IRON 0.0 / SODIUM 0 / CALCIUM 3

AMARETTO-ALMOND SAUCE

3 tablespoons sugar
2 teaspoons cornstarch
½ cup water
3 tablespoons amaretto
½ teaspoon lemon juice
2 tablespoons sliced almonds
¼ teaspoon almond extract

Combine sugar and cornstarch in a small saucepan; stir in water. Place over medium heat; bring to a boil, stirring constantly. Cook 2 minutes or until thickened, stirring constantly.

Stir in amaretto and lemon juice; heat just until mixture comes to a boil. Remove from heat; stir in almonds and extract. Serve warm or chilled over ice milk, angel food cake, fresh fruit, or baked apples. Yield: ¾ cup (31 calories per tablespoon).

PROTEIN 0.2 / FAT 0.5 / CARBOHYDRATE 4.8 / CHOLESTEROL 0 / IRON 0.0 / SODIUM 0 / CALCIUM 3

PLUM SAUCE

¼ cup sugar
2 teaspoons cornstarch
½ teaspoon ground cinnamon
½ cup peach nectar
1 cup sliced fresh plums
½ teaspoon almond extract

Combine sugar, cornstarch, and cinnamon in a medium saucepan; stir well. Add peach nectar; stir until smooth. Stir in plums. Bring to a boil over medium heat, stirring constantly. Reduce heat; simmer 1 minute, stirring constantly. Remove from heat; stir in almond extract. Serve warm or chilled over pancakes or ice milk. Yield: 1⅓ cups (18 calories per tablespoon).

PROTEIN 0.0 / FAT 0.0 / CARBOHYDRATE 4.5 / CHOLESTEROL 0 / IRON 0.0 / SODIUM 0 / CALCIUM 0

MISSISSIPPI MUD SAUCE

⅓ cup miniature marshmallows
1 tablespoon plus 2 teaspoons unsweetened cocoa
1 tablespoon cornstarch
1 cup skim milk
1 tablespoon light corn syrup
1 teaspoon vanilla extract
¼ teaspoon ground cinnamon
¼ cup miniature marshmallows
1 tablespoon chopped pecans

Combine ⅓ cup marshmallows, cocoa, and cornstarch in a small saucepan. Gradually stir in milk and corn syrup. Cook over medium heat, stirring constantly, until thickened. Remove from heat; stir in vanilla and cinnamon. Let cool. Stir in ¼ cup marshmallows and pecans. Serve over ice milk, angel food cake, or fresh fruit. Yield: 1 cup (23 calories per tablespoon).

PROTEIN 0.8 / FAT 0.4 / CARBOHYDRATE 3.9 / CHOLESTEROL 0 / IRON 0.2 / SODIUM 10 / CALCIUM 21

VANILLA CREAM SAUCE

3 tablespoons sugar
2 tablespoons plus ½ teaspoon cornstarch
2¼ cups skim milk
1½ teaspoons vanilla extract

Combine first 3 ingredients in a medium saucepan, stirring well. Cook over medium heat, stirring constantly, until mixture comes to a boil; cook an additional 2 minutes. Remove from heat. Stir in vanilla. Cover and chill. Serve over fresh or baked fruit, baked puddings, or custards. Yield: 2 cups (13 calories per tablespoon).

PROTEIN 0.6 / FAT 0.0 / CARBOHYDRATE 2.5 / CHOLESTEROL 0 / IRON 0.0 / SODIUM 9 / CALCIUM 21

CITRUS MARINADE

1 teaspoon grated orange rind
½ cup unsweetened orange juice
⅓ cup unsweetened grapefruit juice
1 teaspoon grated lime rind
2 tablespoons lime juice
2 tablespoons vegetable oil
2 tablespoons honey
1 tablespoon white wine vinegar
1 teaspoon white wine Worcestershire sauce
½ teaspoon Dijon mustard
¼ teaspoon ground red pepper

Combine first 5 ingredients in a 1-quart jar, stirring well. Gradually add oil; mix well.

Add honey, vinegar, Worcestershire sauce, mustard, and red pepper. Cover jar tightly, and shake vigorously.

Use to marinate chicken before cooking. Remove chicken from marinade, and bring marinade to a boil in a saucepan. Remove from heat, and use for basting while cooking. Yield: 1½ cups (20 calories per tablespoon).

PROTEIN 1.7 / FAT 1.2 / CARBOHYDRATE 2.5 / CHOLESTEROL 0 / IRON 0.1 / SODIUM 6 / CALCIUM 1

CABERNET SAUCE

Vegetable cooking spray
1 tablespoon margarine
¾ cup sliced fresh mushrooms
1 tablespoon minced shallots
2 tablespoons all-purpose flour
1 cup water
3 tablespoons Burgundy or other dry red wine
1 tablespoon minced fresh parsley
1 teaspoon beef-flavored bouillon granules
1 teaspoon low-sodium Worcestershire sauce

Coat a nonstick skillet with cooking spray; add margarine. Place over medium heat until margarine melts. Add mushrooms and shallots; sauté, stirring constantly, until mushrooms are tender. Add flour, and cook 1 minute, stirring constantly. Add water and remaining ingredients; cook until mixture thickens, stirring constantly. Serve with beef. Yield: 1½ cups (10 calories per tablespoon).

PROTEIN 0.1 / FAT 0.6 / CARBOHYDRATE 0.8 / CHOLESTEROL 0 / IRON 0.1 / SODIUM 46 / CALCIUM 1

ZESTY PEPPERCORN SAUCE

½ cup plain nonfat yogurt
½ cup low-fat sour cream
1 tablespoon whole green peppercorns, crushed
2 teaspoons coarse-grained mustard
½ teaspoon ground white pepper

Combine yogurt, sour cream, and remaining ingredients in a small bowl; stir well. Cover and chill. Serve as a meat or sandwich spread. Yield: 1 cup (16 calories per tablespoon).

PROTEIN 0.7 / FAT 1.0 / CARBOHYDRATE 1.2 / CHOLESTEROL 3 / IRON 0.1 / SODIUM 27 / CALCIUM 24

SPINACH-PARMESAN SAUCE

½ pound fresh spinach
½ cup plus 2 tablespoons nonfat buttermilk
¼ cup grated Parmesan cheese
1 tablespoon minced fresh thyme
¼ teaspoon dry mustard

Remove stems from spinach; wash leaves. Place in a large Dutch oven. Cover and cook over medium heat, stirring frequently, until spinach wilts. Drain.

Combine spinach and remaining ingredients in container of an electric blender or food processor; top with cover, and process until smooth. Serve over cooked fresh vegetables. Yield: 1¾ cups (7 calories per tablespoon).

PROTEIN 0.7 / FAT 0.3 / CARBOHYDRATE 0.6 / CHOLESTEROL 1 / IRON 0.3 / SODIUM 25 / CALCIUM 19

GARLIC-TOMATO MAYONNAISE

½ cup reduced-calorie mayonnaise
3 tablespoons no-salt-added tomato sauce
2 cloves garlic, minced
¼ cup plus 2 tablespoons seeded and finely chopped tomato
1 tablespoon chopped fresh parsley

Combine mayonnaise, tomato sauce, and garlic; blend well. Cover and refrigerate at least 3 hours. Stir in tomato and parsley. Serve chilled as a sandwich spread, or warm over vegetables. Yield: 1 cup (23 calories per tablespoon).

PROTEIN 0.2 / FAT 2.0 / CARBOHYDRATE 1.1 / CHOLESTEROL 2 / IRON 0.0 / SODIUM 57 / CALCIUM 1

Fresh herbs add flavor to Chunky Tomato Vinaigrette, which can be served over pasta for a tasty Italian dish.

CREAMY TOMATILLO SAUCE

½ pound fresh tomatillos
¼ cup chopped onion
¼ cup water
1 clove garlic, crushed
¼ teaspoon chicken-flavored bouillon granules
2 tablespoons canned chopped green chiles, drained
2 tablespoons low-fat sour cream

Remove and discard husks from tomatillos; cut tomatillos into quarters, and place in a small saucepan. Add onion and next 3 ingredients. Bring to a boil. Cover, reduce heat, and simmer 7 minutes or until tomatillos are tender.

Pour tomatillo mixture into container of an electric blender or food processor; top with cover, and process until smooth. Press puree through a sieve to remove seeds. Stir in green chiles and sour cream. Serve warm with steaks, hamburgers, or grilled chicken. Yield: 1 cup (7 calories per tablespoon).

PROTEIN 0.3 / FAT 0.3 / CARBOHYDRATE 1.1 / CHOLESTEROL 1 / IRON 0.1 / SODIUM 14 / CALCIUM 4

CHUNKY TOMATO VINAIGRETTE

3 tablespoons red wine vinegar
2 tablespoons balsamic vinegar
2 tablespoons olive oil
½ teaspoon sugar
1¼ pounds tomatoes, peeled, seeded, and chopped (about 1½ cups)
¼ cup minced green onions
1 tablespoon finely chopped fresh basil
1 teaspoon minced fresh thyme
¼ teaspoon dried whole oregano
¼ teaspoon dried whole marjoram
⅛ teaspoon freshly ground pepper

Combine vinegars, olive oil, and sugar in a small bowl; stir with a wire whisk until well blended. Set aside.

Place chopped tomatoes, onions, and remaining ingredients in a large bowl. Gently stir in vinegar mixture. Let stand 1 hour before serving. Serve vinaigrette over hot or cold cooked pasta. Yield: 2 cups (11 calories per tablespoon).

PROTEIN 0.1 / FAT 0.9 / CARBOHYDRATE 0.7 / CHOLESTEROL 0 / IRON 0.1 / SODIUM 1 / CALCIUM 2

CAPONATA SAUCE

Vegetable cooking spray
4 cups diced eggplant (1 medium)
2 cups peeled, seeded, and chopped tomato
1 cup diced celery
1 cup chopped onion
½ cup diced sweet red pepper
½ cup diced green pepper
2 tablespoons cider vinegar
2 cloves garlic, crushed
2 teaspoons dried whole basil
2 teaspoons dried whole tarragon
1 teaspoon olive oil

Coat a Dutch oven with cooking spray; place over medium heat until hot. Add eggplant, tomato, celery, onion, and peppers. Sauté 5 minutes or until vegetables are tender.

Stir in vinegar, garlic, basil, tarragon, and olive oil; cook an additional 10 minutes. Cool. Cover and refrigerate at least 2 hours. Serve as a dip with unsalted tortilla chips or as a sauce with grilled pork or poultry. Yield: 4 cups (6 calories per tablespoon).

PROTEIN 0.2 / FAT 0.1 / CARBOHYDRATE 1.1 / CHOLESTEROL 0 / IRON 0.1 / SODIUM 2 / CALCIUM 6

SEASONED NUT TOPPING

½ cup whole natural almonds
1 slice cracked whole wheat bread
3 sprigs fresh parsley
½ teaspoon dry mustard
¼ teaspoon ground white pepper
⅛ teaspoon garlic powder
Dash of onion powder

Combine all ingredients in container of an electric blender or food processor; top with cover, and process until almonds are coarsely chopped. Sprinkle over cooked fresh vegetables. Yield: 1 cup (30 calories per tablespoon).

PROTEIN 1.0 / FAT 2.6 / CARBOHYDRATE 1.2 / CHOLESTEROL 0 / IRON 0.2 / SODIUM 39 / CALCIUM 12

SPICY PORK SEASONING BLEND

3 tablespoons dried grated orange rind
1 teaspoon onion powder
¾ teaspoon ground cumin
½ teaspoon garlic powder
½ teaspoon ground red pepper
¼ teaspoon ground ginger

Combine all ingredients in a small bowl; stir well. To use, sprinkle over pork and refrigerate 30 minutes before cooking. Yield: ¼ cup (6 calories per tablespoon).

PROTEIN 0.3 / FAT 0.1 / CARBOHYDRATE 2.4 / CHOLESTEROL 0 / IRON 0.3 / SODIUM 1 / CALCIUM 15

CRANBERRY-DATE SPREAD

2 cups fresh cranberries
1 (8-ounce) package pitted whole dates
1 tablespoon grated orange rind

Combine all ingredients in a medium saucepan. Cook over medium heat 8 to 10 minutes or until fruit is tender, stirring frequently.

Position knife blade in food processor bowl; add fruit mixture. Top with cover, and process until smooth. Spoon into hot sterilized jars, leaving ¼-inch headspace. Cover at once with metal lids, and screw on bands. Let stand at room temperature 2 hours; store in refrigerator. Serve with toast or muffins. Yield: 2 cups (22 calories per tablespoon).

PROTEIN 0.2 / FAT 0.0 / CARBOHYDRATE 6.0 / CHOLESTEROL 0 / IRON 0.1 / SODIUM 0 / CALCIUM 3

For a winning combination, spread Raspberry-Mango Freezer Spread on whole wheat toast.

RASPBERRY-MANGO FREEZER SPREAD

2 cups fresh raspberries
1 cup diced ripe mango
1 (1¾-ounce) package powdered pectin
¼ cup sugar
1 tablespoon lime juice

Combine all ingredients in a medium saucepan; bring to a boil. Boil 1 minute, stirring constantly. Remove from heat; stir 3 minutes. Spoon into freezer containers or hot sterilized jars, leaving ¼-inch headspace. Cover at once with metal lids, and screw on bands. Let stand at room temperature 24 hours; freeze. Thaw to serve. Yield: 2 cups (18 calories per tablespoon).

PROTEIN 0.1 / FAT 0.1 / CARBOHYDRATE 4.6 / CHOLESTEROL 0 / IRON 0.1 / SODIUM 0 / CALCIUM 2

FRESH PINEAPPLE SALSA

2 cups diced tomato
1¾ cups diced pineapple
1 cup peeled and diced cucumber
¼ cup diced green onion
1 jalapeño pepper, seeded and minced
3 tablespoons minced fresh cilantro
2 tablespoons red wine vinegar
1 teaspoon vegetable oil

Combine tomato, pineapple, cucumber, onion, jalapeño pepper, and cilantro in a large bowl; toss well. Stir in vinegar and oil. Let stand at room temperature 1 hour. Serve with unsalted chips or roast pork. Yield: 5 cups (4 calories per tablespoon).

PROTEIN 0.1 / FAT 0.1 / CARBOHYDRATE 0.8 / CHOLESTEROL 0 / IRON 0.1 / SODIUM 1 / CALCIUM 1

JALAPEÑO CRANBERRY RELISH

2 cups fresh cranberries
1 small apple, peeled, cored, and quartered
1 jalapeño pepper, seeded and halved
3 tablespoons sugar
1 tablespoon unsweetened apple juice
¼ teaspoon ground nutmeg
⅛ teaspoon chili powder

Position knife blade in food processor bowl;

add cranberries, apple, and pepper. Top with cover, and process until finely chopped. Transfer mixture to a nonaluminum container, and stir in remaining ingredients. Cover and chill thoroughly. Serve with chicken or pork. Yield: 1¾ cups (12 calories per tablespoon).

PROTEIN 0.1 / FAT 0.0 / CARBOHYDRATE 3.1 / CHOLESTEROL 0 / IRON 0.0 / SODIUM 0 / CALCIUM 1

HARVEST REFRIGERATOR RELISH

5 cups shredded cabbage
1½ cups chopped sweet red pepper
1½ cups chopped green pepper
1 cup thinly sliced onion
¼ cup chopped celery
2 cups cider vinegar
½ cup honey
¼ cup hot prepared mustard
2 tablespoons cracked pepper

Combine first 5 ingredients in a large bowl; mix well. Combine vinegar and honey in a small

saucepan. Place over medium heat, and cook just until mixture simmers. Remove from heat. Add vinegar mixture, mustard, and pepper to vegetable mixture; mix well. Let stand 20 minutes to cool.

Spoon into hot sterilized jars, leaving ¼-inch headspace. Cover at once with metal lids, and screw on bands. Refrigerate 3 days before serving. Serve with beef or pork. Yield: 8 half pints (7 calories per tablespoon).

PROTEIN 0.1 / FAT 0.1 / CARBOHYDRATE 1.8 / CHOLESTEROL 0 / IRON 0.1 / SODIUM 6 / CALCIUM 3

Steamed fresh broccoli gets a colorful lift in Broccoli with Parmesan Sauce (page 212).

ARTICHOKE HEART MÉLANGE

2 (9-ounce) packages frozen artichoke hearts
4 cloves garlic, minced
2 teaspoons olive oil
2 teaspoons minced fresh oregano
1 teaspoon minced fresh basil
12 cherry tomatoes, halved
12 small ripe olives

Combine artichoke hearts and garlic in a medium saucepan. Cook artichoke hearts according to package directions, omitting salt and fat. Drain, reserving ¼ cup liquid.

Combine oil, oregano, and basil in a small bowl; stir into reserved liquid. Add herb mixture to artichoke mixture, stirring well. Add tomatoes and olives; stir gently. Cook until thoroughly heated. Yield: 8 servings (48 calories per ½-cup serving).

PROTEIN 2.2 / FAT 1.9 / CARBOHYDRATE 7.4 / CHOLESTEROL 0 / IRON 0.7 / SODIUM 64 / CALCIUM 23

ASPARAGUS AU GRATIN

1 pound fresh asparagus spears
Vegetable cooking spray
1 teaspoon margarine
¼ cup soft whole wheat breadcrumbs
¼ teaspoon dry mustard
⅛ teaspoon salt
⅛ teaspoon ground red pepper
2 teaspoons chopped fresh parsley

Snap off tough ends of asparagus. Remove scales from stalks with a knife or vegetable peeler, if desired. Cook asparagus, covered, in a small amount of boiling water 6 to 8 minutes or until crisp-tender. Drain. Transfer to a 10- x 6- x 2-inch baking dish; set aside and keep warm.

Coat a small nonstick skillet with cooking spray; add margarine. Place over medium-high heat until hot. Add breadcrumbs; cook 2 minutes, stirring constantly, until lightly browned. Add mustard, salt, and red pepper; stir well. Spoon over asparagus. Bake, uncovered, at 400° for 5 minutes or until thoroughly heated. Sprinkle with parsley. Yield: 4 servings (38 calories per serving).

PROTEIN 2.6 / FAT 1.5 / CARBOHYDRATE 5.0 / CHOLESTEROL 0 / IRON 0.7 / SODIUM 98 / CALCIUM 26

BROCCOLI WITH PARMESAN SAUCE

1½ pounds fresh broccoli
1 cup water
Vegetable cooking spray
¼ cup chopped sweet red pepper
¼ cup chopped onion
1 tablespoon margarine
2 teaspoons all-purpose flour
¾ cup skim milk
2 ounces light process cream cheese product
¼ cup grated Parmesan cheese
¼ teaspoon garlic powder

Trim off large leaves of broccoli. Remove tough ends of lower stalks, and wash broccoli thoroughly. Cut into spears. Place broccoli in a Dutch oven; add water. Bring to a boil; cover, reduce heat, and simmer 10 to 15 minutes or until crisp-tender. Drain; arrange broccoli on a serving platter, and keep warm.

Coat a large nonstick skillet with cooking spray; place over medium heat until hot. Add red pepper and onion; cook, stirring constantly, until tender. Remove from skillet, and set aside.

Melt margarine in skillet; stir in flour. Gradually add skim milk. Cook, stirring constantly, until slightly thickened. Add reserved red pepper and onion, cream cheese, Parmesan cheese, and garlic powder; cook over low heat, stirring constantly, until smooth and thoroughly heated. Spoon over broccoli. Serve immediately. Yield: 6 servings (94 calories per serving).

PROTEIN 6.1 / FAT 5.0 / CARBOHYDRATE 8.1 / CHOLESTEROL 3 / IRON 0.9 / SODIUM 175 / CALCIUM 138

BRUSSELS SPROUTS WITH PECANS

1 pound fresh brussels sprouts
1½ cups water
Vegetable cooking spray
1 teaspoon margarine
1 teaspoon vegetable oil
¼ pound fresh mushrooms, sliced
¼ cup coarsely chopped pecans
¼ teaspoon salt
⅛ teaspoon pepper
¼ cup soft whole wheat breadcrumbs
2 tablespoons grated Parmesan cheese

Wash brussels sprouts thoroughly, and remove discolored leaves. Cut off stem ends, and slash bottom of each sprout with a shallow X.

Place brussels sprouts and water in a medium saucepan; bring to a boil. Cover, reduce heat, and simmer 8 to 10 minutes or until crisp-tender. Drain and set aside.

Coat a large nonstick skillet with cooking spray; add margarine and oil. Place over medium-high heat until hot. Add mushrooms and pecans; cook, stirring constantly, until mushrooms are tender. Stir in brussels sprouts. Transfer mixture to an 11- x 7- x 2-inch baking dish.

Combine salt, pepper, breadcrumbs, and Parmesan cheese, stirring well; sprinkle breadcrumb mixture over brussels sprouts. Broil 4 inches from heat 2 to 3 minutes or until breadcrumbs are golden. Yield: 6 servings (81 calories per ½-cup serving).

PROTEIN 3.6 / FAT 5.4 / CARBOHYDRATE 6.4 / CHOLESTEROL 1 / IRON 0.8 / SODIUM 165 / CALCIUM 62

BUTTERNUT PUREE

1 (2-pound) butternut squash, peeled
3 tablespoons unsweetened orange juice
2 tablespoons brown sugar
2 tablespoons reduced-calorie maple syrup
½ teaspoon ground cinnamon
½ teaspoon vanilla extract
¼ teaspoon salt
¼ teaspoon ground nutmeg
Grated orange rind (optional)

Cut squash into 1½-inch pieces. Place squash in a vegetable steamer over boiling water. Cover and steam 15 to 20 minutes or until squash is tender. Cool slightly.

Position knife blade in food processor bowl; add squash and next 7 ingredients. Top with cover, and process until smooth. Transfer squash mixture to a large saucepan; cook over low heat, stirring constantly, until thoroughly heated. Sprinkle with grated orange rind, if desired. Serve warm. Yield: 6 servings (70 calories per ½-cup serving).

PROTEIN 1.1 / FAT 0.2 / CARBOHYDRATE 18.0 / CHOLESTEROL 0 / IRON 1.0 / SODIUM 104 / CALCIUM 49

CAULIFLOWER WITH PEAS AND MUSHROOMS

½ ounce dried shiitake mushrooms
1 small cauliflower, broken into flowerets
Vegetable cooking spray
2 teaspoons reduced-calorie margarine
1 teaspoon vegetable oil
1 clove garlic, minced
½ cup frozen English peas
1 tablespoon lemon juice
¼ teaspoon salt
⅛ teaspoon pepper

Pour boiling water over mushrooms to cover; let stand 30 minutes or until softened. Drain well; pat dry between paper towels. Remove and discard stems. Cut mushrooms into 1-inch pieces. Cover and set aside.

Arrange cauliflower in a vegetable steamer over boiling water. Cover and steam 5 minutes or until crisp-tender.

Coat a large nonstick skillet with cooking spray. Add margarine and oil; place over medium-high heat until hot. Add garlic, and sauté 2 minutes. Add cauliflower, and cook 2 minutes, stirring occasionally. Stir in reserved mushrooms, peas, and remaining ingredients. Cook 5 minutes or until thoroughly heated. Yield: 6 servings (49 calories per ½-cup serving).

PROTEIN 2.1 / FAT 1.8 / CARBOHYDRATE 6.8 / CHOLESTEROL 0 / IRON 0.6 / SODIUM 133 / CALCIUM 23

ROASTED CORN ON THE COB

4 ears fresh corn
¼ cup mild green chile salsa
2 tablespoons Neufchâtel cheese, softened

Lightly dampen corn husks with water; wrap each ear in aluminum foil. Grill over medium-hot coals 15 to 20 minutes, turning occasionally.

Combine salsa and cheese in a small bowl, stirring well. Remove husks and silk from corn; evenly spread each ear with salsa mixture. Serve immediately. Yield: 4 servings (87 calories per serving).

PROTEIN 2.6 / FAT 2.4 / CARBOHYDRATE 15.3 / CHOLESTEROL 5 / IRON 0.4 / SODIUM 131 / CALCIUM 7

Basil, oregano, and garlic add flavor to Grilled Eggplant with Marinara Sauce.

GRILLED EGGPLANT WITH MARINARA SAUCE

½ cup no-salt-added tomato sauce
2 tablespoons chopped fresh mushrooms
1 tablespoon chopped green pepper
1 teaspoon lemon juice
¾ teaspoon minced onion
¼ teaspoon dried whole oregano
¼ teaspoon dried whole basil
Dash of garlic powder
Dash of ground red pepper
1 medium eggplant (about 1 pound)
2 tablespoons vegetable oil
Fresh basil (optional)

Combine first 9 ingredients in a small saucepan; simmer, uncovered, 20 minutes, stirring occasionally. Set aside and keep warm.

Cut eggplant into twelve ½-inch-thick slices. Brush slices with oil on both sides. Grill slices over medium coals 2 minutes on each side or until crisp-tender. Transfer to a serving platter; top with sauce. Garnish with fresh basil, if desired. Yield: 6 servings (67 calories per serving).

PROTEIN 1.1 / FAT 4.6 / CARBOHYDRATE 6.5 / CHOLESTEROL 0 / IRON 0.5 / SODIUM 7 / CALCIUM 28

SANTA FE HOMINY

1 (15½-ounce) can golden hominy, undrained
2 tablespoons chopped onion
2 tablespoons canned chopped green chiles
1 clove garlic, minced
1 teaspoon chopped fresh oregano
¾ teaspoon chili powder
Chopped fresh cilantro (optional)

Combine first 6 ingredients in a medium saucepan; bring to a boil over medium heat. Reduce heat, and simmer 5 minutes. Serve with a slotted spoon. Garnish with cilantro, if desired. Yield: 4 servings (79 calories per ½-cup serving).

PROTEIN 1.5 / FAT 0.5 / CARBOHYDRATE 16.7 / CHOLESTEROL 0 / IRON 0.7 / SODIUM 12 / CALCIUM 5

LEEKS IN ORANGE SAUCE

4 medium leeks
½ cup water
3 tablespoons unsweetened orange juice
2 tablespoons low-sugar orange marmalade
2 teaspoons honey
1 teaspoon margarine
Orange slices (optional)

Remove root, tough outer leaves, and tops from leeks, leaving 2 inches of dark leaves. Wash leeks; split in half lengthwise to within 1 inch of bulb end.

Place water in a large nonstick skillet; bring to a boil. Add leeks; cover, reduce heat, and simmer 8 minutes or until crisp-tender. Drain well.

Add orange juice and next 3 ingredients to leeks in skillet. Bring to a boil. Cover, reduce heat, and simmer 8 minutes or until leeks are glazed and thoroughly heated. Garnish with orange slices, if desired. Yield: 4 servings (119 calories per serving).

PROTEIN 2.1 / FAT 1.4 / CARBOHYDRATE 26.2 / CHOLESTEROL 0 / IRON 2.9 / SODIUM 38 / CALCIUM 81

BARBECUED LIMA BEANS

1 (10-ounce) package frozen baby lima beans
½ cup frozen whole kernel corn
Vegetable cooking spray
1 tablespoon diced onion
2 teaspoons diced green pepper
¼ cup no-salt-added tomato sauce
3 tablespoons vinegar
1 tablespoon brown sugar
1 tablespoon diced pimiento
1 tablespoon low-sodium Worcestershire sauce
2 teaspoons prepared mustard
½ teaspoon chili powder

Combine lima beans and corn in a medium saucepan. Cook according to package directions, omitting salt. Drain and set aside.

Coat a medium nonstick skillet with cooking spray. Place over medium heat until hot. Add onion and green pepper; sauté until tender. Stir in tomato sauce and next 6 ingredients; reduce heat, and simmer 5 minutes. Stir in lima beans and corn. Bring to a boil. Cover, reduce heat, and simmer 5 minutes. Yield: 4 servings (124 calories per ½-cup serving).

PROTEIN 6.2 / FAT 0.6 / CARBOHYDRATE 24.9 / CHOLESTEROL 0 / IRON 2.3 / SODIUM 161 / CALCIUM 34

TEXAN-STYLE MUSHROOMS

Vegetable cooking spray
2 teaspoons commercial picante sauce
1 teaspoon vegetable oil
1 clove garlic, minced
1 pound small fresh mushrooms, sliced
2 teaspoons chopped fresh cilantro
¼ teaspoon onion powder
Fresh cilantro sprigs (optional)

Coat a large nonstick skillet with cooking spray; add picante sauce and oil. Place over medium heat until hot. Add garlic, and sauté 1 minute. Add mushrooms, cilantro, and onion powder; sauté 3 to 5 minutes. Garnish with fresh cilantro, if desired. Serve immediately. Yield: 4 servings (42 calories per ½-cup serving).

PROTEIN 2.4 / FAT 1.7 / CARBOHYDRATE 5.8 / CHOLESTEROL 0 / IRON 1.5 / SODIUM 23 / CALCIUM 9

HORSERADISH PARSNIPS

1¼ pounds parsnips, scraped and diagonally sliced
¼ cup low-fat sour cream
2 tablespoons skim milk
1 tablespoon prepared horseradish
¼ teaspoon ground white pepper
1 tablespoon chopped fresh parsley

Cook parsnips, covered, in a small amount of boiling water 10 minutes or until tender. Drain and set aside.

Combine sour cream, milk, horseradish, and pepper in a small bowl; stir into parsnips. Cook just until thoroughly heated. Transfer to a serving dish. Sprinkle with parsley. Yield: 6 servings (79 calories per ½-cup serving).

PROTEIN 1.5 / FAT 1.5 / CARBOHYDRATE 15.9 / CHOLESTEROL 4 / IRON 0.6 / SODIUM 18 / CALCIUM 49

SUGARED ONIONS

1½ pounds boiling onions, peeled
3 tablespoons brown sugar
3 tablespoons reduced-calorie margarine
¼ cup water
¼ teaspoon salt
1 teaspoon ground cinnamon

Arrange onions in a vegetable steamer over boiling water. Cover and steam 15 minutes or until crisp-tender; set aside.

Combine brown sugar, margarine, water, and salt in a medium-size heavy skillet; cook over low heat until margarine melts, stirring constantly. Add onions; cover and cook over low heat 20 minutes, stirring occasionally. Stir in cinnamon. Yield: 4 servings (124 calories per ½-cup serving).

PROTEIN 1.3 / FAT 5.5 / CARBOHYDRATE 20.1 / CHOLESTEROL 0 / IRON 0.9 / SODIUM 244 / CALCIUM 66

EASY BAKED POTATO HALVES

2 medium-size baking potatoes
2 tablespoons commercial reduced-calorie buttermilk dressing
1 tablespoon reduced-calorie margarine, melted
¼ teaspoon pepper

Slice potatoes in half lengthwise. Combine remaining ingredients. Spread mixture evenly over potatoes. Place potatoes in a 10- x 6- x 2-inch baking dish. Cover and bake at 400° for 30 to 45 minutes or until done. Yield: 4 servings (110 calories per serving).

PROTEIN 2.2 / FAT 4.1 / CARBOHYDRATE 19.0 / CHOLESTEROL 0 / IRON 1.3 / SODIUM 35 / CALCIUM 14

ORIENTAL PEAS

1 (10-ounce) package frozen English peas
¼ cup sliced green onions
1 (8-ounce) can sliced water chestnuts, drained
2 teaspoons reduced-sodium soy sauce
2 teaspoons dry sherry
½ teaspoon sugar
½ teaspoon chicken-flavored bouillon granules

Combine peas and onions; cook according to package directions, omitting salt and fat. Drain, reserving 2 tablespoons cooking liquid. Add cooking liquid, water chestnuts, and remaining ingredients to peas; stir well. Bring to a boil. Reduce heat, and simmer 3 minutes or until thoroughly heated. Yield: 4 servings (99 calories per ½-cup serving).

PROTEIN 4.5 / FAT 0.4 / CARBOHYDRATE 19.4 / CHOLESTEROL 0 / IRON 1.5 / SODIUM 287 / CALCIUM 24

MUSTARD-GLAZED TOMATOES

4 medium tomatoes, halved crosswise
Vegetable cooking spray
3 tablespoons coarse-grained mustard
1 tablespoon brown sugar
1 tablespoon minced fresh parsley

Arrange tomatoes on rack of a broiler pan that has been coated with cooking spray. Combine mustard and sugar; stir well. Spread 1½ teaspoons mustard mixture over the cut side of each tomato. Broil 6 inches from heat 6 minutes or until browned and bubbly. Sprinkle with parsley. Yield: 8 servings (33 calories per serving).

PROTEIN 1.0 / FAT 0.7 / CARBOHYDRATE 6.4 / CHOLESTEROL 0 / IRON 0.6 / SODIUM 177 / CALCIUM 10

THE SKIN OF A POTATO?

Not only is the skin a source of fiber, but also many of the nutrients of the potato—vitamin C and iron, for example—concentrate next to the skin. The only time to be concerned about the skin is when a potato is old. As potatoes age, they develop higher than normal concentrations of a natural toxin called solanine. Large doses of this toxin can cause nausea, vomiting, and diarrhea.

Avoid potatoes that have sprouted "eyes;" have a spongy, soft texture; or have a green-tinted skin. Green skin is perhaps the strongest indicator of high solanine levels. Even though it would probably take a steady diet of green skins, say four or five skins a day, to make most people sick, play it safe. Make it a point to avoid and discard old potatoes. When shopping, search for unblemished potatoes with no green coloring. Then, store potatoes in a cool, dry place to slow aging.

Orange juice and soy sauce give an Oriental flair to Sweet Potato-Broccoli Stir-Fry.

SWEET POTATO-BROCCOLI STIR-FRY

2 medium-size sweet potatoes
Vegetable cooking spray
1 tablespoon sesame oil
1 clove garlic, minced
1 cup sliced broccoli stems (¼-inch thick)
½ cup sliced green onions, cut into 1-inch pieces
¼ cup sliced sweet red pepper
1 tablespoon reduced-sodium soy sauce
1½ teaspoons unsweetened orange juice
⅛ teaspoon ground red pepper

Peel sweet potatoes; slice into ¼-inch-thick slices. Coat a wok or large nonstick skillet with cooking spray. Add oil; place over medium-high heat until hot. Add sweet potatoes and garlic; stir-fry 4 minutes. Add broccoli, green onions, and red pepper slices; stir-fry 3 minutes or until vegetables are crisp-tender.

Combine soy sauce, orange juice, and ground red pepper. Add to vegetables, and stir until thoroughly heated. Yield: 8 servings (102 calories per ½-cup serving).

PROTEIN 1.9 / FAT 2.1 / CARBOHYDRATE 19.7 / CHOLESTEROL 0 / IRON 0.8 / SODIUM 89 / CALCIUM 28

POACHED APPLE SLICES

3 medium cooking apples, peeled, cored, and
    sliced (about 1½ pounds)
1 tablespoon lemon juice
¾ cup water
¼ cup sugar
6 whole cloves
1 (3-inch) stick cinnamon

Place apple slices in a large bowl; add lemon
juice, tossing well. Set aside.

Combine water, sugar, cloves, and cinnamon
stick in a large nonstick skillet; bring to a boil.
Reduce heat, and simmer, uncovered, until mixture is reduced to ⅓ cup. Remove and discard
spices. Add apple slices. Cover and simmer 10
minutes or until apples are tender, stirring occasionally. Serve with a slotted spoon. Yield: 6 servings (76 calories per ½-cup serving).

PROTEIN 0.1 / FAT 0.2 / CARBOHYDRATE 19.7 / CHOLESTEROL 0 /
IRON 0.1 / SODIUM 0 / CALCIUM 3

BROILED BRANDIED APRICOTS

1 (16-ounce) can unsweetened apricot halves,
    undrained
¼ cup brandy
1 (3-inch) stick cinnamon
Vegetable cooking spray
2 tablespoons plus 1 teaspoon no-sugar-added
    apricot spread
½ teaspoon brandy
Nutmeg (optional)

Drain apricots, reserving ½ cup juice. Combine juice, ¼ cup brandy, and cinnamon stick in
a small saucepan; bring to a boil. Reduce heat,
and simmer, uncovered, 10 minutes. Remove
and discard cinnamon stick. Pour mixture over
apricots; cover and chill.

Drain apricots, and arrange in an 8-inch
square baking dish that has been coated with
cooking spray. Combine apricot spread and ½
teaspoon brandy. Fill each apricot half with ½
teaspoon mixture. Sprinkle with nutmeg, if desired, and broil 6 inches from heat 5 minutes or
until lightly browned and bubbly. Serve warm.
Yield: 4 servings (71 calories per serving).

PROTEIN 1.0 / FAT 0.4 / CARBOHYDRATE 16.7 / CHOLESTEROL 0 /
IRON 0.5 / SODIUM 11 / CALCIUM 13

SAUTÉED BANANAS AND PINEAPPLE

1 tablespoon reduced-calorie margarine
1 tablespoon crème de bananes
2 medium bananas, peeled and sliced
½ cup pineapple chunks
1 tablespoon brown sugar

Melt margarine in a nonstick skillet over medium heat; add crème de bananes. Stir in bananas and pineapple; sprinkle sugar over fruit.
Cook until thoroughly heated. Yield: 4 servings
(123 calories per ½-cup serving).

PROTEIN 0.8 / FAT 2.2 / CARBOHYDRATE 27.4 / CHOLESTEROL 0 /
IRON 0.4 / SODIUM 30 / CALCIUM 10

THE BEST TIME TO EXERCISE

While the health benefits of a sunrise jog or
a late-night aerobics class are clearly the
same, exercising in the evening may offer calorie-
burning advantages. In the after-dinner hours, metabolism becomes sluggish. The body shifts into low
gear, using less fuel to function. Late-night exercise
can rev up this low metabolic rate. But be sure to
wait at least an hour after eating before jumping
into motion. This gives the body adequate time to
digest the food. And if you begin having problems
getting to sleep, change to a daytime routine.

STIR-FRIED COMPOTE

Vegetable cooking spray
2 teaspoons margarine
2 tablespoons unsweetened pineapple juice
1 tablespoon honey
¼ teaspoon ground cinnamon
6 kumquats, sliced and seeded
¾ cup halved red seedless grapes
½ cup chopped fresh pineapple
½ cup peeled and sliced banana

Coat a large nonstick skillet or wok with cooking spray. Add margarine; place over medium
heat until margarine melts. Stir in juice, honey,
and cinnamon. Add kumquats; stir-fry 1 minute.
Add grapes and pineapple; stir-fry 1 minute. Stir
in banana, and cook until thoroughly heated.
Yield: 4 servings (96 calories per ½-cup serving).

PROTEIN 0.7 / FAT 2.4 / CARBOHYDRATE 20.0 / CHOLESTEROL 0 /
IRON 0.4 / SODIUM 25 / CALCIUM 16

Serve Pepper-Stuffed Nectarines garnished with cilantro as a surprising new side dish.

PEPPER-STUFFED NECTARINES

2 tablespoons minced sweet red pepper
2 tablespoons minced sweet yellow pepper
1 tablespoon plus 1 teaspoon chopped fresh cilantro
1 tablespoon minced purple onion
2 teaspoons white wine vinegar
1 teaspoon vegetable oil
½ teaspoon chili powder, divided
2¼ teaspoons sugar, divided
1 cup water
¼ cup white wine vinegar
4 medium-size fresh nectarines, peeled, halved, and pitted
Fresh cilantro sprigs (optional)

Combine first 6 ingredients, ¼ teaspoon chili powder, and ¼ teaspoon sugar in a small bowl; stir well. Let mixture stand at room temperature for 2 hours.

Combine remaining ¼ teaspoon chili powder, water, vinegar, and remaining 2 teaspoons sugar in a small skillet; bring to a boil. Add nectarine halves; spoon liquid over fruit. Cover, reduce heat, and simmer 5 minutes or until nectarines are tender. Drain.

To serve, spoon 2 teaspoons pepper mixture into each nectarine half. Garnish with cilantro sprigs, if desired. Yield: 4 servings (57 calories per serving).

PROTEIN 0.7 / FAT 1.6 / CARBOHYDRATE 10.8 / CHOLESTEROL 0 / IRON 0.4 / SODIUM 6 / CALCIUM 7

TANGY PEACH MOUSSE

¼ cup vinegar
¼ cup water
1 tablespoon unflavored gelatin
1 (16-ounce) can unsweetened peach slices, undrained
1 teaspoon dry mustard
¼ teaspoon ground ginger
¼ teaspoon almond extract
¼ cup low-fat sour cream
½ cup peach low-fat yogurt
Vegetable cooking spray

Combine vinegar and water in a small saucepan. Sprinkle gelatin over vinegar mixture; let stand 1 minute. Cook over low heat, stirring constantly, until gelatin dissolves; set aside.

Place peaches and next 3 ingredients in container of an electric blender or food processor; top with cover, and process until smooth. Combine peach mixture and gelatin mixture in a medium bowl; stir well. Chill to consistency of unbeaten egg white. Fold in sour cream and yogurt.

Spoon into individual ½-cup molds that have been coated with cooking spray. Chill until firm. Unmold and place on individual serving plates. Yield: 6 servings (75 calories per ½-cup serving).

PROTEIN 2.9 / FAT 1.7 / CARBOHYDRATE 13.3 / CHOLESTEROL 5 /
IRON 0.2 / SODIUM 19 / CALCIUM 42

MUSTARD-GLAZED PINEAPPLE STICKS

1 medium-size fresh pineapple
Vegetable cooking spray
2 teaspoons margarine
2 tablespoons unsweetened pineapple juice
1 tablespoon spicy brown mustard
2 teaspoons light corn syrup

Peel and trim eyes from pineapple; remove core. Cut lengthwise into 12 sticks; set aside.

Coat a nonstick skillet with cooking spray; add margarine. Place over medium-low heat until margarine melts. Add juice, mustard, and syrup; stir well. Add pineapple sticks; cook, stirring frequently, 5 minutes or until thoroughly heated. Yield: 4 servings (121 calories per serving).

PROTEIN 0.7 / FAT 3.1 / CARBOHYDRATE 24.9 / CHOLESTEROL 0 /
IRON 0.7 / SODIUM 140 / CALCIUM 14

SAUCY RHUBARB

1½ pounds fresh rhubarb, trimmed and cut into 1-inch pieces
½ cup water
2 tablespoons sugar
1½ teaspoons cornstarch
⅔ cup cranberry juice cocktail
½ cup no-sugar-added strawberry spread
¼ teaspoon grated orange rind
⅛ teaspoon ground cloves
⅛ teaspoon ground mace

Combine rhubarb and water in a medium saucepan; bring to a boil. Reduce heat, cover, and simmer 10 minutes or until very tender. Drain and set aside.

Combine sugar and cornstarch in a medium saucepan. Stir in cranberry juice and strawberry spread. Cook over medium heat, stirring constantly, until smooth and thickened. Add cooked rhubarb, orange rind, cloves, and mace. Cook until thoroughly heated. Yield: 8 servings (55 calories per ½-cup serving).

PROTEIN 0.6 / FAT 0.2 / CARBOHYDRATE 13.3 / CHOLESTEROL 0 /
IRON 0.2 / SODIUM 4 / CALCIUM 68

Fresh fruits blend to form an attractive garnish in each serving of chilled Berry-Peach Soup (page 222).

Soups & Stews

MINTY CANTALOUPE SOUP

1 (3-pound) cantaloupe, peeled, seeded, and cut
  into chunks
¾ cup unsweetened orange juice
3 tablespoons lime juice
¼ teaspoon peppermint extract
1 cup skim milk
Fresh mint sprigs (optional)

Combine first 4 ingredients in container of an
electric blender or food processor; top with
cover, and process until smooth. Transfer mixture to a bowl. Stir in milk. Cover and chill at
least 2 hours. Stir soup before serving. Ladle
soup into individual bowls, and garnish with
fresh mint sprigs, if desired. Yield: 6 cups (86
calories per 1-cup serving).

PROTEIN 3.0 / FAT 0.5 / CARBOHYDRATE 19.0 / CHOLESTEROL 1 /
IRON 0.4 / SODIUM 36 / CALCIUM 71

CHILLED CHERRY BORSCH

3 cups water
2 tablespoons brown sugar
2 teaspoons beef-flavored bouillon granules
1 teaspoon mixed pickling spices
1 (3-inch) stick cinnamon
1 (15-ounce) can sliced beets, undrained
1 pound fresh or frozen sweet cherries, thawed and
  drained
1 tablespoon vinegar
¼ cup plus 1 tablespoon cherry low-fat yogurt

Combine first 5 ingredients in a large saucepan. Bring mixture to a boil. Cover, reduce heat,
and simmer 15 minutes. Strain mixture through
a sieve, and discard spices. Return mixture to
saucepan. Stir in beets and cherries, and bring to
a boil. Cover, reduce heat, and simmer 15 minutes or until cherries are tender.

Transfer mixture in batches into container of
an electric blender or food processor; top with
cover, and process until very smooth. Repeat
with remaining mixture. Pour into a bowl; stir in
vinegar. Cover and chill thoroughly.

Ladle soup into individual bowls. Top each
serving with 1 tablespoon yogurt. Yield: 5 cups
(87 calories per 1-cup serving).

PROTEIN 1.5 / FAT 1.4 / CARBOHYDRATE 18.8 / CHOLESTEROL 1 /
IRON 0.5 / SODIUM 387 / CALCIUM 37

BERRY-PEACH SOUP

1 cup fresh raspberries
3 cups fresh or frozen sliced peaches, thawed
3 tablespoons lemon juice
1 cup peach nectar
1 (8-ounce) carton plain nonfat yogurt
1 teaspoon almond extract

Place raspberries in container of an electric
blender or food processor. Top with cover, and
process until smooth. Press berry mixture
through a sieve; discard seeds. Cover and chill.

Place peaches and lemon juice in container
of an electric blender; top with cover, and process until smooth. Pour into a large bowl. Stir in
nectar, yogurt, and extract. Cover and chill.

Spoon peach mixture into individual soup
bowls. Drizzle 1 tablespoon raspberry sauce in a
circle on top of each serving. Draw a wooden
pick through sauce, spoke-fashion, at regular intervals to create a webbed effect. Yield: 4 cups
(141 calories per 1-cup serving).

PROTEIN 4.6 / FAT 0.5 / CARBOHYDRATE 31.8 / CHOLESTEROL 1 /
IRON 0.5 / SODIUM 48 / CALCIUM 130

SUMMER STRAWBERRY-RHUBARB SOUP

1¼ cups peeled, diced fresh rhubarb
1¾ cups plus 2 tablespoons water, divided
1 cup unsweetened orange juice
¼ cup sugar
1 teaspoon grated orange rind
1 (3-inch) stick cinnamon
1 tablespoon cornstarch
2 tablespoons grenadine
1½ cups sliced fresh strawberries

Combine rhubarb, 1¾ cups water, and next 4
ingredients in a saucepan. Bring to a boil; reduce heat, and simmer, uncovered, 20 minutes
or until tender. Discard cinnamon stick.

Combine cornstarch and remaining 2 tablespoons water, stirring until smooth. Add cornstarch mixture to rhubarb mixture. Cook, stirring
constantly, until thickened. Remove from heat;
stir in grenadine and strawberries. Pour fruit mixture into a serving bowl. Cover and chill. Yield: 4
cups (115 calories per 1-cup serving).

PROTEIN 1.2 / FAT 0.3 / CARBOHYDRATE 28.5 / CHOLESTEROL 0 /
IRON 0.4 / SODIUM 4 / CALCIUM 54

Oriental Beef-Noodle Soup has a wonderful flavor and takes just minutes to make. Served with breadsticks, crackers, or warm bread, it's a good choice to serve for lunch or dinner.

ORIENTAL BEEF-NOODLE SOUP

½ pound lean boneless top round steak
4½ cups water
1 tablespoon cornstarch
2 teaspoons beef-flavored bouillon granules
Vegetable cooking spray
2 teaspoons peanut oil
½ cup thinly sliced celery
¼ cup sliced green onions
1 teaspoon minced fresh gingerroot
2 cups sliced fresh mushrooms
1 (8-ounce) can sliced water chestnuts, drained
½ teaspoon cracked pepper
2 cups hot cooked fine egg noodles (cooked without salt or fat)
1½ cups fresh snow pea pods, trimmed and cut diagonally into 1-inch pieces
2 teaspoons sesame oil

Partially freeze steak; trim fat from steak. Slice steak diagonally across grain into ⅛-inch strips. Set aside.

Combine water, cornstarch, and bouillon granules in a medium bowl; stir until smooth, and set aside.

Coat a wok or large nonstick skillet with cooking spray; add peanut oil. Place over medium-high heat until hot. Add celery, onions, and gingerroot; stir-fry 3 minutes or until vegetables are crisp-tender. Remove from wok. Add steak; stir-fry 3 minutes or until browned. Add cornstarch mixture, mushrooms, water chestnuts, and pepper, stirring well. Cover and cook over medium heat 10 minutes. Stir in noodles, snow peas, and sesame oil; cook an additional 5 minutes or until thoroughly heated. Yield: 7 cups (181 calories per 1-cup serving).

PROTEIN 10.7 / FAT 5.1 / CARBOHYDRATE 22.4 / CHOLESTEROL 33 / IRON 2.0 / SODIUM 302 / CALCIUM 24

EASY BEEF MINESTRONE

½ pound fresh green beans
Vegetable cooking spray
¾ pound ground chuck
½ cup minced onion
2 cloves garlic, minced
4 cups water
2 (14½-ounce) cans no-salt-added stewed
  tomatoes, undrained
1 teaspoon beef-flavored bouillon granules
¼ teaspoon salt
2 cups shredded cabbage
1 (19-ounce) can cannellini beans, drained
1½ cups diced zucchini
4 ounces vermicelli, uncooked and broken into
  2-inch pieces
½ cup grated Parmesan cheese
¼ cup minced fresh basil

Wash green beans; remove strings. Cut into
1-inch pieces. Set aside. Coat a Dutch oven with
cooking spray; place over medium heat until
hot. Add ground chuck, onion, and garlic; cook
until meat is browned, stirring to crumble. Drain
and pat dry with paper towels. Wipe drippings
from Dutch oven with a paper towel.

Return meat to Dutch oven; add green beans,
water, tomatoes, granules, and salt. Bring to a
boil; cover, reduce heat, and simmer 15 minutes. Add cabbage and next 3 ingredients. Return to a boil; cover and cook 15 minutes or
until tender. Sprinkle each serving with 2 teaspoons cheese and 1 teaspoon basil. Yield: 12
cups (166 calories per 1-cup serving).

PROTEIN 11.4 / FAT 4.9 / CARBOHYDRATE 19.7 / CHOLESTEROL 20 /
IRON 2.3 / SODIUM 216 / CALCIUM 100

CHICKEN-ESCAROLE SOUP

Vegetable cooking spray
½ cup chopped onion
3 cloves garlic, minced
2 quarts water
2 teaspoons chicken-flavored bouillon granules
4 (6-ounce) skinned chicken breast halves
1 head escarole, cut into ½-inch slices
½ (8-ounce) package spaghetti, uncooked and
  broken into 2-inch pieces
3 tablespoons plus 1 teaspoon grated Parmesan
  cheese

Coat a Dutch oven with cooking spray; place
over medium-high heat until hot. Add onion
and garlic, and sauté until tender. Add water,
bouillon granules, and chicken. Bring to a boil.
Cover, reduce heat, and simmer 30 minutes or
until chicken is done. Remove chicken from
broth, and set broth aside. Remove bone from
chicken, and cut meat into ½-inch pieces. Set
meat aside.

Add escarole to broth; bring to a boil. Cover,
reduce heat, and simmer 10 minutes. Add spaghetti, and simmer 10 minutes. Stir in chicken,
and cook until thoroughly heated. Ladle soup
into individual bowls. Sprinkle 1 teaspoon
cheese over each serving. Yield: 10 cups (124
calories per 1-cup serving).

PROTEIN 15.5 / FAT 1.8 / CARBOHYDRATE 11.1 / CHOLESTEROL 33 /
IRON 1.1 / SODIUM 322 / CALCIUM 58

SPINACH-WONTON SOUP

½ (10-ounce) package frozen chopped spinach,
  thawed and well drained
½ cup part-skim ricotta cheese
2 tablespoons minced fresh basil
½ teaspoon ground white pepper
2½ dozen fresh or frozen wonton skins, thawed
6 cups canned no-salt-added chicken broth,
  undiluted
2 cups peeled, chopped tomatoes
1 (8-ounce) can no-salt-added whole kernel corn,
  drained
¼ teaspoon salt

Combine first 4 ingredients in container of an
electric blender; top with cover, and process
until smooth. Place 1 teaspoon filling in center
of each wonton. Fold top corner of wonton over
filling. Fold left and right corners over filling.
Lightly brush remaining corner with water.
Tightly roll filled end toward exposed corner in
jellyroll fashion. Moisten edges with water to
seal. Cover and set aside.

Bring chicken broth to a boil in a large Dutch
oven. Add wontons, tomatoes, corn, and salt.
Return to a boil. Cover, reduce heat, and simmer 3 minutes or until wontons are tende
Yield: 9 cups (91 calories per 1-cup serving).

PROTEIN 5.2 / FAT 3.2 / CARBOHYDRATE 9.8 / CHOLESTEROL 29
IRON 0.9 / SODIUM 244 / CALCIUM 68

TARRAGON POTATO SOUP

Vegetable cooking spray
3 cups thinly sliced leeks
2 cups thinly sliced fresh mushrooms
4 cups peeled, diced potatoes
4¼ cups water
1 cup sliced celery
1 tablespoon chicken-flavored bouillon granules
1 tablespoon minced fresh tarragon
1 tablespoon lemon juice
2 teaspoons low-sodium Worcestershire sauce
½ teaspoon ground white pepper
3 tablespoons minced fresh chives

Coat a Dutch oven with cooking spray; place over medium-high heat until hot. Add leeks and mushrooms; sauté 5 minutes or until tender. Add potatoes and next 3 ingredients. Bring to a boil. Cover, reduce heat, and simmer 30 to 35 minutes or until potatoes are tender.

Place 1 cup vegetable mixture in container of an electric blender; top with cover, and process until smooth. Add vegetable puree to remaining vegetable mixture. Stir in tarragon, lemon juice, Worcestershire sauce, and pepper. Cook until thoroughly heated. Ladle soup into individual bowls, and sprinkle evenly with chives. Yield: 8 cups (91 calories per 1-cup serving).

PROTEIN 2.7 / FAT 0.7 / CARBOHYDRATE 19.8 / CHOLESTEROL 0 / IRON 1.6 / SODIUM 336 / CALCIUM 32

MEXICAN LENTIL SOUP

Vegetable cooking spray
2¼ cups chopped onion
¾ cup chopped parsnips
½ cup chopped carrot
½ cup chopped celery
4 cups Spicy Vegetable Broth (recipe below)
2 cups water
½ pound dried lentils
1 teaspoon ground cumin
1 teaspoon chili powder
1 (14½-ounce) can no-salt-added whole tomatoes, undrained and chopped
1 jalapeño pepper, seeded and chopped
¼ teaspoon hot sauce

Coat a large Dutch oven with cooking spray; place over medium-high heat until hot. Add chopped onion, and sauté 5 minutes or until tender.

Add parsnips and next 7 ingredients, stirring well. Bring vegetable mixture to a boil; cover, reduce heat, and simmer 30 minutes. Stir in tomatoes, chopped jalapeño pepper, and hot sauce; simmer an additional 45 minutes or until lentils are tender. To serve, ladle soup into individual bowls. Yield: 8 cups (141 calories per 1-cup serving).

PROTEIN 9.4 / FAT 0.7 / CARBOHYDRATE 26.0 / CHOLESTEROL 0 / IRON 3.8 / SODIUM 27 / CALCIUM 59

SPICY VEGETABLE BROTH

Vegetable cooking spray
3 cups peeled, diced turnips
1 cup diced carrot
1 cup diced onion
1 cup diced celery
1 cup diced sweet red pepper
6 cups water
2 cups spicy hot vegetable juice cocktail
¼ cup minced fresh parsley
2 teaspoons dried Italian seasoning
5 peppercorns
1 jalapeño pepper, seeded and diced
½ teaspoon ground red pepper

Coat a Dutch oven with cooking spray; place over medium-high heat until hot. Add turnips, carrot, onion, celery, and sweet red pepper; sauté 15 minutes.

Stir in water and remaining ingredients. Bring to a boil. Cover, reduce heat, and simmer 2 hours. Strain broth through a double layer of cheesecloth; reserve vegetables for other uses. Cover and chill broth. Store in refrigerator or freezer. Use as a base for vegetable soups. Yield: 6 cups (24 calories per 1-cup serving).

PROTEIN 0.7 / FAT 0.2 / CARBOHYDRATE 4.8 / CHOLESTEROL 0 / IRON 1.1 / SODIUM 2 / CALCIUM 19

FRESH VEGETABLE SOUP

½ pound fresh green beans
1 (46-ounce) can no-salt-added tomato juice
2½ cups peeled, chopped tomatoes
2 cups finely shredded cabbage
1½ cups sliced fresh okra
2 cups peeled, cubed potatoes
1 cup sliced carrots
½ cup chopped onion
½ cup uncooked pearl barley
2 teaspoons minced fresh oregano
1½ teaspoons hot sauce
½ teaspoon salt
½ teaspoon pepper
½ cup fresh corn kernels (about 1 ear fresh corn)

Wash beans, and remove strings. Cut beans into 1-inch pieces.

Combine beans, tomato juice, and next 11 ingredients in a large Dutch oven. Bring to a boil. Cover, reduce heat, and simmer 45 minutes. Stir in corn kernels; cover and cook an additional 15 minutes or until vegetables are tender, stirring occasionally. To serve, ladle soup into individual bowls. Yield: 12 cups (105 calories per 1-cup serving).

PROTEIN 3.9 / FAT 0.4 / CARBOHYDRATE 24.0 / CHOLESTEROL 0 / IRON 1.0 / SODIUM 126 / CALCIUM 37

VEGETABLE-WILD RICE SOUP

Vegetable cooking spray
1 cup thinly sliced carrots
1 cup diced zucchini
1 cup diced yellow squash
½ cup chopped onion
¼ cup chopped celery
3 cups no-salt-added vegetable juice cocktail
1 cup water
½ cup Chablis or other dry white wine
¾ teaspoon cracked pepper
¼ teaspoon salt
1 cup cooked wild rice (cooked without salt or fat)
1 cup broccoli flowerets

Coat a large Dutch oven with cooking spray; place over medium-high heat until hot. Add carrots, zucchini, yellow squash, onion, and celery,

and sauté until tender.

Stir in vegetable juice cocktail, 1 cup water, white wine, cracked pepper, and salt; bring to a boil. Cover, reduce heat, and simmer 30 minutes. Stir in cooked wild rice and broccoli flowerets. Cover and cook an additional 15 minutes or until broccoli is crisp-tender. Yield: 6 cups (81 calories per 1-cup serving).

PROTEIN 3.5 / FAT 0.8 / CARBOHYDRATE 16.3 / CHOLESTEROL 1 / IRON 1.7 / SODIUM 144 / CALCIUM 46

CREAM OF ASPARAGUS SOUP

1 pound fresh asparagus spears
2 cups water
¼ cup sliced green onions
3 tablespoons chopped fresh chives
1 teaspoon chicken-flavored bouillon granules
¼ teaspoon salt
¼ teaspoon dried whole dillweed
1 tablespoon reduced-calorie margarine
1 tablespoon all-purpose flour
1 teaspoon dry mustard
1 cup skim milk

Snap off tough ends of asparagus. Remove scales from stalks with a knife or vegetable peeler, if desired. Cut asparagus into 2-inch pieces.

Place asparagus pieces in a medium saucepan. Add water and next 5 ingredients; bring to a boil. Cover, reduce heat, and simmer 12 to 15 minutes or until vegetables are tender. Place vegetable mixture in container of an electric blender; top with cover, and process until smooth. Set aside.

Melt margarine in a large saucepan over medium-low heat. Combine flour and dry mustard; add to margarine, stirring with a wire whisk until mixture is smooth. Cook 1 minute, stirring constantly. Gradually add milk; cook over medium heat, stirring constantly, until mixture is thickened and bubbly.

Stir in reserved vegetable mixture; cook over medium heat until hot. To serve, ladle soup into individual bowls. Serve immediately. Yield: 4 cups (68 calories per 1-cup serving).

PROTEIN 5.1 / FAT 2.5 / CARBOHYDRATE 8.1 / CHOLESTEROL 1 / IRON 0.8 / SODIUM 413 / CALCIUM 101

ROASTED RED PEPPER SOUP

6 large sweet red peppers
2 medium leeks
Vegetable cooking spray
1 tablespoon all-purpose flour
½ teaspoon ground cumin
¼ teaspoon ground red pepper
1 cup evaporated skimmed milk
1 cup water
1 teaspoon chicken-flavored bouillon granules

Cut peppers in half lengthwise; remove and discard seeds and membrane. Place peppers, skin side up, on a baking sheet; flatten with palm of hand. Broil 4 inches from heat 15 to 20 minutes or until charred. Place in ice water, and chill 5 minutes. Remove peppers from water; peel and discard skins. Cut peppers into 1-inch pieces; set aside.

Remove and discard root, tough outer leaves, and tops from leeks to where dark green begins to pale. Cut leeks crosswise into ⅛-inch slices. Coat a nonstick skillet with cooking spray. Place over medium-high heat until hot. Add leeks; sauté 3 minutes or until tender. Combine flour, cumin, and ground red pepper; sprinkle over leeks, stirring well.

Combine pepper pieces and leek mixture in container of an electric blender or food processor; top with cover, and process until smooth. Transfer pureed mixture to a large saucepan; add milk, water, and bouillon granules, stirring well. Cook over medium heat, stirring frequently, until hot (do not boil). Serve immediately. Yield: 4 cups (114 calories per 1-cup serving).

PROTEIN 6.8 / FAT 1.3 / CARBOHYDRATE 20.5 / CHOLESTEROL 3 / IRON 2.7 / SODIUM 289 / CALCIUM 213

CLAM AND SHRIMP CHOWDER

Vegetable cooking spray
1 cup chopped onion
¾ cup chopped celery
¾ cup chopped green pepper
1 clove garlic, minced
7 cups water, divided
1 (14½-ounce) can no-salt-added whole tomatoes, undrained and chopped
2 cups no-salt-added tomato juice
1 tablespoon chicken-flavored bouillon granules
½ cup uncooked long-grain rice
½ teaspoon dried whole thyme
¼ teaspoon crushed red pepper
1 (6½-ounce) can minced clams, undrained
1 tablespoon cornstarch
¾ pound unpeeled medium-size fresh shrimp
2 tablespoons vermouth

Coat a Dutch oven with cooking spray; place over medium-high heat until hot. Add onion, celery, green pepper, and garlic; sauté until tender. Add 4 cups water, tomatoes, tomato juice, and bouillon granules. Bring to a boil. Stir in rice, thyme, and red pepper. Cover, reduce heat, and simmer 30 minutes or until rice is tender.

Drain clams, reserving liquid. Combine cornstarch and liquid in a small bowl; set aside.

Bring remaining 3 cups water to a boil; add shrimp, and cook 3 to 5 minutes. Drain well; rinse with cold water. Peel and devein shrimp. Add clams, shrimp, vermouth, and cornstarch mixture to tomato mixture. Stir well. Cook until thoroughly heated and slightly thickened. Yield: 10 cups (106 calories per 1-cup serving).

PROTEIN 8.6 / FAT 1.1 / CARBOHYDRATE 15.8 / CHOLESTEROL 45 / IRON 2.1 / SODIUM 409 / CALCIUM 50

A VITAMIN FOR YOUR EYES

Vitamin A, one of the first vitamins to be discovered, has numerous functions. Crucial to eye health, this vitamin keeps the tissues of the eye healthy.

But new research from the University of Illinois points to another reason why vitamin A is good for the eyes. Vitamin A may help stop the formation of free radicals, substances that can damage the eye.

In fact, people who regularly eat vitamin A-rich fruits and vegetables—carrots, broccoli, and spinach, for example—appear 60 percent less likely to develop a serious eye problem called macular degeneration. Macular degeneration is one of the most common causes of blindness in later years—one for which no treatment is available. That's all the more reason to stock up on vitamin A-rich vegetables.

HEARTY MUSHROOM CHOWDER

Vegetable cooking spray
½ cup cracked wheat
4½ cups Spicy Vegetable Broth (page 225)
1 teaspoon beef-flavored bouillon granules
¾ cup chopped onion
1 clove garlic, minced
2½ cups thinly sliced fresh mushrooms
1 cup shredded carrots
1 (14½-ounce) can no-salt-added stewed tomatoes,
   undrained
2 cups chopped fresh spinach
2 tablespoons Marsala wine

Coat a Dutch oven with cooking spray; place over medium-high heat until hot. Add cracked wheat; cook until lightly browned, stirring constantly. Add broth; bring to a boil. Stir in bouillon granules. Cover, reduce heat, and simmer 50 minutes or until cracked wheat is tender.

Coat a large nonstick skillet with cooking spray; place over medium-high heat until hot. Add onion and garlic, and sauté 2 minutes. Add mushrooms and shredded carrot; sauté 5 minutes or until tender. Stir mushroom mixture, tomatoes, spinach, and wine into cracked wheat mixture. Simmer 10 minutes or until chowder is thoroughly heated. Yield: 8 cups (85 calories per 1-cup serving).

PROTEIN 3.0 / FAT 0.7 / CARBOHYDRATE 17.8 / CHOLESTEROL 0 / IRON 2.0 / SODIUM 141 / CALCIUM 46

EASY OVEN STEW

1½ pounds lean boneless round steak (½-inch thick)
¼ cup all-purpose flour
½ teaspoon cracked black pepper
Vegetable cooking spray
1 (12-ounce) can flat light beer
¾ cup water
2 tablespoons prepared mustard
2 teaspoons beef-flavored bouillon granules
1 teaspoon sugar
3 cups peeled, diced potatoes
2 cups thinly sliced mushrooms
2 medium carrots, scraped and cut into 1-inch
   julienne strips
½ cup frozen pearl onions

Trim fat from steak, and cut into 1-inch cubes. Combine flour and pepper in a large zip-top plastic bag; add steak, and shake until meat is well coated. Place steak in a 3-quart casserole that has been coated with cooking spray.

Combine beer, water, mustard, bouillon granules, and sugar; pour over steak. Bake, covered, at 350° for 1 hour.

Add potatoes, mushrooms, carrots, and onions to steak mixture, stirring well. Bake, covered, an additional 55 minutes or until meat and vegetables are tender. Yield: 8 cups (200 calories per 1-cup serving).

PROTEIN 19.6 / FAT 4.5 / CARBOHYDRATE 19.8 / CHOLESTEROL 45 / IRON 2.7 / SODIUM 342 / CALCIUM 22

BEEF AND SQUASH STEW

1½ pounds lean boneless round steak (½-inch thick)
Vegetable cooking spray
½ cup chopped onion
1 (14½-ounce) can no-salt-added whole tomatoes,
   undrained and chopped
1 cup unsweetened apple juice
½ cup water
½ teaspoon dried whole thyme
½ teaspoon ground nutmeg
¼ teaspoon ground white pepper
2 cups peeled, cubed sweet potatoes
2 medium carrots, scraped and cut into ½-inch slices
2 cups cubed yellow squash
1 cup cubed zucchini

Trim fat from steak, and cut into 1-inch cubes. Set aside.

Coat a Dutch oven with cooking spray; place over medium-high heat until hot. Add onion, and sauté 2 minutes or until tender. Reduce heat to medium; add steak, and cook until browned, stirring often. Add tomatoes and next 5 ingredients; bring to a boil. Cover, reduce heat, and simmer 1 hour. Add sweet potatoes and carrots. Cover and cook 25 minutes. Add yellow squash and zucchini; cover and cook an additional 20 minutes or until vegetables are tender. Yield: 8 cups (195 calories per 1-cup serving).

PROTEIN 20.1 / FAT 4.5 / CARBOHYDRATE 18.2 / CHOLESTEROL 48 / IRON 2.7 / SODIUM 65 / CALCIUM 46

Hearty Acorn Squash-Beef Stew is filling enough to be a meal by itself.

ACORN SQUASH-BEEF STEW

1½ pounds lean boneless round steak (½-inch thick)
Vegetable cooking spray
2½ cups water
1 medium onion, sliced
2 stalks celery, cut into ½-inch slices
2 tablespoons dry sherry
2 teaspoons beef-flavored bouillon granules
½ teaspoon ground coriander
½ teaspoon ground cumin
½ teaspoon ground ginger
¼ teaspoon ground red pepper
2 cups cubed acorn squash (about 1 medium)
1 (15½-ounce) can red kidney beans, drained
2 tablespoons chopped fresh parsley

Trim fat from steak; cut into 1-inch pieces.

Coat a Dutch oven with cooking spray; place over medium-high heat until hot. Add steak; cook until browned on all sides, stirring frequently. Drain and pat dry with paper towels. Wipe pan drippings from Dutch oven with a paper towel. Return meat to Dutch oven; add water and next 8 ingredients. Bring to a boil; cover, reduce heat, and simmer 1½ hours. Add squash and beans; cook, covered, an additional 10 minutes or until meat and squash are tender. Ladle stew into individual bowls, and sprinkle 1 teaspoon parsley over each serving. Yield: 6 cups (250 calories per 1-cup serving).

PROTEIN 31.3 / FAT 6.1 / CARBOHYDRATE 16.8 / CHOLESTEROL 71 / IRON 4.3 / SODIUM 383 / CALCIUM 48

CURRIED CHICKEN STEW

1 (20-ounce) can unsweetened pineapple tidbits, undrained
4 (4-ounce) skinned, boned chicken breast halves, cut into 1-inch pieces
½ teaspoon cracked pepper
Vegetable cooking spray
½ cup chopped onion
½ cup chopped sweet red pepper
2 teaspoons curry powder
½ cup unsweetened apple juice
4 cups water
¼ teaspoon salt
1 Granny Smith apple, peeled, cored, and diced
2 tablespoons all-purpose flour
2 tablespoons water
¾ teaspoon coconut extract
4 cups hot cooked long-grain rice (cooked without salt or fat)
¼ cup raisins

Drain pineapple, reserving juice. Set pineapple aside.

Sprinkle chicken with cracked pepper. Coat a large nonstick skillet with cooking spray; place over medium-high heat until hot. Add chicken, and sauté until browned, stirring frequently. Drain well on paper towels. Wipe pan drippings from skillet with a paper towel.

Add onion, red pepper, and curry powder to skillet; sauté 5 minutes or until tender. Return chicken to skillet. Add reserved pineapple juice, apple juice, 4 cups water, and salt; bring to a boil. Cover, reduce heat, and simmer 45 minutes. Stir in reserved pineapple and apple.

Combine flour and 2 tablespoons water; stir until smooth. Stir into chicken mixture in skillet. Cook over medium heat until thickened and bubbly. Stir in extract.

Place ½ cup rice in each of 8 individual bowls. Ladle stew evenly over rice, and sprinkle each serving with 1½ teaspoons raisins. Yield: 8 servings (290 calories per serving).

PROTEIN 16.6 / FAT 1.2 / CARBOHYDRATE 52.7 / CHOLESTEROL 33 / IRON 2.3 / SODIUM 114 / CALCIUM 38

HEARTY TURKEY STEW

Vegetable cooking spray
1 (1-pound) package fresh raw ground turkey
½ cup chopped onion
1 (16-ounce) can red kidney beans, undrained
1 (14½-ounce) can no-salt-added whole tomatoes, undrained and chopped
1 (8-ounce) can no-salt-added tomato sauce
1 cup elbow macaroni, uncooked
¾ cup water
1 teaspoon chili powder
½ teaspoon garlic powder
½ teaspoon ground cumin
¼ teaspoon pepper
¼ cup plus 2 tablespoons (2½ ounces) shredded 40% less-fat Cheddar cheese

Coat a Dutch oven with cooking spray; place over medium-high heat until hot. Add ground turkey and onion; cook until meat is browned, stirring to crumble. Drain meat mixture in a colander; pat dry with paper towels. Wipe pan drippings from Dutch oven with a paper towel.

Return meat mixture to Dutch oven. Add kidney beans and next 8 ingredients, stirring well. Bring to a boil; cover, reduce heat, and simmer 30 minutes, stirring occasionally. Ladle stew into individual bowls; sprinkle each serving with 1 tablespoon cheese. Serve immediately. Yield: 6 cups (300 calories per 1-cup serving).

PROTEIN 26.5 / FAT 5.2 / CARBOHYDRATE 37.4 / CHOLESTEROL 43 / IRON 3.1 / SODIUM 387 / CALCIUM 150

Save the best for last: Serve Fresh Strawberry Trifle (page 233) for an elegant finale to a delicious meal.

TROPICAL FRUIT COMPOTE

1 medium mango, peeled, seeded, and sliced
1 kiwifruit, peeled and sliced
2 tablespoons lime juice
⅛ teaspoon almond extract
1 cup fresh raspberries
2 tablespoons chopped pistachios, toasted

Combine mango and kiwifruit in a medium bowl. Combine lime juice and almond extract; pour over fruit, and toss gently. Cover and chill at least 2 hours.

Gently fold in raspberries. Spoon fruit mixture into individual dessert bowls. Sprinkle each serving with 1 teaspoon pistachios. Yield: 6 servings (67 calories per ½-cup serving).

PROTEIN 1.2 / FAT 1.7 / CARBOHYDRATE 13.1 / CHOLESTEROL 0 /
IRON 0.5 / SODIUM 1 / CALCIUM 18

PEACHES WITH CRISPY TOPPING

½ cup plain low-fat yogurt
1 teaspoon apple pie spice, divided
Vegetable cooking spray
1 tablespoon margarine
½ cup nutlike cereal nuggets
1 teaspoon brown sugar
4 cups sliced fresh peaches
Fresh mint sprigs (optional)

Combine yogurt and ½ teaspoon apple pie spice in a small bowl, stirring well. Cover and chill thoroughly.

Coat a small skillet with cooking spray; add margarine, and place over medium heat until margarine melts. Combine cereal nuggets, brown sugar, and remaining apple pie spice in a small bowl; add mixture to skillet, and cook over medium heat 2 minutes or until margarine is absorbed, stirring frequently. Remove from heat, and set aside to cool.

To serve, spoon peaches into 4 individual dessert bowls. Drizzle each serving with 2 tablespoons chilled yogurt mixture; sprinkle 2 tablespoons cereal mixture over each. Garnish with mint sprigs, if desired. Yield: 4 servings (173 calories per serving).

PROTEIN 4.4 / FAT 3.7 / CARBOHYDRATE 33.6 / CHOLESTEROL 2 /
IRON 1.0 / SODIUM 153 / CALCIUM 72

FLAMING PEARS FOSTER

3 cups peeled, sliced bananas, cut diagonally into
    ¼-inch slices
1 cup peeled, sliced fresh pears
Vegetable cooking spray
½ cup unsweetened orange juice
3 tablespoons rum, divided
1 tablespoon brown sugar
1 tablespoon lime juice
2 whole cloves
1 (3-inch) stick cinnamon
¼ teaspoon ground cinnamon

Place banana and pear slices in an 11- x 7- x 1½-inch baking dish that has been coated with cooking spray. Set aside.

Combine orange juice, 2 tablespoons rum, and next 4 ingredients in a small saucepan; stir well. Bring to a boil, stirring occasionally. Remove cinnamon stick and cloves; discard. Pour orange juice mixture over fruit, and bake at 400° for 15 minutes, basting every 5 minutes.

Place remaining 1 tablespoon rum in a small, long-handled pan; heat just until warm (do not boil). Ignite with a long match, and pour over fruit mixture. Stir gently until flames die down. Spoon fruit mixture into individual dessert dishes. Sprinkle with cinnamon. Yield: 6 servings (83 calories per ½-cup serving).

PROTEIN 0.8 / FAT 0.4 / CARBOHYDRATE 21.1 / CHOLESTEROL 0 /
IRON 0.5 / SODIUM 1 / CALCIUM 14

ORANGE-POACHED PEARS

6 medium-size ripe pears
1 cup unsweetened orange juice
⅓ cup Grand Marnier or other orange-flavored
    liqueur
½ teaspoon grated orange rind
2 teaspoons cornstarch
3 tablespoons water
Orange rind strips (optional)

Peel pears and core from bottom, cutting to, but not through, stem end.

Combine orange juice, liqueur, and orange rind in a large Dutch oven; bring to a boil. Place pears, stem end up, in Dutch oven; baste pears with juice mixture. Cover, reduce heat, and simmer 10 to 15 minutes or until pears are tender. Remove pears with a slotted spoon; place in dessert dishes, and set aside.

Combine cornstarch and water; stir well. Add cornstarch mixture to juice mixture; cook over low heat, stirring constantly, until thickened. Pour orange sauce evenly over pears. Garnish each serving with a strip of orange rind, if desired. Yield: 6 servings (62 calories per serving).

PROTEIN 0.5 / FAT 0.3 / CARBOHYDRATE 15.6 / CHOLESTEROL 0 / IRON 0.2 / SODIUM 0 / CALCIUM 12

FRESH STRAWBERRY TRIFLE

2 cups skim milk, divided
1 egg, beaten
3 tablespoons cornstarch
2 tablespoons honey
1 teaspoon vanilla extract
¼ teaspoon orange extract
6 ladyfingers, split lengthwise
1 tablespoon Triple Sec or other orange-flavored liqueur
3 cups sliced fresh strawberries, divided
Whole fresh strawberries (optional)

Combine 1¾ cups milk and egg in a medium saucepan; beat with a wire whisk 1 to 2 minutes or until foamy. Combine remaining ¼ cup milk and cornstarch; stir until smooth. Add honey and stir well. Add to milk and egg mixture, and cook over medium heat, stirring constantly, until thickened. Remove from heat, and stir in flavorings. Cover and chill.

Sprinkle ladyfingers with liqueur. Arrange half of ladyfingers on bottom of a 1-quart soufflé or trifle dish. Arrange 1 cup sliced strawberries on top of ladyfingers and, cut side out, around lower edge of dish. Top with half of chilled custard and remaining ladyfingers. Arrange 1 cup strawberries on top of ladyfingers and, cut side out, around edge of dish. Top with remaining custard and remaining 1 cup strawberries. Cover and chill at least 2 hours. Garnish with whole strawberries, if desired. Yield: 6 servings (136 calories per serving).

PROTEIN 5.0 / FAT 1.7 / CARBOHYDRATE 24.6 / CHOLESTEROL 35 / IRON 1.6 / SODIUM 111 / CALCIUM 117

BLUEBERRY SLUSH

5 cups frozen blueberries
1 (8-ounce) carton vanilla low-fat yogurt
3 tablespoons superfine sugar
2 tablespoons Kahlúa or other coffee-flavored liqueur

Combine all ingredients in container of an electric blender or food processor; top with cover, and process until smooth. Spoon into individual dessert bowls, and serve immediately. Yield: 4 cups (98 calories per ½-cup serving).

PROTEIN 1.7 / FAT 0.9 / CARBOHYDRATE 20.0 / CHOLESTEROL 1 / IRON 0.2 / SODIUM 20 / CALCIUM 55

GRAPEFRUIT-MINT SORBET

4 cups unsweetened pink grapefruit juice, divided
¼ cup plus 2 tablespoons honey
⅓ cup minced fresh mint
1 envelope unflavored gelatin
¼ cup lemon juice

Combine ½ cup grapefruit juice and honey in a small saucepan. Cook over low heat until honey melts. Place mint in a large bowl. Pour honey mixture over mint; stir well. Let cool.

Line a colander or sieve with a double layer of cheesecloth that has been rinsed out and squeezed dry. Allow cheesecloth to extend over outside edges of colander. Place colander in a large bowl to drain. Pour honey-mint mixture into colander. Discard mint. Transfer honey mixture to a small saucepan.

Sprinkle gelatin over honey mixture in saucepan; let stand 5 minutes. Cook over low heat, stirring constantly, until gelatin dissolves. Combine gelatin mixture, remaining 3½ cups grapefruit juice, and lemon juice in a large bowl; stir well. Cover and freeze until firm. Remove from freezer; let stand 10 minutes.

Position knife blade in food processor bowl; add frozen mixture. Top with cover, and process until smooth. Scoop sorbet into individual dessert bowls, and serve immediately. Yield: 6 cups (67 calories per ½-cup serving).

PROTEIN 1.0 / FAT 0.1 / CARBOHYDRATE 16.7 / CHOLESTEROL 0 / IRON 1.8 / SODIUM 3 / CALCIUM 9

(From left): A trio of delicate flavors are featured in Rosy Pineapple Ice, Tropical Fruit Sherbet, and Apricot Sorbet.

APRICOT SORBET

2 (16-ounce) cans unsweetened apricot halves, undrained
2 tablespoons lemon juice
½ teaspoon almond extract
1 cup white grape juice
¼ cup sugar
2 egg whites

Drain apricots, reserving 1 cup liquid. Place apricots, lemon juice, and almond extract in container of an electric blender. Top with cover, and process until smooth; stir in reserved liquid. Set aside.

Combine grape juice and sugar in a medium saucepan; cook over low heat until sugar dissolves. Remove from heat, and let cool to room temperature. Stir grape juice mixture into apricot mixture. Pour mixture into 2 freezer trays, and freeze until mixture is almost firm, stirring several times.

Beat egg whites (at room temperature) in a small mixing bowl at high speed of an electric mixer until stiff peaks form. Spoon apricot mixture into a large mixing bowl; beat with an electric mixer until smooth. Fold in beaten egg whites. Spoon into 2 freezer trays; freeze at least 8 hours, stirring several times.

Before serving, transfer one tray of mixture to container of an electric blender; top with cover, and process until smooth. Scoop sorbet into individual serving bowls. Repeat procedure with remaining mixture. Serve immediately. Yield: 5 cups (83 calories per ½-cup serving).

PROTEIN 1.5 / FAT 0.2 / CARBOHYDRATE 19.8 / CHOLESTEROL 0 / IRON 0.5 / SODIUM 12 / CALCIUM 14

ROSY PINEAPPLE ICE

2½ cups unsweetened pineapple juice, divided
3 tablespoons honey
1½ cups cranberry juice cocktail

Combine ½ cup pineapple juice and honey in a large saucepan. Cook over low heat until honey melts. Remove from heat. Stir in remaining pineapple juice and cranberry juice cocktail. Pour into a 13- x 9- x 2-inch pan. Cover and freeze until firm.

Position knife blade in food processor bowl; add half of frozen mixture. Top with cover, and process until smooth. Repeat procedure with remaining mixture. Spoon ice into individual dessert bowls, and serve immediately. Yield: 6 cups (64 calories per ½-cup serving).

PROTEIN 0.2 / FAT 0.1 / CARBOHYDRATE 16.4 / CHOLESTEROL 0 / IRON 0.2 / SODIUM 2 / CALCIUM 10

TROPICAL FRUIT SHERBET

2¼ cups nonfat buttermilk
1 cup peeled, cubed mango
3 medium kiwifruit, peeled and quartered
1 (6-ounce) can frozen orange juice concentrate, thawed and undiluted
1 medium banana, peeled and sliced
¼ cup lime juice
3 tablespoons honey
¼ teaspoon coconut extract

Combine all ingredients in container of an electric blender or food processor; top with cover, and process until smooth.

Pour mixture into freezer can of a 1-gallon hand-turned or electric freezer. Freeze according to manufacturer's instructions. Scoop into individual dessert bowls, and serve immediately. Yield: 7 cups (73 calories per ½-cup serving).

PROTEIN 2.1 / FAT 0.4 / CARBOHYDRATE 16.4 / CHOLESTEROL 0 / IRON 0.2 / SODIUM 42 / CALCIUM 10

FROZEN RUM-CURRANT YOGURT

3 tablespoons currants
2 tablespoons powdered sugar
3 tablespoons dark rum
3 (8-ounce) cartons vanilla low-fat yogurt

Combine currants, sugar, and rum in a small bowl. Let stand 30 minutes. Combine yogurt and rum mixture, stirring well.

Pour yogurt mixture into freezer can of a 2-quart hand-turned or electric freezer. Freeze according to manufacturer's instructions. Scoop frozen yogurt into individual dessert bowls, and serve immediately. Yield: 3 cups (136 calories per ½-cup serving).

PROTEIN 5.7 / FAT 1.5 / CARBOHYDRATE 21.2 / CHOLESTEROL 6 / IRON 0.2 / SODIUM 77 / CALCIUM 198

MINI BAKED ALASKAS

1 (8-ounce) can unsweetened pineapple slices, drained
Vegetable cooking spray
2 cups raspberry sherbet
3 egg whites
1/8 teaspoon cream of tartar
3 tablespoons sugar
1/4 teaspoon almond extract

Place pineapple slices on a baking sheet that has been coated with cooking spray. Freeze until firm.

Remove pineapple from freezer. Top each slice with a scoop of sherbet. Freeze until firm.

Beat egg whites (at room temperature) and cream of tartar in a large bowl at high speed of an electric mixer until foamy. Gradually add sugar, 1 tablespoon at a time, beating until stiff peaks form and sugar dissolves (2 to 4 minutes). Fold in extract.

Remove sherbet-topped pineapple from freezer. Spread meringue over sherbet, making sure edges are sealed. Cover loosely and freeze until firm.

Remove alaskas from freezer. Broil 6 inches from heat 1 to 2 minutes or until lightly golden. Serve immediately. Yield: 4 servings (178 calories per serving).

PROTEIN 3.5 / FAT 1.1 / CARBOHYDRATE 39.3 / CHOLESTEROL 0 / IRON 0.2 / SODIUM 114 / CALCIUM 41

APRICOT TORTONI

1/4 cup evaporated skimmed milk
6 plain oatmeal cookies, crushed
1 tablespoon plus 1 teaspoon low-sugar apricot spread, melted
2 (8-ounce) cans unsweetened apricot halves, drained and chopped
3 tablespoons sugar
1 egg white
1 teaspoon lime juice
1/2 teaspoon almond extract
2 tablespoons chopped almonds, toasted

Place evaporated skimmed milk in a small, narrow glass or stainless steel bowl; freeze 20

minutes or until a 1/8-inch-thick layer of ice forms on surface.

Combine cookie crumbs and apricot spread in a small bowl; stir well. Press crumb mixture evenly into bottoms of 6 paper-lined muffin cups. Set aside.

Combine apricots, sugar, egg white, lime juice, and almond extract in a large mixing bowl. Beat at low speed of an electric mixer until well blended.

Beat partially frozen milk at high speed of an electric mixer 5 minutes or until stiff peaks form. Fold whipped milk into apricot mixture.

Spoon apricot mixture evenly into prepared muffin cups. Sprinkle each with 1 teaspoon toasted almonds. Freeze several hours or until firm. Let stand at room temperature 5 minutes before serving. Yield: 6 servings (159 calories per serving).

PROTEIN 3.8 / FAT 5.5 / CARBOHYDRATE 24.3 / CHOLESTEROL 12 / IRON 0.9 / SODIUM 80 / CALCIUM 65

FROZEN CHOCOLATE-CHERRY SQUARES

6 chocolate wafers, crushed
2 teaspoons unsalted margarine, melted
Vegetable cooking spray
1 cup diced, pitted fresh sweet cherries
2 tablespoons rum
6 cups chocolate ice milk, softened
1 ounce semisweet chocolate morsels
1 teaspoon skim milk

Combine wafer crumbs and margarine; stir well. Sprinkle half of crumb mixture on bottom of an 8-inch square pan that has been coated with cooking spray. Set aside.

Gently fold cherries and rum into ice milk. Spread into prepared pan.

Combine chocolate morsels and milk in a small saucepan. Cook over low heat just until chocolate melts. Drizzle chocolate mixture over ice milk mixture. Sprinkle with remaining crumb mixture. Freeze until firm. Cut into 9 squares, and serve immediately. Yield: 9 servings (149 calories per serving).

PROTEIN 2.1 / FAT 4.5 / CARBOHYDRATE 19.5 / CHOLESTEROL 3 / IRON 0.2 / SODIUM 15 / CALCIUM 9

The chocolate custard in Black Bottom Parfaits adds an irresistible flavor to this mouth-watering dessert.

PROFILING PEANUT BUTTER

While peanut butter is a good source of protein and contains plenty of iron and B vitamins, remember that a tablespoon of it contains about 100 calories, 75 percent of which come from fat. Granted, most of that fat is the heart-healthy monounsaturated variety, but it is still fat.

Consider, too, that several brands of peanut butter add saturated fats to keep the consistency smooth. "Natural" peanut butters made from 100 percent fresh ground peanuts solves the saturated fat dilemma. But to cut down on total fat calories—unless you are feeding a growing child—be sure to spread this coating thin.

BLACK BOTTOM PARFAITS

½ cup plus 2 tablespoons sugar, divided
2 tablespoons cornstarch
2 cups skim milk
2 eggs, separated
½ teaspoon unflavored gelatin
¼ cup Dutch process cocoa, sifted
1 tablespoon dark rum
¼ teaspoon cream of tartar
½ teaspoon vanilla extract
Grated chocolate (optional)
Fresh cherries (optional)

Combine ½ cup sugar and cornstarch in a medium saucepan; gradually stir in milk. Cook over medium heat, stirring constantly, until mixture comes to a boil. Cook 1 minute, stirring constantly. Remove from heat.

Beat egg yolks at medium speed of an electric mixer until thick and lemon colored. Gradually stir about one-fourth of hot mixture into yolks; add to remaining hot mixture, stirring constantly. Bring mixture to a boil over low heat, and cook 1 minute, stirring constantly. Remove from heat, and transfer 1 cup mixture to a small mixing bowl. Add gelatin to hot custard in small mixing bowl; beat with a wire whisk until gelatin dissolves. Set aside gelatin mixture to cool completely.

Add cocoa and dark rum to remaining custard in saucepan. Beat with a wire whisk until cocoa thoroughly dissolves. Spoon chocolate custard equally into 6 parfait glasses, and set aside to cool completely.

Beat egg whites (at room temperature) in a medium mixing bowl at high speed of an electric mixer until foamy. Add cream of tartar and continue to beat until soft peaks form. Gradually add remaining sugar, one tablespoon at a time, beating until stiff peaks form and sugar dissolves. Fold in vanilla.

Beat reserved cooled custard in small mixing bowl with a wire whisk until smooth; fold in beaten egg white mixture. Spoon meringue mixture evenly over chocolate layer in parfait glasses. Cover and chill thoroughly. If desired, garnish with grated chocolate, and fresh cherries. Yield: 6 servings (161 calories per serving).

PROTEIN 5.7 / FAT 2.6 / CARBOHYDRATE 29.0 / CHOLESTEROL 68 / IRON 0.7 / SODIUM 99 / CALCIUM 113

PINEAPPLE CHIFFON DESSERT

1 (8-ounce) can unsweetened crushed pineapple,
  undrained
1 envelope unflavored gelatin
4 eggs, separated
½ cup sugar, divided
2 tablespoons lemon juice
¼ cup vanilla wafer crumbs
Fresh mint leaves (optional)

Drain pineapple, reserving juice. Set pineapple aside. Add enough cold water to juice to equal ½ cup. Sprinkle gelatin over pineapple juice mixture; set aside.

Beat egg yolks in a small saucepan until smooth. Add ¼ cup sugar, reserved drained pineapple, and lemon juice; stir until well blended. Cook over medium-low heat, stirring constantly, 5 minutes or until mixture begins to thicken. Remove from heat; add gelatin mixture, stirring until gelatin dissolves. Cool to room temperature. Chill thoroughly.

Beat egg whites (at room temperature) in a large mixing bowl at high speed of an electric mixer until foamy. Gradually add remaining ¼ cup sugar, 1 tablespoon at a time, beating until stiff peaks form. Fold into pineapple mixture.

Sprinkle vanilla wafer crumbs evenly over bottom of an 8-inch square pan. Spoon filling over crumbs. Chill until firm. Cut into squares to serve; garnish with mint leaves, if desired. Yield: 8 servings (117 calories per serving).

PROTEIN 4.1 / FAT 3.0 / CARBOHYDRATE 19.1 / CHOLESTEROL 101 / IRON 0.6 / SODIUM 44 / CALCIUM 18

PEAR PUDDING

1 (16-ounce) can unsweetened pear halves,
  undrained
2 tablespoons margarine
2 tablespoons all-purpose flour
¾ cup water
2 teaspoons vanilla extract
¼ teaspoon salt
⅛ teaspoon ground nutmeg
Vegetable cooking spray
¼ cup fine, dry breadcrumbs
1 tablespoon brown sugar

Drain pears, reserving ¾ cup liquid. Mash pears, and press between paper towels to remove excess moisture. Set aside.

Melt margarine in a small saucepan over medium heat. Gradually stir in flour. Cook, stirring constantly, 1 minute. Combine reserved liquid and water; gradually add to flour mixture. Cook, stirring constantly, until thickened and smooth. Stir in vanilla, salt, nutmeg, and pears. Pour mixture into a 1-quart baking dish that has been coated with cooking spray. Combine breadcrumbs and sugar; sprinkle over pears. Bake at 350° for 15 minutes. Yield: 6 servings (99 calories per ½-cup serving).

PROTEIN 0.9 / FAT 4.2 / CARBOHYDRATE 13.9 / CHOLESTEROL 0 / IRON 0.3 / SODIUM 175 / CALCIUM 11

HEARTY RICE PUDDING

1¼ cups water
½ cup uncooked brown rice
1 (8-ounce) can unsweetened crushed pineapple,
  undrained
1½ cups skim milk
¼ cup raisins
¼ cup firmly packed brown sugar
½ teaspoon ground cinnamon
3 tablespoons whole wheat flour
1 teaspoon vanilla extract
¼ cup slivered almonds, toasted

Bring water to a boil in a medium saucepan. Add rice; cover, reduce heat, and simmer 45 minutes.

Drain pineapple, reserving juice; set pineapple juice aside. Add pineapple and milk to rice, stirring well. Place over medium-low heat; cover and cook 15 minutes. Stir in raisins, sugar, and cinnamon.

Combine reserved pineapple juice and flour, stirring until blended. Gradually add flour mixture to rice mixture; cook over medium heat until thickened and bubbly. Remove from heat; stir in vanilla. Spoon into individual dessert dishes; top each with 1½ teaspoons slivered almonds. Serve warm or chilled. Yield: 8 servings (157 calories per ½-cup serving).

PROTEIN 4.1 / FAT 3.2 / CARBOHYDRATE 29.2 / CHOLESTEROL 1 / IRON 0.9 / SODIUM 29 / CALCIUM 89

PUMPKIN CUSTARD

2 eggs
1 (12-ounce) can evaporated skimmed milk
1 (16-ounce) can pumpkin
¼ cup firmly packed brown sugar
1 teaspoon pumpkin pie spice
2 teaspoons vanilla extract
Vegetable cooking spray
Plain nonfat yogurt (optional)

Combine eggs and half of milk in a medium mixing bowl; beat at medium speed of an electric mixer until well blended. Add remaining milk, pumpkin, brown sugar, pumpkin pie spice, and vanilla; beat at low speed until well blended.

Spoon pumpkin mixture into a 1-quart casserole that has been coated with cooking spray. Bake, uncovered, at 325° for 1 hour and 25 minutes or until custard is set. Cool slightly on a wire rack.

Spoon into individual serving dishes, and top with yogurt, if desired. Yield: 6 servings (135 calories per ½-cup serving).

PROTEIN 7.2 / FAT 2.1 / CARBOHYDRATE 22.3 / CHOLESTEROL 69 / IRON 1.8 / SODIUM 93 / CALCIUM 202

BANANA-COFFEE SOUFFLÉ

¼ cup sugar
2 tablespoons cornstarch
1 tablespoon instant coffee granules
¾ cup mashed ripe banana
¼ cup evaporated skimmed milk
1 tablespoon lemon juice
1 tablespoon Kahlúa or other coffee-flavored liqueur
1½ teaspoons vanilla extract
6 egg whites
½ teaspoon cream of tartar
¼ teaspoon ground cinnamon

Combine sugar, cornstarch, and coffee granules in a medium saucepan; stir in banana and milk. Cook over medium heat, stirring constantly, until thickened and bubbly. Cook an additional minute or until very thick. Remove from heat; stir in juice, liqueur, and vanilla. Transfer to a large mixing bowl. Cover with plastic wrap, gently pressing directly on mixture. Set aside.

Beat egg whites (at room temperature),
cream of tartar, and cinnamon in a large mixing bowl at high speed of an electric mixer until stiff peaks form. Fold one-third of egg whites into banana mixture; carefully fold in remaining egg whites. Spoon into a 2½-quart soufflé dish. Bake at 375° for 20 to 25 minutes or until puffed and golden. Serve immediately. Yield: 6 servings (107 calories per serving).

PROTEIN 4.5 / FAT 0.2 / CARBOHYDRATE 20.3 / CHOLESTEROL 0 / IRON 0.2 / SODIUM 80 / CALCIUM 38

BUTTERSCOTCH SOUFFLÉ

Vegetable cooking spray
¾ cup skim milk
1 teaspoon cornstarch
¼ cup butterscotch morsels
3 eggs, separated
½ teaspoon maple flavoring
1 egg white
½ teaspoon cream of tartar
2 tablespoons brown sugar
2 tablespoons finely chopped pecans, toasted

Coat bottom of a 1½-quart soufflé dish with cooking spray; set aside.

Combine milk and cornstarch in top of a double boiler, stirring to blend. Place over boiling water and cook, stirring constantly, until slightly thickened. Add butterscotch morsels, stirring until morsels melt.

Beat egg yolks slightly. Gradually stir about one-fourth of hot mixture into egg yolks; add to remaining hot mixture, stirring constantly. Cook 5 minutes over boiling water, stirring constantly with a wire whisk, until mixture is thickened. Remove from heat, and let cool to room temperature. Stir in maple flavoring.

Beat 4 egg whites (at room temperature) and cream of tartar in a large bowl at high speed of an electric mixer until soft peaks form. Gradually add brown sugar, 1 tablespoon at a time, beating until stiff peaks form. Gently fold beaten egg whites into cooled butterscotch mixture.

Pour into prepared soufflé dish; sprinkle with pecans. Bake at 350° for 30 minutes or until puffed and golden. Serve immediately. Yield: 6 servings (124 calories per serving).

PROTEIN 5.2 / FAT 6.7 / CARBOHYDRATE 10.6 / CHOLESTEROL 101 / IRON 0.6 / SODIUM 80 / CALCIUM 64

WARM PINEAPPLE SOUFFLÉ

1 (8-ounce) can unsweetened crushed pineapple
⅓ cup sugar
2 tablespoons cornstarch
2 egg yolks
1 teaspoon vanilla extract
⅛ teaspoon salt
6 egg whites
½ teaspoon cream of tartar
Vegetable cooking spray

Drain pineapple, reserving juice; set pineapple aside. Add water to juice to measure ¾ cup. Combine juice mixture, sugar, and cornstarch in a medium saucepan, stirring well. Cook over medium heat, stirring constantly, until mixture thickens and comes to a boil.

Beat egg yolks, vanilla, and salt in a medium bowl with a wire whisk. Gradually stir about one-fourth of hot mixture into egg yolk mixture; add to remaining hot mixture, stirring constantly. Cook 1 minute; remove from heat. Stir in reserved pineapple.

Beat egg whites (at room temperature) and cream of tartar in a large bowl at high speed of an electric mixer until stiff peaks form. Gently stir one-fourth of egg white mixture into pineapple mixture. Gently fold remaining egg white mixture into pineapple mixture. Spoon into a 2-quart soufflé dish that has been coated with cooking spray. Bake at 375° for 30 to 35 minutes or until puffed and golden. Serve immediately. Yield: 8 servings (87 calories per serving).

PROTEIN 3.3 / FAT 1.5 / CARBOHYDRATE 15.0 / CHOLESTEROL 68 / IRON 0.3 / SODIUM 89 / CALCIUM 13

SPECIAL BLUEBERRY PIE

2½ cups fresh blueberries
2 cups diced fresh mango
¼ cup sugar
2 tablespoons cornstarch
2 teaspoons minced crystallized ginger
1 teaspoon grated lemon rind
2 teaspoons lemon juice
Vegetable cooking spray
4 sheets commercial frozen phyllo pastry, thawed
2 tablespoons margarine, melted

Combine first 7 ingredients in a large bowl; stir well. Set aside.

Coat a 9-inch pieplate with cooking spray. Place 1 sheet of phyllo on a damp towel (keep remaining phyllo covered). Lightly brush phyllo with melted margarine; place phyllo, margarine side up, in pieplate, allowing ends to extend over sides. Repeat process with remaining phyllo, crisscrossing sheets alternately. Gently press phyllo so that layers conform to sides of pieplate. Roll overhanging phyllo to form a rim. Brush rim with remaining margarine.

Spoon blueberry mixture into pieplate; place on a baking sheet. Bake at 350° for 45 minutes or until crust is golden. Cool slightly. Yield: 8 servings (144 calories per serving).

PROTEIN 1.6 / FAT 3.3 / CARBOHYDRATE 28.8 / CHOLESTEROL 0 / IRON 0.2 / SODIUM 37 / CALCIUM 9

CHOCO-BANANA PIE

1 cup chocolate wafer crumbs
3 tablespoons reduced-calorie margarine, melted
Vegetable cooking spray
½ cup plus 2 tablespoons instant nonfat dry milk powder
¼ cup cornstarch
¼ cup unsweetened cocoa
3 tablespoons sugar
2¼ cups water
½ teaspoon vanilla extract
2 medium bananas, peeled and sliced

Combine crumbs and margarine, mixing well. Firmly press crumb mixture evenly over bottom of a 9-inch pieplate that has been coated with cooking spray. Bake at 350° for 10 minutes. Set aside, and cool completely.

Combine milk powder, cornstarch, cocoa, and sugar in a medium saucepan. Stir in water. Cook over medium heat, stirring constantly, until mixture thickens and comes to a boil. Boil 1 minute, stirring constantly. Remove from heat; stir in vanilla. Let cool 10 minutes, stirring occasionally.

Arrange banana slices over prepared crust. Spoon cocoa mixture over bananas. Cover and chill at least 8 hours. Yield: 8 servings (194 calories per serving).

PROTEIN 5.4 / FAT 6.3 / CARBOHYDRATE 30.3 / CHOLESTEROL 13 / IRON 0.9 / SODIUM 144 / CALCIUM 139

PUMPKIN PRALINE PIE

1 envelope unflavored gelatin
¼ cup unsweetened apple juice
1 (16-ounce) can pumpkin
1 (8-ounce) carton vanilla low-fat yogurt
⅓ cup firmly packed brown sugar
1 teaspoon pumpkin pie spice
Vegetable cooking spray
8 gingersnaps
¼ cup chopped pecans, toasted

Sprinkle gelatin over apple juice in a small saucepan; let stand 1 minute. Cook over low heat, stirring constantly, until gelatin dissolves.

Place pumpkin in a large bowl; stir gelatin mixture into pumpkin. Add yogurt, brown sugar, and pumpkin pie spice; stir until smooth. Coat a 9-inch pieplate with cooking spray.

Cut gingersnaps in half using a bread knife. Line side of pieplate with cookie halves, cut side down. Spoon pumpkin mixture into prepared pieplate. Sprinkle with pecans. Cover and chill 6 hours or until set. Yield: 8 servings (124 calories per serving).

PROTEIN 3.3 / FAT 3.6 / CARBOHYDRATE 21.2 / CHOLESTEROL 3 /
IRON 1.4 / SODIUM 30 / CALCIUM 80

GRAPEFRUIT TARTS

1½ teaspoons unflavored gelatin
2 tablespoons cold water
½ (8-ounce) package Neufchâtel cheese, softened
¼ cup sifted powdered sugar
¾ cup unsweetened grapefruit juice
⅛ teaspoon vanilla extract
Tart Shells
1 small pink grapefruit, peeled and sectioned
Grapefruit Glaze
Fresh mint leaves (optional)

Sprinkle gelatin over cold water in a small saucepan; let stand 1 minute. Cook over low heat, stirring constantly, until gelatin dissolves. Set aside.

Combine Neufchâtel cheese, sugar, juice, and vanilla in container of an electric blender; top with cover, and process until smooth. Add gelatin mixture, and process 5 seconds. Chill slightly. Spoon cheese mixture evenly into Tart Shells.

Top each with grapefruit sections. Drizzle glaze evenly over grapefruit. Chill thoroughly before serving. Garnish with mint leaves, if desired. Yield: 10 servings. (182 calories each).

Tart Shells:

1 cup all-purpose flour
¼ cup finely ground unsalted almonds
¼ cup plus 1 tablespoon margarine, chilled
3 tablespoons cold water
½ teaspoon vanilla extract
¼ teaspoon orange extract

Combine flour and almonds in a small mixing bowl; cut in margarine with a pastry blender until mixture resembles coarse meal. Sprinkle water and flavorings evenly over surface; stir with a fork until dry ingredients are moistened. Shape dough into a ball; cover and chill 1 hour. Divide dough into 10 equal portions. Press dough into ten 3½-inch tart shells. Prick bottoms and sides of shells with a fork. Bake at 350° for 25 minutes or until golden. Cool completely on a wire rack. Remove pastry shells from pans before filling. Yield: 10 tart shells.

Grapefruit Glaze:

1 teaspoon cornstarch
¼ cup unsweetened grapefruit juice
2 tablespoons water
2 teaspoons sugar

Combine all ingredients in a small saucepan, stirring until well blended. Bring to a boil; cook over medium heat 1 minute, stirring constantly.

Remove from heat, and let cool, stirring occasionally. Yield: about ¼ cup.

PROTEIN 3.8 / FAT 10.0 / CARBOHYDRATE 19.3 / CHOLESTEROL 9 /
IRON 1.1 / SODIUM 114 / CALCIUM 24

 ## MORE AEROBIC CHOICES

Don't feel confined to only aerobic dance classes to achieve cardiovascular fitness. Other actitivies such as brisk walking, jogging, swimming, rowing, cross-country skiing, and cycling also offer cardiovascular benefits. Include a variety of these aerobic activities in your schedule for a varied exercise routine.

APPLE-RAISIN CAKE ROLL

Vegetable cooking spray
3 eggs
½ cup firmly packed brown sugar
½ cup peeled, shredded apple
1 teaspoon vanilla extract
½ cup all-purpose flour
¼ cup whole wheat flour
1 teaspoon baking powder
2 teaspoons ground cinnamon
1 teaspoon grated lemon rind
½ teaspoon ground cardamom
½ teaspoon ground nutmeg
¼ teaspoon salt
2 tablespoons powdered sugar
Applesauce Filling

Coat a 15- x 10- x 1-inch jellyroll pan with cooking spray. Line pan with wax paper, and coat wax paper with cooking spray. Set jellyroll pan aside.

Beat eggs at high speed of an electric mixer 5 minutes or until fluffy. Gradually add brown sugar, 1 tablespoon at a time, beating well after each addition. Fold in apple and vanilla.

Combine flours and next 6 ingredients; stir well. Fold flour mixture into apple mixture. Spread batter evenly in prepared pan. Bake at 375° for 10 to 12 minutes.

Sift powdered sugar in a 15- x 10-inch rectangle on a linen towel. When cake is done, immediately loosen from sides of pan, and invert onto powdered sugar; peel off wax paper. Starting at narrow end, roll up cake and towel together, and let cake cool completely on a wire rack, seam side down.

Unroll cake. Spread Applesauce Filling evenly over cake, and carefully reroll cake, without towel. Place on a serving platter, seam side down. Cut cake roll into 1-inch slices to serve. Yield: 10 servings (189 calories per serving).

Applesauce Filling:

1 (8-ounce) package Neufchâtel cheese, softened
½ cup unsweetened applesauce
2 tablespoons brown sugar
¼ teaspoon ground nutmeg
2 tablespoons chopped raisins

Combine first 4 ingredients in a small mixing bowl; beat at medium speed of an electric mixer until well blended. Stir in raisins. Cover and chill 1 hour. Yield: 1½ cups.

PROTEIN 5.4 / FAT 7.1 / CARBOHYDRATE 26.9 / CHOLESTEROL 77 / IRON 1.3 / SODIUM 203 / CALCIUM 65

APPLE SUNDAE CAKE

2¼ cups vanilla ice milk, softened
1 teaspoon apple pie spice, divided
1 medium baking apple, peeled, cored, and thinly sliced
1 medium pear, peeled, cored, and thinly sliced
2 teaspoons lemon juice
1 cup all-purpose flour
½ cup unsweetened apple juice
2 tablespoons sugar
1 egg
1 teaspoon baking powder
½ teaspoon salt
¼ cup firmly packed brown sugar
2 tablespoons chopped pecans
2 tablespoons raisins, chopped
1 cup boiling water

Combine ice milk and ½ teaspoon apple pie spice in a medium bowl. Freeze until firm.

Arrange apple and pear slices in bottom of an ungreased 9-inch square baking pan. Sprinkle with lemon juice; set aside.

Combine flour and next 5 ingredients in a large mixing bowl. Beat at high speed of an electric mixer until smooth. Spoon batter over fruit slices.

Combine brown sugar, pecans, raisins, and remaining ½ teaspoon apple pie spice in a small bowl. Sprinkle over batter. Pour boiling water over batter in a slow, steady stream. Bake at 375° for 30 minutes. Let cool 10 minutes. Cut into 3-inch squares. Place on individual plates; top with ¼ cup ice milk mixture. Serve immediately. Yield: 9 servings (194 calories per serving).

PROTEIN 4.0 / FAT 3.4 / CARBOHYDRATE 38.1 / CHOLESTEROL 27 / IRON 1.1 / SODIUM 200 / CALCIUM 84

Cheesecake lovers will savor the spicy creaminess of Pumpkin Cheesecake.

EASY PEACH CAKE

1⅓ cups all-purpose flour
1 teaspoon baking soda
1 teaspoon ground cinnamon
½ teaspoon ground ginger
½ teaspoon ground cloves
⅔ cup plain nonfat yogurt
⅓ cup honey
¼ cup vegetable oil
1 egg, beaten
1 cup peeled, chopped fresh peaches
1 tablespoon all-purpose flour
Vegetable cooking spray
2 teaspoons powdered sugar

Combine flour, soda, cinnamon, ginger, and cloves in a large bowl; stir well.

Combine yogurt, honey, oil, and egg in a small bowl; stir until smooth. Add yogurt mixture to dry ingredients; stir until smooth.

Combine peaches and 1 tablespoon flour, tossing gently to coat. Fold peaches into batter. Spoon batter into an 8-inch square pan that has been coated with cooking spray. Bake at 350° for 25 minutes or until a wooden pick inserted in center comes out clean. Let cool completely in pan on a wire rack. Sift powdered sugar over cooled cake. Yield: 12 servings (148 calories per serving).

PROTEIN 3.0 / FAT 5.2 / CARBOHYDRATE 22.9 / CHOLESTEROL 17 / IRON 0.7 / SODIUM 85 / CALCIUM 48

PUMPKIN CHEESECAKE

Vegetable cooking spray
2 tablespoons cinnamon graham cracker crumbs
1 (16-ounce) can pumpkin
12 ounces Neufchâtel cheese, softened
1 cup part-skim ricotta cheese
½ cup firmly packed dark brown sugar
1 tablespoon plus 1½ teaspoons all-purpose flour
1 tablespoon grated orange rind
1½ teaspoons pumpkin pie spice
1¼ teaspoons vanilla extract
1 teaspoon brandy flavoring
2 eggs

Coat bottom of a 9-inch springform pan with cooking spray. Dust with cracker crumbs.

Combine pumpkin and next 8 ingredients in container of an electric blender or food processor; top with cover, and process until smooth. Add eggs, one at a time, and process just until blended. Pour batter into prepared pan, and place pan in a large shallow baking pan. Pour hot water to depth of 1 inch into larger pan. Bake at 350° for 50 minutes or until cheesecake is almost set.

Turn oven off, and partially open oven door; leave cake in oven 30 minutes. Remove cake from water bath, and let cool to room temperature on a wire rack. Cover and chill thoroughly. Remove sides of pan before serving. Yield: 12 servings (174 calories per serving).

PROTEIN 6.8 / FAT 9.4 / CARBOHYDRATE 16.0 / CHOLESTEROL 61 / IRON 1.3 / SODIUM 162 / CALCIUM 102

ORANGE SPICE POUND CAKE

Vegetable cooking spray
2 teaspoons all-purpose flour
2½ cups sifted cake flour
1½ teaspoons baking powder
½ teaspoon baking soda
¼ teaspoon salt
¼ teaspoon ground cinnamon
¼ teaspoon ground allspice
¼ teaspoon ground nutmeg
⅛ teaspoon ground cloves
½ cup unsalted margarine, softened
⅔ cup firmly packed brown sugar
3 egg whites
1 cup nonfat buttermilk
1 tablespoon grated orange rind
1 teaspoon vanilla extract
½ teaspoon orange extract

Coat bottom of a 9- x 5- x 3-inch loafpan with cooking spray; dust with 2 teaspoons flour, and set aside.

Combine cake flour and next 7 ingredients; stir well, and set aside.

Cream margarine; gradually add brown sugar, beating well at medium speed of an electric mixer. Add egg whites; beat 4 minutes or until well blended.

Add reserved flour mixture to creamed mixture alternately with buttermilk, beginning and ending with flour mixture. Mix just until blended after adding each addition. Stir in orange rind and flavorings.

Pour batter into prepared pan. Bake at 350° for 50 minutes or until a wooden pick inserted in center comes out clean. Cool in pan 10 minutes; remove from pan, and cool on a wire rack. Yield: 18 servings (135 calories per ½-inch slice).

PROTEIN 2.1 / FAT 5.2 / CARBOHYDRATE 19.8 / CHOLESTEROL 0 / IRON 0.4 / SODIUM 106 / CALCIUM 33

CARROT CAKE WITH CREAM CHEESE FROSTING

2 cups all-purpose flour
1 teaspoon baking powder
1 teaspoon baking soda
½ teaspoon salt
2 teaspoons ground cinnamon
1 (8-ounce) can unsweetened crushed pineapple, undrained
2 eggs
¾ cup plus 2 tablespoons sugar
¼ cup vegetable oil
¾ cup nonfat buttermilk
2 teaspoons vanilla extract
2 cups shredded carrots
Vegetable cooking spray
1 (8-ounce) package light process cream cheese product

Combine first 5 ingredients in a medium bowl, stirring well. Set aside. Drain pineapple, reserving 1 tablespoon plus 2 teaspoons juice. Set pineapple and juice aside.

Beat eggs in a large bowl at high speed of an electric mixer 5 minutes or until light and fluffy. Beat in sugar, oil, buttermilk, and vanilla. Gently stir in flour mixture, reserved pineapple, and shredded carrot.

Pour batter into a 13- x 9- x 2-inch baking pan that has been coated with cooking spray. Bake at 350° for 35 minutes or until a wooden pick inserted in center comes out clean. Cool completely in pan.

Beat cream cheese and reserved pineapple juice in a small bowl at high speed of an electric mixer until light and fluffy. Spread over cooled cake, and cut into squares. Yield: 16 servings (192 calories per serving).

PROTEIN 4.7 / FAT 6.8 / CARBOHYDRATE 28.8 / CHOLESTEROL 25 / IRON 0.8 / SODIUM 248 / CALCIUM 57

SELECTING A BREAKFAST CEREAL

It's easy to spot sugar-coated cereals, but hidden sugars are not so obvious. Take a look at the nutrition label; cereals with less than 3 grams of sugar per serving are best. Check granolas and "natural" cereals, and avoid those that contain saturated fats such as coconut oil. When it comes to fiber, look for cereals that list "whole grains" (whole wheat, rolled oats, corn bran) on the label. Cereals that list flour or wheat flour as the major ingredient are much lower in fiber content.

MARBLED BROWNIES

¼ cup plus 2 tablespoons reduced-calorie
  margarine, softened
⅓ cup Neufchâtel cheese, softened
⅔ cup sugar
2 eggs, beaten
1 teaspoon vanilla extract
¾ cup all-purpose flour
½ teaspoon baking powder
¼ teaspoon salt
3 tablespoons unsweetened cocoa
Vegetable cooking spray

Cream margarine and cheese; gradually add
sugar, beating at medium speed of an electric
mixer until light and fluffy. Add eggs and vanilla, beating well.

Combine flour, baking powder, and salt; add
to creamed mixture, beating well. Divide batter
in half. Sift cocoa over half of batter, and fold in
gently. Spoon cocoa mixture into an 8-inch
square baking pan that has been coated with
cooking spray. Pour remaining half of batter into
pan. Cut through mixture in pan with a knife to
create a marbled effect.

Bake at 350° for 25 minutes or until a
wooden pick inserted in center comes out
clean. Cool brownies in pan on a wire rack. Cut
brownies into 2- x 1¼-inch bars. Yield: 2 dozen
(70 calories each).

PROTEIN 1.5 / FAT 3.1 / CARBOHYDRATE 9.3 / CHOLESTEROL 19 /
IRON 0.3 / SODIUM 76 / CALCIUM 10

MOLASSES-OAT BARS

⅓ cup reduced-calorie margarine
½ cup nutlike cereal nuggets
⅓ cup firmly packed brown sugar
2 tablespoons molasses
1 teaspoon vanilla extract
1 egg, beaten
½ cup all-purpose flour
¼ cup whole wheat flour
⅓ cup quick-cooking oats, uncooked
½ teaspoon baking powder
⅛ teaspoon baking soda
Vegetable cooking spray
2 teaspoons powdered sugar

Melt margarine in a medium saucepan over
medium heat; add cereal. Cook 2 minutes, stirring constantly. Remove from heat; add brown
sugar, molasses, vanilla, and egg, stirring until
well blended.

Combine flours and next 3 ingredients in a
medium bowl. Add to cereal mixture; stir well.
Spread into an 8-inch square pan that has been
coated with cooking spray. Bake at 350° for 18
minutes. Let cool. Sprinkle with powdered sugar.
Cut into 2- x 1½-inch bars. Yield: 20 bars (79
calories each).

PROTEIN 1.6 / FAT 2.5 / CARBOHYDRATE 13.2 / CHOLESTEROL 10 /
IRON 0.7 / SODIUM 67 / CALCIUM 20

OLD-FASHIONED HERMITS

⅓ cup margarine, softened
⅔ cup firmly packed brown sugar
1 egg, beaten
½ teaspoon lemon extract
¼ teaspoon vanilla extract
1½ cups all-purpose flour
1½ teaspoons baking powder
½ teaspoon ground allspice
½ teaspoon ground cinnamon
¼ teaspoon ground cloves
¼ teaspoon ground nutmeg
¼ cup unsweetened apple juice
Vegetable cooking spray
56 raisins

Cream margarine; gradually add brown sugar,
beating at medium speed of an electric mixer
until light and fluffy. Add beaten egg and flavorings, beating well.

Combine flour and next 5 ingredients, mixing
well. Add to creamed mixture alternately with
apple juice, beginning and ending with flour
mixture, mixing well after each addition.

Drop dough by rounded teaspoonfuls 2 inches
apart onto cookie sheets that have been coated
with cooking spray. Press a raisin in center of
each cookie. Bake at 325° for 15 to 20 minutes.
Cool slightly on cookie sheets. Remove to wire
racks to cool completely. Yield: 56 cookies (37
calories each).

PROTEIN 0.5 / FAT 1.2 / CARBOHYDRATE 5.9 / CHOLESTEROL 4 /
IRON 0.2 / SODIUM 23 / CALCIUM 10

(From top): Poppy Seed Ice Box Cookies, Marbled Brownies (page 245), and Lemon Sugar Cookies.

POPPY SEED ICEBOX COOKIES

⅓ cup margarine, softened
⅔ cup sugar
1 egg, beaten
2 tablespoons skim milk
½ teaspoon almond extract
1¾ cups all-purpose flour
½ teaspoon baking soda
¼ teaspoon salt
¼ teaspoon ground nutmeg
¼ cup poppy seeds

Cream margarine; gradually add sugar, beating well at medium speed of an electric mixer until light and fluffy. Add egg, beating well. Add skim milk and almond extract. Combine flour and next 3 ingredients; add to creamed mixture, beating well. Stir in poppy seeds.

Divide dough into 4 equal portions; place each portion on a sheet of plastic wrap, and shape into a 4- x 2-inch log. Wrap logs in plastic wrap, and refrigerate or freeze until firm.

Unwrap logs, and cut into ¼-inch slices. Place 1 inch apart on ungreased cookie sheets. Bake at 350° for 6 to 8 minutes or until lightly browned. Cool on wire racks. Yield: 64 cookies (35 calories each).

PROTEIN 0.6 / FAT 1.3 / CARBOHYDRATE 5.1 / CHOLESTEROL 3 / IRON 0.2 / SODIUM 28 / CALCIUM 11

LEMON SUGAR COOKIES

¼ cup plus 2 tablespoons reduced-calorie margarine
⅔ cup sugar
1 egg
½ teaspoon lemon extract
1¾ cups all-purpose flour
1 teaspoon grated lemon rind
¾ teaspoon cream of tartar
½ teaspoon baking soda
⅛ teaspoon salt
Vegetable cooking spray
2 tablespoons sugar

Cream margarine; gradually add ⅔ cup sugar, beating well at medium speed of an electric mixer. (Reduced-calorie margarine will separate while beating.) Add egg and lemon extract,

beating well. Combine flour, lemon rind, cream of tartar, soda, and salt; gradually add to creamed mixture, beating until well blended. Cover and freeze dough 1 hour.

Shape dough into 1-inch balls. Place on cookie sheets that have been coated with cooking spray. Flatten cookies slightly. Sprinkle cookies evenly with 2 tablespoons sugar. Bake at 375° for 8 minutes or until lightly browned. Cool on wire racks. Yield: 2½ dozen cookies (65 calories each).

PROTEIN 1.0 / FAT 1.7 / CARBOHYDRATE 11.4 / CHOLESTEROL 7 / IRON 0.3 / SODIUM 53 / CALCIUM 5

MOCHA THUMBPRINT COOKIES

1 tablespoon plus 1 teaspoon instant coffee granules, divided
2½ teaspoons hot water, divided
¼ cup light process cream cheese product
2 teaspoons powdered sugar
¼ cup margarine, softened
½ cup sugar
1 egg
½ teaspoon vanilla extract
1½ cups plus 2 tablespoons sifted cake flour
2 tablespoons unsweetened cocoa
½ teaspoon baking soda

Dissolve 1 teaspoon coffee granules in ½ teaspoon hot water; add cream cheese and powdered sugar, beating until smooth. Set aside.

Dissolve remaining 1 tablespoon coffee granules in 2 teaspoons hot water; set aside. Cream margarine; gradually add sugar, beating at medium speed of an electric mixer until light and fluffy. Add egg and vanilla; beat well. Combine flour, cocoa, and soda; add to creamed mixture, mixing well. Chill dough at least 30 minutes.

Shape dough into ¾-inch balls; place 2 inches apart on ungreased cookie sheets. Press thumb into each cookie, leaving an indentation. Bake at 350° for 8 minutes. Remove to wire racks. Spoon ¼ teaspoon reserved cream cheese mixture into each cookie indentation, and let cool completely. Yield: 5½ dozen cookies (25 calories each).

PROTEIN 0.4 / FAT 1.0 / CARBOHYDRATE 3.6 / CHOLESTEROL 4 / IRON 0.1 / SODIUM 20 / CALCIUM 4

Cooking Light 1990 Menu Plans

This plan for seven days of calorie-controlled meals provides a healthful approach to weight loss. Follow the plan precisely, or use it as a model for planning your own balanced meals by substituting foods of comparable calories and nutrients. Refer to the Calorie/Nutrient Chart on pages 250-261 for these values. The items with an asterisk represent recipes that can be located in the menu and recipe sections. When planning your own menus, remember that of the total calories provided, at least 50 percent should be from carbohydrate, less than 30 percent from fat, and less than 20 percent from protein.

Most women can safely lose weight while eating 1,200 calories per day; most men can lose while eating 1,600. Once weight is lost, modify the menu plan according to the calories needed to maintain your ideal weight. If you feel you are losing weight too slowly, keep in mind that eating fewer calories to speed up weight loss may rob you of the nutrients your body needs to stay healthy. Also, your metabolism may slow down to accommodate a very limited food supply. Exercising is the key to speeding up weight loss.

1200 calories		DAY 1	1600 calories	
		Breakfast		
2 pancakes	140	*Whole Wheat Pancakes	2 pancakes	140
2 tablespoons	12	Reduced-Calorie Maple Syrup	2 tablespoons	12
—	—	*Peppered Pork Links	1 serving	124
1 cup	45	Fresh Strawberries	1 cup	45
1 cup	86	Skim Milk	1 cup	86
	283			407
		Lunch		
1 serving	170	*Garden Patch Pitas	1 serving	170
½ cup	94	*Lentil Salad	½ cup	94
1 serving	117	*Pineapple Chiffon Dessert	1 serving	117
—	—	*Peachy Tea	1 cup	85
	381			466
		Dinner		
1 serving	189	*Broiled Lamb Chops with Rosemary Sauce	1 serving	189
½ cup	81	*Brussels Sprouts with Pecans	½ cup	81
½ cup	67	*Wild Rice, Fennel, and Orange Salad	½ cup	67
—	—	*Sesame-Parmesan Crescents	1 crescent	99
½ cup	83	*Flaming Pears Foster	½ cup	83
	420			519
		Snack		
¾ cup	103	*Hot Malted Nog	¾ cup	103
—	—	*Strawberry-Banana Muffin Bites	3 each	108
	103			211
Total	1187		Total	1603

1200 calories		DAY 2	1600 calories	
		Breakfast		
1 slice	132	*Peanut Butter and Jelly Coffee Cake	1 slice	132
—	—	Lean Cooked Ham	2 ounces	82
½ cup	76	*Poached Apple Slices	½ cup	76
1 cup	86	Skim Milk	1 cup	86
	294			376
		Lunch		
1 cup	124	*Smoked Turkey, Potato, and Green Bean Salad	1 cup	124
—	—	*Sugared Onions	½ cup	124
1 wedge	86	*Rosemary Flatbread	1 wedge	86
2 tea cakes	130	*Lemon Tea Cakes	2 tea cakes	130
1 cup	79	*Spicy Orange-Almond Tea	1 cup	79
	419			543
		Dinner		
1 serving	188	*Seashell Tuna Bake	1 serving	188
1 cup	55	*Marinated Cucumber Salad	1 cup	55
1 wedge	7	Lettuce Wedge	1 wedge	7
1 tablespoon	15	*Garlic-Dill Buttermilk Dressing	1 tablespoon	15
—	—	*Pesto Swirl-Yogurt Bread	1 slice	150
2 cookies	98	*Giant Gingersnaps	2 cookies	98
	363			513
		Snack		
¾ cup	119	*Chocolate Milk Shake	¾ cup	119
—	—	*Grahamy Bananas	3 pieces	39
	119			158
Total	1195		Total	1590

1200 calories		DAY 3	1600 calories	
		Breakfast		
1 serving	146	*Vegetable Omelet	1 serving	146
—	—	Bagel	1 whole	161
1 cup	140	*Honeybees	1 cup	140
—	—	Skim Milk	1 cup	86
	286			533
		Lunch		
1 serving	154	*Turkey-Broccoli Patties	1 serving	154
½ cup	55	*Saucy Rhubarb	½ cup	55
1 serving	33	*Mustard-Glazed Tomatoes	1 serving	33
1 slice	124	*Pumpkin Praline Pie	1 slice	124
	366			366
		Dinner		
1 serving	168	*Jalisco-Style Roast	1 serving	168
1 serving	110	*Easy Baked Potato Halves	1 serving	110
½ cup	42	*Texan-Style Mushrooms	½ cup	42
—	—	Commercial Hard Roll	1 roll	156
1 slice	144	*Special Blueberry Pie	1 slice	144
	464			620
		Snacks		
1 serving	58	*Kiwifruit Colada Popsicles	1 serving	58
Total	1174		Total	1577

DAY 4

1200 calories			1600 calories	
Breakfast				
1 egg	71	Poached Egg	1 egg	71
1 slice	105	*Whole Wheat-Apricot Twist	1 slice	105
—	—	Oatmeal	½ cup	73
1 cup	67	*Morning Milk Punch	1 cup	67
	243			316
Lunch				
1 serving	204	*Grilled Cheese with Pineapple	1 serving	204
1 cup	102	*Easy Tomato-Bean Soup	1 cup	102
—	—	Skim Milk	1 cup	86
—	—	*Old-Fashioned Hermits	2 cookies	74
	306			466
Dinner				
1 serving	189	*Chicken Thighs au Poivre	1 serving	189
½ cup	130	*Savory Rice	½ cup	130
1 serving	60	*Green Salad with Warm Brie Dressing	1 serving	60
1 slice	166	Angel Food Cake	1 slice	166
1 tablespoon	31	*Amaretto-Almond Sauce	3 tablespoons	91
	576			636
Snack				
1 tablespoon	25	*Apple-Peanut Butter Spread	2 tablespoons	50
4 crackers	44	Melba Toast	12 crackers	132
	69			182
Total	1194		Total	1600

DAY 6

1200 calories			1600 calories	
Breakfast				
½ cup	64	Bran Flakes Cereal	½ cup	64
—	—	*Pumpkin Muffins	1 muffin	110
1 serving	112	*Fresh Fruit Medley	1 serving	112
1 cup	86	Skim Milk	1 cup	86
	262			372
Lunch				
1 serving	208	*Chiles Rellenos Casserole	1 serving	208
½ cup	19	*Zucchini Toss	½ cup	19
—	—	Whole Wheat Roll	1 roll	123
—	—	*Raspberry-Mango Freezer Spread	1 tablespoon	18
1 cookie	35	*Poppy Seed Icebox Cookies	2 cookies	70
	262			438
Dinner				
1 cup	236	*Straw and Hay	1 cup	236
1 cup	60	*Mixed Greens, Mushroom, and Hazelnut Salad	1 cup	60
1 slice	122	*Tangy French Bread	1 slice	122
1 serving	124	*Butterscotch Soufflé	1 serving	124
	542			542
Snack				
1 cup	118	*Bahamian Cocoa	1 cup	118
—	—	*Sesame-Whole Wheat Pretzels	1 pretzel	108
	118			226
Total	1184		Total	1578

DAY 5

1200 calories			1600 calories	
Breakfast				
1 slice	83	*Raisin Bran English Muffin Loaf	2 slices	166
1 ounce	41	Lean Cooked Ham	2 ounces	82
1 cup	86	Skim Milk	1 cup	86
½ grapefruit	43	Grapefruit	½ grapefruit	43
	253			377
Lunch				
1 serving	215	*Turkey Joes	1 serving	215
1 cup	76	*Apple-Orange Slaw	1 cup	76
—	—	*Barbecued Lima Beans	½ cup	124
1 brownie	70	*Marbled Brownies	1 brownie	70
	361			485
Dinner				
1 serving	108	*Bass with Champagne Sauce	1 serving	108
1 serving	117	*Greek Tomatoes with Rice	1 serving	117
1 serving	33	*Asparagus Salad with Watercress Dressing	1 serving	33
⅔ cup	113	White Wine	⅔ cup	113
1 serving	149	*Frozen Chocolate-Cherry Squares	1 serving	149
	520			520
Snack				
1 nectarine	67	Fresh Nectarine	1 nectarine	67
—	—	Plain Nonfat Yogurt	1 cup	127
	67			194
Total	1201		Total	1576

DAY 7

1200 calories			1600 calories	
Breakfast				
1 serving	57	*Baked Canadian Bacon	1 serving	57
1 serving	104	*Golden Oat Slices	1 serving	104
—	—	*Ambrosia Cup Cooler	½ cup	69
1 cup	86	Skim Milk	1 cup	86
	247			316
Lunch				
1 cup	105	*Fresh Vegetable Soup	1 cup	105
1 cup	51	*Warm Spinach Salad with Feta Cheese	1 cup	51
—	—	*Hearty California Bread	1 slice	143
—	—	*Cranberry-Date Spread	1 tablespoon	22
1 serving	136	*Fresh Strawberry Trifle	1 serving	136
	292			457
Dinner				
1 serving	241	*Oriental Grilled Flank Steak	1 serving	241
½ cup	145	*Chinese "Not Fried" Rice	½ cup	145
½ cup	37	*Lemony Baby Carrots	½ cup	37
—	—	*Mixed Grains-Buttermilk Bread	1 slice	105
½ cup	83	*Apricot Sorbet	½ cup	83
	506			611
Snack				
1 cup	86	Skim Milk	1 cup	86
1 cookie	65	*Lemon Sugar Cookies	2 cookies	130
	151			216
Total	1196		Total	1600

Calorie/Nutrient Chart

FOOD	APPROXIMATE MEASURE	FOOD ENERGY (CALORIES)	PROTEIN (GRAMS)	FAT (GRAMS)	CARBOHYDRATES (GRAMS)	CHOLESTEROL (MILLIGRAMS)	IRON (MILLIGRAMS)	SODIUM (MILLIGRAMS)	CALCIUM (MILLIGRAMS)
Apple									
Cider	½ cup	58	0.1	0.1	14.5	0	0.5	4	9
Fresh, with skin	1 medium	81	0.2	0.5	21.0	0	0.2	0	10
Juice, unsweetened	½ cup	58	0.1	0.1	14.5	0	0.5	4	9
Applesauce, unsweetened	½ cup	52	0.2	0.1	13.8	0	0.1	2	4
Apricot									
Canned, in light syrup	½ cup	75	0.7	0.1	19.0	—	0.3	1	12
Dried, uncooked	1 each	17	0.3	0.0	4.3	0	0.3	1	3
Fresh	1 each	18	0.4	0.1	4.1	0	0.2	0	5
Nectar	½ cup	70	0.5	0.1	18.0	0	0.5	4	9
Artichoke									
Fresh, cooked	1 each	53	2.6	0.2	12.4	0	1.6	79	47
Hearts, cooked	½ cup	37	1.8	0.1	8.7	0	1.1	55	33
Asparagus, fresh, cooked	½ cup	23	2.3	0.3	4.0	0	0.6	4	22
Arugula	3 ounces	20	2.2	0.3	3.3	0	1.0	—	263
Avocado	1 medium	322	3.9	30.6	14.8	0	2.0	20	22
Bacon									
Canadian-style	1 ounce	52	6.9	2.4	0.3	16	0.2	438	3
Cured, broiled	1 slice	29	1.4	2.6	0.1	4	0.1	95	0
Bamboo shoots, cooked	½ cup	7	0.9	0.1	1.1	0	0.1	2	7
Banana									
Mashed	½ cup	101	1.1	0.5	25.8	0	0.3	1	7
Whole	1 medium	109	1.2	0.5	27.6	0	0.4	1	7
Barley, dry	½ cup	349	8.1	1.0	78.8	0	2.0	3	16
Bean sprouts, raw	½ cup	16	1.6	0.1	3.1	0	0.5	3	7
Beans									
Black, cooked	½ cup	114	7.6	0.5	20.4	0	1.8	1	23
Garbanzo, cooked	½ cup	134	7.3	2.1	22.5	0	2.4	6	40
Great Northern, cooked	½ cup	132	9.3	0.5	23.7	0	2.4	2	76
Green, canned, regular pack	½ cup	18	1.0	0.1	4.2	0	1.0	442	29
Green, fresh, cooked	½ cup	22	1.2	0.2	4.9	0	0.8	2	29
Kidney, cooked	½ cup	112	7.7	0.4	20.2	0	2.6	2	25
Lima, frozen, baby	½ cup	94	6	0.3	17.5	0	1.8	26	25
Pinto, cooked	½ cup	117	7.0	0.4	21.9	0	2.2	2	41
Red, cooked	½ cup	112	7.7	0.4	20.2	0	2.6	2	25
Yellow or wax, canned, regular pack	½ cup	17	0.9	0.2	3.6	—	1.1	208	32
Beef, trimmed of fat									
Flank steak, broiled	3 ounces	207	21.6	12.7	0.0	60	2.2	71	5
Ground, extra-lean	3 ounces	213	22.5	13.7	0.0	70	1.9	42	6
Liver, braised	3 ounces	137	20.7	4.2	2.9	331	5.7	60	6
Roast	3 ounces	204	23.1	11.7	0.0	69	2.2	63	9
Round, bottom, braised	3 ounces	189	26.9	8.2	0.0	82	2.9	43	4
Round, eye of, cooked	3 ounces	156	24.7	5.5	0.0	59	1.7	53	4
Sirloin, broiled	3 ounces	177	25.8	7.4	0.0	76	2.9	56	9
Beverages									
Beer	12 fluid ounces	146	1.1	0.0	13.1	0	0.1	18	18
Beer, light	12 fluid ounces	99	0.7	0.0	4.6	0	0.1	11	18
Champagne	6 fluid ounces	134	0.5	0.0	2.1	0	0.9	7	5
Coffee, black	1 cup	5	0.2	0.0	0.9	0	1.0	5	5

Dash (-) indicates insufficient data available

FOOD	APPROXIMATE MEASURE	FOOD ENERGY (CALORIES)	PROTEIN (GRAMS)	FAT (GRAMS)	CARBOHYDRATES (GRAMS)	CHOLESTEROL (MILLIGRAMS)	IRON (MILLIGRAMS)	SODIUM (MILLIGRAMS)	CALCIUM (MILLIGRAMS)
Beverages (continued)									
Coffee liqueur	1 fluid ounce	99	0.0	0.1	13.9	0	0.0	2	0
Cognac brandy	1 fluid ounce	72	—	—	—	0	—	—	0
Crème de menthe liqueur	1 tablespoon	62	0.0	0.1	7.0	0	0.0	1	0
Gin, rum, vodka, or whiskey, 80 proof	1 fluid ounce	68	0.0	0.0	0.0	0	0.0	0.0	0
Sherry, sweet	1 fluid ounce	39	0.1	0.0	2.0	0	0.1	4	2
Vermouth, dry	1 fluid ounce	33	0.0	0.0	1.6	0	0.1	5	2
Vermouth, sweet	1 fluid ounce	43	0.0	0.0	4.5	0	0.1	8	2
Wine, port	6 fluid ounces	267	0.2	0.0	20.4	0	0.7	7	7
Wine, red	6 fluid ounces	116	0.3	0.0	0.4	0	1.4	16	12
Wine, white, dry	6 fluid ounces	113	0.2	0.0	1.1	0	0.9	7.5	15
Beets									
Canned, regular pack	½ cup	30	0.8	0.1	7.2	—	0.5	209	15
Fresh, diced, cooked	½ cup	26	0.9	0.4	5.7	0	0.5	42	9
Blackberries, fresh	½ cup	37	0.5	0.3	9.2	0	0.4	0	23
Blueberries, fresh	½ cup	41	0.5	0.3	10.2	0	0.1	4	4
Bouillon, dry									
Beef-flavored cubes	1 cube	3	0.1	0.0	0.2	—	—	400	—
Beef-flavored granules	1 teaspoon	5	0.0	0.5	0.0	—	—	461	—
Chicken-flavored cubes	1 cube	7	0.2	0.1	0.5	—	—	800	—
Chicken-flavored granules	1 teaspoon	5	0.2	0.5	0.2	—	0.0	381	—
Bran									
Oat, dry, uncooked	½ cup	153	8.0	3.0	23.5	0	2.6	1	31
Wheat, raw	½ cup	59	4.0	1.3	7.5	0	4.4	3	36
Bread									
Bagel, plain	1 each	161	5.9	1.5	30.5	—	1.4	196	23
Bun, hamburger or hot dog	1 each	136	3.2	3.4	22.4	13	0.8	112	19
Cornbread	2-ounce square	168	3.8	6.6	23.1	61	0.8	298	105
English muffin	1 each	174	5.3	1.4	34.6	0	1.9	334	107
French/vienna	1 slice	73	2.3	0.5	13.9	1	0.6	145	11
Light, wheatberry or 7-grain	1 slice	40	2.0	1.0	7.0	5	0.7	11	20
Pita, whole wheat	1 medium	122	2.4	0.9	23.5	0	1.4	—	39
Pumpernickel	1 slice	76	2.8	0.4	16.4	0	0.7	176	26
Raisin	1 slice	66	1.6	0.7	13.4	1	0.3	91	18
Rye	1 slice	61	2.3	0.3	13.0	0	0.4	139	19
White	1 slice	67	2.2	0.8	12.6	1	0.6	127	18
Whole wheat	1 slice	61	2.6	0.8	11.9	1	0.6	132	25
Breadcrumbs, fine, dry	½ cup	196	6.3	2.2	36.7	2	1.7	368	61
Broccoli, fresh, chopped, cooked	½ cup	26	2.8	0.1	4.9	0	0.6	22	47
Broth, beef, homemade	1 cup	22	0.5	0.0	1.9	0	0.0	7	0
Brussels sprouts, fresh, cooked	½ cup	30	2.0	0.4	6.8	0	0.9	16	28
Bulgur, uncooked	½ cup	301	9.5	1.3	64.3	0	3.1	3	25
Butter									
Regular	1 tablespoon	102	0.1	11.5	0.0	31	0.0	117	3
Unsalted	1 tablespoon	102	0.1	11.5	0.0	31	0.0	2	3
Whipped	1 tablespoon	68	0.1	7.7	0.0	21	0.0	78	2
Cabbage									
Bok choy	1 cup	9	1.0	0.1	1.5	0	0.6	45	73
Common varieties, raw, shredded	½ cup	8	0.4	0.1	1.9	0	0.2	6	16
Cake, without frosting									
Angel food	2-ounce slice	166	3.3	0.1	38.1	—	0.1	56	4
Pound	1-ounce slice	305	3.6	17.5	33.7	134	0.5	245	27
Sponge, cut into 12 slices	1 slice	183	3.6	5.0	30.8	221	0.8	99	44
Yellow, cut into 12 slices	1 slice	227	3.6	9.0	33.0	80	0.5	404	30
Candy									
Fudge, chocolate	1 ounce	113	0.8	3.4	21.3	0	0.3	54	22

FOOD	APPROXIMATE MEASURE	FOOD ENERGY (CALORIES)	PROTEIN (GRAMS)	FAT (GRAMS)	CARBOHYDRATES (GRAMS)	CHOLESTEROL (MILLIGRAMS)	IRON (MILLIGRAMS)	SODIUM (MILLIGRAMS)	CALCIUM (MILLIGRAMS)
Candy (*continued*)									
Gumdrops	1 ounce	98	0.0	0.2	24.8	0	0.1	10	2
Hard	1 each	27	0.0	0.0	6.8	0	0.1	2	1
Jelly beans	1 ounce	104	0.0	0.1	26.4	0	0.3	3	3
Marshmallows, large	1 each	26	0.2	0.0	6.4	0	0.1	3	1
Milk chocolate	1 ounce	149	2.0	7.9	16.9	6	—	23	60
Cantaloupe, raw, diced	½ cup	28	0.7	0.2	6.7	0	0.2	7	9
Capers	1 tablespoon	4	0.4	0.0	0.6	0	—	670	—
Carambola	1 medium	42	0.7	0.4	9.9	0	0.3	3	5
Carrot									
Raw	1 medium	30	0.7	0.1	7.1	0	0.3	25	19
Cooked, sliced	½ cup	35	0.8	0.1	8.1	0	0.5	51	24
Catsup									
Regular	1 tablespoon	18	0.3	0.1	4.3	0	0.1	178	4
No-salt-added	1 tablespoon	15	0.0	0.0	4.0	—	—	6	—
Reduced-calorie	1 tablespoon	7	0.0	0.0	1.2	—	0.0	3	0
Cauliflower									
Raw, flowerets	½ cup	10	0.8	0.1	2.1	0	0.2	6	12
Cooked, flowerets	½ cup	15	1.2	0.1	2.8	0	0.2	4	17
Caviar	1 tablespoon	54	5.8	2.8	0.8	65	2.0	374	47
Celeriac, raw, shredded	½ cup	30	1.2	0.2	7.2	0	0.5	78	34
Celery									
Raw, diced	½ cup	10	0.4	0.1	2.2	0	0.3	53	23
Cooked	½ cup	11	0.4	0.1	2.6	0	0.1	48	27
Cereal									
Bran, whole	½ cup	106	6.1	0.7	31.6	0	6.7	480	34
Bran flakes	½ cup	64	2.5	0.4	15.3	0	5.6	182	10
Corn flakes	½ cup	44	0.9	0.0	9.8	0	0.7	140	0
Cream of rice	½ cup	48	0.9	0.1	10.8	0	0.1	303	5
Cream of wheat	½ cup	52	1.5	0.3	10.8	0	4.0	330	23
Granola	½ cup	251	5.7	9.8	37.7	0	1.9	116	36
Crispy rice	½ cup	55	0.9	0.1	12.4	0	0.3	103	3
Whole-grain wheat flakes	½ cup	79	1.9	0.2	18.6	0	0.6	150	6
Puffed wheat	½ cup	28	1.6	0.1	5.5	—	0.1	2	32
Raisin bran	½ cup	77	2.7	0.5	18.6	0	3.0	179	9
Shredded wheat miniatures	½ cup	76	2.3	0.5	17.0	0	0.9	2	8
Toasted oat	½ cup	44	1.7	0.7	7.8	0	1.8	123	19
Cheese									
American, processed, skim	1 ounce	69	6.0	5.0	1.0	10	—	—	149
American, processed	1 ounce	106	6.3	8.9	0.5	27	0.1	405	175
Blue	1 ounce	100	6.0	8.1	0.7	21	0.1	395	150
Brie	1 ounce	95	5.9	7.8	0.1	28	0.1	178	52
Cheddar	1 ounce	114	7.0	9.4	0.3	30	0.2	176	204
Cheddar, 40% less-fat	1 ounce	71	5.0	4.1	6.0	—	0.1	150	192
Cottage, dry curd, no-salt-added	½ cup	62	12.5	0.3	1.3	5	0.2	9	23
Cottage, low-fat, (1% milk-fat)	½ cup	81	14.0	1.1	3.1	5	0.2	459	69
Cottage, low-fat, (2% milk-fat)	½ cup	102	15.5	2.2	4.1	9	0.2	459	77
Cottage, (4% milk-fat)	½ cup	108	13.1	4.7	2.8	16	0.1	425	63
Cream, light	1 ounce	60	3.0	5.0	2.0	—	—	159	40
Farmers	1 ounce	40	4.0	3.0	1.0	—	—	—	30
Feta	1 ounce	75	4.0	6.0	1.2	25	0.2	316	139
Fontina	1 ounce	110	7.3	8.8	0.4	33	0.1	—	156
Gouda	1 ounce	101	7.1	7.8	0.6	32	0.1	232	198
Gruyère	1 ounce	117	8.4	9.2	0.1	31	—	95	287
Monterey Jack	1 ounce	64	9.9	3.0	1.0	9	—	64	298
Mozzarella, part-skim	1 ounce	72	6.9	4.5	0.8	16	0.1	132	183
Mozzarella, whole milk	1 ounce	80	5.5	6.1	0.6	22	0.0	106	147
Muenster	1 ounce	104	6.6	8.5	0.3	27	0.1	178	203

Dash (-) indicates insufficient data available

FOOD	APPROXIMATE MEASURE	FOOD ENERGY (CALORIES)	PROTEIN (GRAMS)	FAT (GRAMS)	CARBOHYDRATES (GRAMS)	CHOLESTEROL (MILLIGRAMS)	IRON (MILLIGRAMS)	SODIUM (MILLIGRAMS)	CALCIUM (MILLIGRAMS)
Cheese (continued)									
Neufchâtel	1 ounce	74	2.8	6.6	0.8	22	0.1	113	21
Parmesan, grated	1 ounce	111	10.1	7.3	0.9	19	0.2	454	336
Provolone	1 ounce	100	7.2	7.5	0.6	20	0.1	248	214
Ricotta, part-skim	1 ounce	39	3.2	2.2	1.5	9	0.1	35	77
Romano, grated	1 ounce	110	9.0	7.6	1.0	29	—	340	302
Swiss	1 ounce	107	8.1	7.8	1.0	26	0.0	74	272
Cherries									
Fresh, sweet	½ cup	52	0.9	0.7	12.0	0	0.3	0	11
Sour, sweetened	½ cup	127	1.0	1.1	33.1	0	1.7	10	14
Sour, unsweetened	½ cup	36	0.7	0.3	8.5	0	0.4	1	10
Chicken, skinned, boned and roasted									
White meat	3 ounces	140	26.4	3.0	0.0	72	0.9	63	13
Dark meat	3 ounces	174	23.3	8.3	0.0	79	1.1	79	13
Liver	3 ounces	134	20.7	4.6	0.7	537	7.2	43	12
Chili sauce	1 tablespoon	18	0.4	0.1	4.2	0	0.1	228	3
Chives, raw, chopped	1 tablespoon	1	0.1	0.0	0.1	0	0.0	0	2
Chocolate									
Semisweet	1 ounce	144	1.2	10.1	16.2	0	0.7	1	9
Sweet	1 ounce	150	1.2	9.9	16.4	0	0.4	9	27
Syrup, fudge	1 tablespoon	65	0.9	2.5	9.6	—	0.2	22	19
Unsweetened, baking	1 ounce	141	3.1	14.7	8.5	0	2.0	1	23
Chutney	1 tablespoon	41	0.2	0.0	10.5	—	0.2	34	5
Cilantro, fresh, minced	1 tablespoon	1	0.1	0.0	0.3	0	0.2	1	5
Clams									
Canned, drained	½ cup	118	20.4	1.6	4.1	54	22.4	90	74
Raw	½ cup	92	15.8	1.2	3.2	42	17.3	69	57
Cocoa powder, unsweetened	1 tablespoon	24	1.6	0.7	2.6	—	0.9	0	8
Coconut									
Fresh, grated	1 cup	526	5.5	51.4	18.8	0	2.6	30	21
Dried, unsweetened, shredded	1 cup	526	5.5	51.4	18.8	0	2.6	30	21
Dried, sweetened, shredded	1 cup	463	2.7	32.8	44.0	0	1.8	242	14
Collard greens, cooked	½ cup	12	0.9	0.1	2.2	0	0.3	16	66
Cookies									
Brownie	2-ounce bar	243	2.7	10.1	39.0	10	1.3	153	25
Chocolate	1 each	72	1.0	3.4	9.4	13	0.4	61	18
Chocolate chip, homemade	1 each	69	0.9	4.6	6.8	7	0.3	30	7
Oatmeal, plain	1 each	57	0.9	2.7	7.2	9	0.3	46	13
Sandwich, with creme	1 each	40	0.3	1.7	6.0	—	0.2	41	2
Sugar	1 each	50	0.3	2.7	6.6	—	0.1	38	2
Vanilla wafers	1 each	19	0.2	0.9	2.5	—	0.1	16	2
Corn									
Cream-style, regular pack	½ cup	92	2.2	0.5	23.2	0	0.5	365	4
Fresh, kernels, cooked	½ cup	89	2.6	1.0	20.6	0	0.5	14	2
Cornmeal									
Enriched, dry	1 cup	453	10.9	1.7	95.2	0	4.0	1	8
Self-rising	1 cup	465	11.4	4.3	95.8	0	2.3	1849	402
Cornstarch	1 tablespoon	29	0.0	0.0	7.0	0	0.0	0	0
Couscous, cooked	½ cup	98	3.5	0.0	20.6	—	0.5	—	10
Crab									
Blue, cooked	3 ounces	87	17.2	1.5	0.0	85	0.8	237	88
Imitation	3 ounces	75	10.2	0.0	8.4	—	0.6	—	255
Crackers									
Animal	1 each	14	0.2	0.4	2.3	—	—	11	—
Butter	1 each	17	0.0	1.0	2.0	—	0.1	32	4
Graham, plain	1 each	54	1.1	1.3	10.3	0	0.2	94	6
Melba rounds, plain	1 each	11	0.4	0.2	2.0	—	0.1	26	—
Saltine	1 each	13	0.3	0.3	2.0	—	0.1	43	5
Whole wheat	1 each	27	0.5	1.0	3.5	—	0.1	50	0

FOOD	APPROXIMATE MEASURE	FOOD ENERGY (CALORIES)	PROTEIN (GRAMS)	FAT (GRAMS)	CARBOHYDRATES (GRAMS)	CHOLESTEROL (MILLIGRAMS)	IRON (MILLIGRAMS)	SODIUM (MILLIGRAMS)	CALCIUM (MILLIGRAMS)
Cranberry									
Fresh, whole	½ cup	23	0.2	0.1	6.0	0	0.1	0	3
Juice cocktail, reduced-calorie	½ cup	24	0.0	0.0	5.9	—	2.8	4	7
Juice cocktail, regular	½ cup	75	0.0	0.1	19.2	0	0.2	5	4
Sauce, sweetened	¼ cup	105	0.1	0.1	26.9	0	0.1	20	3
Cream									
Half-and-half	1 tablespoon	20	0.5	1.7	0.7	6	0.0	6	16
Whipping	1 tablespoon	51	0.3	5.5	0.4	20	0.0	6	10
Sour	1 tablespoon	31	0.5	0.3	0.6	6	0.0	8	17
Sour, reduced-calorie	1 tablespoon	20	0.4	1.8	0.6	6	0.0	6	16
Creamer, non-dairy	1 teaspoon	11	0.1	0.7	1.1	0	0.0	4	16
Croutons, seasoned	1 ounce	139	3.0	5.0	18.9	—	0.3	—	20
Cucumbers, raw, whole	1 medium	32	1.3	0.3	7.1	0	0.7	5	34
Currants	1 tablespoon	25	0.3	0.2	6.1	—	0.3	3	8
Dates, pitted, unsweetened	5 each	114	0.8	0.2	30.5	0	0.5	1	13
Doughnut									
Cake type	1 each	156	1.8	7.4	20.6	24	0.5	200	16
Plain, yeast	1 each	166	2.5	10.7	15.1	10	0.6	94	15
Egg									
White	1 each	16	3.5	0.0	0.4	0	0.0	49	4
Whole	1 each	75	6.4	5.1	0.6	213	1.0	69	28
Yolk	1 each	59	2.8	5.1	0.0	213	0.9	8	26
Substitute	¼ cup	30	6.0	0.0	1.0	0	1.1	90	20
Eggplant, cooked without salt	½ cup	13	0.4	0.1	3.2	0	0.2	1	3
Extracts									
Almond	1 teaspoon	10	—	—	—	—	—	—	—
Coconut	1 teaspoon	6	—	—	—	—	—	—	—
Peppermint	1 teaspoon	22	—	—	—	—	—	—	—
Vanilla	1 teaspoon	12	—	—	—	—	—	—	—
Fennel, leaves, raw	½ cup	13	1.2	0.2	2.3	0	1.2	4	45
Figs									
Fresh	1 medium	37	0.4	0.2	9.9	0	0.2	1	18
Dried	1 each	48	0.6	0.2	12.2	0	0.4	2	27
Fish, cooked									
Catfish, farm-raised	3 ounces	195	15.4	11.3	6.8	69	1.2	238	37
Cod	3 ounces	89	19.4	0.7	0.0	47	0.4	66	12
Flounder	3 ounces	100	20.5	1.3	0.0	58	0.3	89	15
Grouper	3 ounces	100	21.1	1.1	0.0	40	1.0	45	18
Haddock	3 ounces	95	20.6	0.8	0.0	63	1.1	74	36
Halibut	3 ounces	119	22.7	2.5	0.0	35	0.9	59	51
Mackerel	3 ounces	134	20.1	5.4	0.0	62	0.6	56	11
Perch	3 ounces	100	21.1	1.0	0.0	98	1.0	67	87
Pollock	3 ounces	96	20.0	1.0	0.0	82	0.2	99	5
Pompano	3 ounces	179	20.1	10.3	0.0	54	0.6	65	37
Salmon	3 ounces	184	23.2	9.3	0.0	74	0.5	56	6
Scrod	3 ounces	89	19.4	0.7	0.0	47	0.4	66	12
Snapper	3 ounces	109	22.4	1.5	0.0	40	0.2	48	34
Sole	3 ounces	100	20.5	1.3	0.0	58	0.3	89	15
Swordfish	3 ounces	132	21.6	4.4	0.0	43	0.9	98	5
Trout	3 ounces	128	22.4	3.7	0.0	62	2.1	29	73
Tuna, canned in water	6½ ounces	251	49.1	4.5	0.0	77	1.1	722	—
Tuna, canned in oil	6½ ounces	343	48.9	14.9	0.0	57	1.2	730	7

Dash (-) indicates insufficient data available

FOOD	APPROXIMATE MEASURE	FOOD ENERGY (CALORIES)	PROTEIN (GRAMS)	FAT (GRAMS)	CARBOHYDRATES (GRAMS)	CHOLESTEROL (MILLIGRAMS)	IRON (MILLIGRAMS)	SODIUM (MILLIGRAMS)	CALCIUM (MILLIGRAMS)
Flour									
All-purpose, unsifted	1 cup	499	14.4	1.4	104.1	0	4.0	3	22
Bread, sifted	1 cup	420	13.6	1.3	85.8	0	3.3	2	18
Buckwheat, light, unsifted	1 cup	340	6.3	1.2	77.9	0	1.0	2	11
Cake, sifted	1 cup	349	7.2	0.8	76.2	0	0.5	2	16
Rye, light, sifted	1 cup	314	8.2	0.9	68.6	0	1.0	1	19
Whole wheat, unsifted	1 cup	400	16.0	2.4	85.2	0	3.8	4	49
Frankfurter									
All-meat	1 each	130	5.8	11.2	1.1	29	0.8	484	3
Chicken	1 each	113	5.7	8.6	3.0	44	0.9	603	42
Turkey	1 each	63	3.8	5.3	0.1	—	0.3	299	33
Fruit bits, dried	1 ounce	93	1.3	0.0	20.0	0	0.5	24	—
Fruit cocktail, canned, packed in juice	½ cup	57	0.6	0.0	14.6	0	0.2	5	10
Garlic, raw	1 clove	4	0.2	0.0	1.0	0	0.1	1	5
Gelatin									
Flavored, prepared with water	½ cup	80	2.0	—	18.9	—	—	90	—
Unflavored	1 teaspoon	10	2.6	0.0	0.0	—	—	3	—
Grape juice									
Concord	½ cup	77	0.7	0.1	18.9	0	0.3	4	11
White	½ cup	84	0.0	0.0	21.5	0	0.4	5	17
Grapefruit									
Fresh	1 medium	77	1.5	0.2	19.3	0	0.2	0	29
Juice, unsweetened	½ cup	47	0.6	0.1	11.1	0	2.5	1	9
Grapes, green, seedless	1 cup	114	1.1	0.9	28.4	0	0.4	3	18
Grits, cooked	½ cup	73	1.6	0.2	15.7	0	0.8	0	0
Ham									
Cured, roasted, extra-lean	3 ounces	123	17.8	4.7	1.3	45	1.3	1023	7
Turkey ham	3 ounces	105	16.7	4.3	0.0	48	2.3	587	9
Hominy									
Golden	½ cup	80	1.5	0.5	17.1	0	0.6	—	—
White	½ cup	75	2.1	0.0	17.1	0	0.7	—	—
Honey	1 tablespoon	64	0.1	0.0	17.5	0	0.1	1	1
Honeydew, raw, diced	1 cup	59	0.8	0.2	15.6	0	0.1	17	10
Horseradish, prepared	1 tablespoon	6	0.2	0.0	1.4	0	0.1	14	9
Hot sauce, bottled	¼ teaspoon	0	0.0	0.0	0.0	0	0.0	9	0
Ice cream, vanilla, regular	½ cup	134	2.3	7.2	15.9	30	0.0	58	88
Ice milk, vanilla	½ cup	92	2.6	2.8	14.5	9	0.1	52	88
Ice, cherry	½ cup	82	0.2	0.0	10.3	—	—	0	—
Jams and Jellies									
Regular	1 tablespoon	51	0.0	0.0	13.2	0	0.3	3	4
Reduced-calorie	1 tablespoon	29	0.1	0.0	7.4	0	0.0	16	1
Jicama	1 cup	49	1.6	0.2	10.5	0	0.7	7	18
Kiwifruit	1 each	44	1.0	0.5	8.9	0	0.4	0	20
Kumquat	1 each	11	0.2	0.0	3.0	0	0.1	1	8
Lamb									
Leg, roasted	3 ounces	158	24.4	6.0	0.0	85	1.9	60	11
Loin, broiled	3 ounces	156	24.0	6.0	0.0	85	1.7	60	9
Chop	3 ounces	160	24.0	6.4	0.0	85	1.7	60	10
Ground, cooked	3 ounces	160	24.0	6.4	0.0	85	1.7	60	10

FOOD	APPROXIMATE MEASURE	FOOD ENERGY (CALORIES)	PROTEIN (GRAMS)	FAT (GRAMS)	CARBOHYDRATES (GRAMS)	CHOLESTEROL (MILLIGRAMS)	IRON (MILLIGRAMS)	SODIUM (MILLIGRAMS)	CALCIUM (MILLIGRAMS)
Lard	1 tablespoon	116	0.0	12.8	0.0	12	0.0	0	0
Leeks, bulb, raw	½ cup	32	0.8	0.2	7.3	0	1.0	10	31
Lemon									
Fresh	1 each	16	0.6	0.2	5.2	0	0.3	1	15
Juice	1 tablespoon	4	0.1	0.0	1.3	0	0.0	0	1
Lemonade, sweetened	1 cup	99	0.2	0.0	26.0	0	0.4	7	7
Lentils, cooked	½ cup	115	8.9	0.4	19.9	0	3.3	2	19
Lettuce									
Boston or Bibb, shredded	1 cup	7	0.7	0.1	1.3	0	0.2	3	—
Belgian endive	1 cup	14	0.9	0.1	2.9	0	0.5	6	—
Curly endive or escarole	1 cup	8	0.6	0.1	1.7	0	0.4	11	26
Iceberg, chopped	1 cup	7	0.5	0.1	1.1	0	0.3	5	10
Romaine, chopped	1 cup	9	0.9	0.1	1.3	0	0.6	4	20
Lime									
Fresh	1 each	20	0.4	0.1	6.8	0	0.4	1	21
Juice	1 tablespoon	4	0.1	0.0	1.4	0	0.0	0	1
Lobster, cooked, meat only	3 ounces	83	17.4	0.5	1.1	61	0.3	323	52
Luncheon meats									
Bologna	1 slice	74	2.5	6.9	0.4	13	0.2	241	2
Deviled ham	1 ounce	78	4.3	6.7	0.0	—	0.3	—	1
Salami	1 ounce	74	4.0	6.2	0.6	—	0.4	393	—
Turkey ham	1 ounce	35	5.6	1.4	0.0	16	0.8	196	3
Turkey pastrami	1 ounce	34	5.3	1.4	0.0	16	0.5	218	3
Lychees, raw	1 each	6	0.1	0.0	1.6	0	0.0	0	0
Mango, raw	½ cup	54	0.4	0.2	14.0	0	0.1	2	8
Margarine									
Regular	1 tablespoon	101	0.1	11.4	0.1	0	0.0	133	4
Reduced-calorie, stick	1 tablespoon	60	0.0	7.3	0.0	0	0.0	110	0
Salt-free	1 tablespoon	101	0.1	11.3	0.1	0	0.0	0	2
Marmalade, orange, low-sugar	1 tablespoon	24	0.0	0.0	6.0	—	—	0.0	—
Mayonnaise									
Regular	1 tablespoon	99	0.2	10.9	0.4	8	0.1	78	2
Reduced-calorie	1 tablespoon	44	0.1	4.6	0.7	6	0.0	88	1
Milk									
Buttermilk, nonfat	1 cup	90	9.0	1.0	12.0	—	—	255	285
Chocolate, low-fat	1 cup	158	8.1	2.5	26.1	8	0.6	153	288
Condensed, sweetened	1 cup	982	24.2	26.3	166.5	104	0.5	389	869
Evaporated, skim, canned	1 cup	200	19.3	0.5	29.1	10	0.7	294	742
Low-fat, 2% fat	1 cup	122	8.1	4.7	11.7	20	0.1	122	298
Low-fat, 1% fat	1 cup	102	8.0	2.5	11.6	10	0.1	122	300
Nonfat dry	⅓ cup	145	14.5	0.3	20.8	8	0.1	214	503
Powder, malted	1 tablespoon	35	1.0	0.6	6.2	—	0.1	43	26
Skim	1 cup	86	8.3	0.4	11.9	5	0.1	127	301
Whole	1 cup	156	8.0	8.9	11.3	34	0.1	120	290
Molasses, cane, light	1 tablespoon	52	0.0	0.0	13.3	0	0.9	3	34
Mushrooms									
Fresh	½ cup	9	0.7	0.1	1.6	0	0.4	1	2
Canned	¼ cup	13	0.1	0.1	2.5	0	0.0	1	1
Shiitake, dried	1 each	14	0.3	0.0	2.6	0	0.1	0	0
Mussels, blue, cooked	3 ounces	146	20.2	3.8	6.3	48	5.7	314	28
Mustard									
Dijon	1 tablespoon	18	0.0	1.0	1.0	0	—	446	—
Prepared, yellow	1 tablespoon	12	0.7	0.7	1.0	0	0.3	196	13
Nectarine, fresh	1 each	67	1.3	0.6	16.1	0	0.2	0	7

Dash (-) indicates insufficient data available

FOOD	APPROXIMATE MEASURE	FOOD ENERGY (CALORIES)	PROTEIN (GRAMS)	FAT (GRAMS)	CARBOHYDRATES (GRAMS)	CHOLESTEROL (MILLIGRAMS)	IRON (MILLIGRAMS)	SODIUM (MILLIGRAMS)	CALCIUM (MILLIGRAMS)
Nuts									
Almonds, chopped	1 tablespoon	48	1.6	4.2	1.7	0	0.3	1	22
Hazelnuts, chopped	1 tablespoon	45	0.9	4.5	1.1	0	0.2	0	14
Peanuts, roasted, unsalted	1 tablespoon	53	2.4	4.5	1.7	0	0.2	1	8
Pecans, chopped	1 tablespoon	50	0.6	5.0	1.4	0	0.2	0	3
Pine	1 tablespoon	52	2.4	5.1	1.4	0	0.9	0	3
Pistachio nuts	1 tablespoon	46	1.6	3.9	2.0	0	0.5	0	11
Walnuts, black	1 tablespoon	47	1.9	4.4	0.9	0	0.2	0	5
Oats									
Cooked	1 cup	145	5.8	2.3	25.3	0	1.6	374	19
Rolled, dry	½ cup	154	6.4	2.5	26.8	0	1.7	—	21
Oil									
Canola (rapeseed)	1 tablespoon	117	0.0	13.6	0.0	0	0.0	0	0
Vegetable	1 tablespoon	121	0.0	13.6	0.0	0	0.0	0	0
Olive	1 tablespoon	119	0.0	13.5	0.0	0	0.0	0	0
Sesame	1 teaspoon	40	0.0	4.5	0.0	0	0.0	0	0
Okra, cooked	½ cup	26	1.5	0.1	5.8	0	0.3	4	50
Olives									
Black	1 medium	5	0.0	0.4	0.3	0	0.1	35	4
Green, stuffed	½ cup	54	0.7	4.6	3.8	0	2.2	606	63
Onions									
Green	1 tablespoon	2	0.1	0.0	0.3	0	0.1	0	4
Cooked, yellow or white	½ cup	15	0.4	0.1	3.3	0	0.1	4	14
Raw, chopped	½ cup	29	1.0	0.2	6.2	0	0.3	2	21
Orange									
Fresh	1 medium	62	1.2	0.2	15.4	0	0.1	0	52
Juice	½ cup	56	0.8	0.1	13.4	0	0.1	1	11
Mandarin, canned, packed in juice	½ cup	46	0.7	0.0	12.0	0	0.4	6	14
Oysters, raw	1 cup	171	17.5	6.1	9.7	136	16.6	278	112
Papaya									
Fresh, cubed	½ cup	27	0.4	0.1	6.9	0	0.1	2	17
Nectar, canned	½ cup	71	0.3	0.3	18.1	0	0.4	6	13
Parsley, raw	1 tablespoon	1	0.1	0.0	0.3	0	0.2	1	5
Parsnip, cooked, diced	½ cup	63	1.0	0.2	15.1	0	0.4	8	29
Passion fruit	1 medium	17	0.4	0.1	4.2	0	0.3	5	2
Pasta, cooked									
Macaroni	½ cup	78	2.4	0.3	16.1	0	0.6	1	6
Medium egg noodles	½ cup	100	3.2	1.2	18.6	25	0.6	2	8
Lasagna noodles	½ cup	100	3.2	1.2	18.6	25	0.6	2	8
Rice noodles	½ cup	138	3.1	1.3	28.6	0	2.2	—	40
Spinach noodles	½ cup	100	3.8	1.0	18.9	0	1.8	22	46
Spaghetti	½ cup	96	3.2	0.3	19.6	0	0.7	1	7
Whole wheat	½ cup	100	3.7	1.4	19.8	0	1.0	1	12
Peaches									
Fresh	1 medium	54	0.9	0.1	13.9	0	0.1	0	6
Canned, packed in juice	½ cup	56	0.8	0.0	14.7	0	0.3	5	8
Peanut butter									
Regular	1 tablespoon	95	4.6	8.3	2.6	0	0.3	79	5
No-salt-added	1 tablespoon	95	4.6	8.3	2.6	0	0.3	3	5
Pear									
Fresh	1 medium	97	0.6	0.7	24.9	0	0.4	0	18
Canned, packed in juice	½ cup	62	0.4	0.1	16.0	0	0.3	5	11
Juice	½ cup	59	0.0	0.0	14.2	—	—	6	—
Peas									
Black-eyed, cooked	½ cup	90	6.7	0.7	15.0	0	1.2	3	23
Chinese, pods	½ cup	34	2.6	0.2	5.6	0	1.6	3	34

FOOD	APPROXIMATE MEASURE	FOOD ENERGY (CALORIES)	PROTEIN (GRAMS)	FAT (GRAMS)	CARBOHYDRATES (GRAMS)	CHOLESTEROL (MILLIGRAMS)	IRON (MILLIGRAMS)	SODIUM (MILLIGRAMS)	CALCIUM (MILLIGRAMS)
Peas (continued)									
English, cooked	½ cup	62	4.1	0.2	11.4	0	1.2	70	19
Split, cooked	½ cup	116	8.2	0.4	20.7	0	1.3	2	14
Peppers									
Sweet, raw, green, red or yellow	1 medium	23	0.7	0.5	4.8	0	1.1	3	5
Sweet, chopped	½ cup	19	0.6	0.3	4.0	0	0.9	2	4
Jalapeño, green	1 each	4	0.2	0.0	0.9	0	0.1	1	2
Picante sauce	1 tablespoon	5	0.2	0.0	0.9	—	0.1	108	2
Pickle									
Dill, sliced	¼ cup	4	0.2	0.1	0.9	0	0.4	553	10
Relish, chopped, sour	1 tablespoon	3	0.1	0.1	0.4	0	0.2	207	4
Sweet, sliced	¼ cup	57	0.2	0.2	14.1	0	0.5	276	5
Pimiento, diced	1 tablespoon	5	0.2	0.1	1.1	0	0.3	5	1
Pie, baked, 9-inch diameter, cut into 8 slices									
Apple, fresh	1 slice	409	3.3	15.3	67.7	12	0.8	229	37
Chocolate meringue	1 slice	354	6.8	13.4	53.8	109	1.2	307	130
Egg custard	1 slice	248	7.3	11.6	28.6	149	0.9	229	129
Peach	1 slice	327	3.2	11.0	55.1	0	1.0	339	35
Pecan	1 slice	478	5.8	20.3	71.1	141	2.4	324	51
Pumpkin	1 slice	181	4.0	6.8	27.0	61	1.1	210	78
Pineapple									
Fresh, diced	½ cup	38	0.3	0.3	9.6	0	0.3	1	5
Canned, packed in light syrup	½ cup	82	0.4	0.1	21.3	—	0.4	1	15
Canned, packed in juice	½ cup	81	0.6	0.1	21.0	—	0.6	1	22
Juice, unsweetened	½ cup	70	0.4	0.1	17.2	0	0.3	1	21
Plum, fresh	1 medium	35	0.5	0.4	8.3	0	0.1	0	3
Popcorn, hot-air popped	1 cup	23	0.8	0.3	4.6	0	0.2	0	1
Poppy seeds	1 tablespoon	47	1.6	3.9	2.1	0	0.8	2	127
Pork, cooked									
Roast	3 ounces	208	21.6	12.7	0.0	82	1.3	65	7
Tenderloin	3 ounces	141	24.5	4.1	0.0	79	1.3	57	8
Chop, center-loin	3 ounces	204	24.2	11.1	0.0	77	0.9	59	5
Spareribs	3 ounces	338	24.7	25.7	0.0	103	1.5	79	40
Sausage	1 link	44	2.4	3.7	0.1	10	0.1	155	4
Sausage patty	1 ounce	105	5.6	8.8	0.3	24	0.3	367	9
Potatoes									
Baked, with skin	1 each	218	4.4	0.2	50.4	0	2.7	16	20
Boiled, diced	½ cup	67	1.3	0.1	15.6	0	0.2	4	6
Fried	½ cup	228	3.4	12.0	27.6	0	0.9	190	13
Potato chips									
Regular	10 each	105	1.3	7.1	10.4	0	0.2	94	5
No-salt-added	10 each	105	1.3	7.1	10.4	0	0.2	2	5
Pretzel sticks	10 each	106	2.1	0.0	23.3	—	1.4	772	9
Prunes									
Dried, pitted	5 large	127	1.1	1.4	30.9	—	1.1	23	21
Juice	½ cup	91	0.8	0.0	22.3	0	1.5	5	15
Pumpkin, canned	½ cup	42	1.3	0.3	9.9	0	1.7	6	32
Radish, fresh, sliced	½ cup	10	0.3	0.3	2.1	0	0.2	14	12
Raisins	1 tablespoon	27	0.3	0.0	7.2	0	0.2	1	4
Raspberries									
Black, fresh	½ cup	33	0.6	0.4	7.7	0	0.4	0	15
Red, fresh	½ cup	30	0.6	0.3	7.1	0	0.3	0	14
Rhubarb									
Diced, raw	½ cup	13	0.5	0.1	2.8	0	0.1	2	52
Cooked, with sugar	½ cup	157	0.5	0.1	42.1	0	0.3	1	196

Dash (-) indicates insufficient data available

FOOD	APPROXIMATE MEASURE	FOOD ENERGY (CALORIES)	PROTEIN (GRAMS)	FAT (GRAMS)	CARBOHYDRATES (GRAMS)	CHOLESTEROL (MILLIGRAMS)	IRON (MILLIGRAMS)	SODIUM (MILLIGRAMS)	CALCIUM (MILLIGRAMS)
Rice cake, plain	1 each	36	0.7	0.2	7.7	0	0.2	1	1
Rice, cooked without salt or fat									
Brown	½ cup	102	2.0	0.6	21.9	0	0.4	2	9
White, long-grain	½ cup	103	1.8	0.1	22.7	0	0.8	1	7
White, enriched	½ cup	93	1.7	0.1	20.3	0	0.7	313	17
Wild	½ cup	85	3.1	1.2	16.2	3	0.8	12	4
Roll									
Croissant	1 each	272	4.6	17.3	24.6	47	1.1	384	32
Plain, brown-and-serve	1 each	84	2.2	1.9	14.1	2	0.5	144	13
Hard	1 each	156	4.9	1.6	29.8	2	1.1	313	24
Whole wheat	1 each	72	2.3	1.8	12.0	9	0.5	149	16
Rutabaga, cooked, cubed	½ cup	29	0.9	0.2	6.6	0	0.4	15	36
Salad dressing									
Blue cheese	1 tablespoon	84	0.4	9.2	0.3	0	0.0	216	3
Blue cheese, low calorie	1 tablespoon	14	0.7	1.1	1.0	3	0.0	307	18
French	1 tablespoon	96	0.3	9.4	2.9	8	0.1	205	6
French, low calorie	1 tablespoon	22	0.0	0.9	3.5	1	0.1	128	2
Italian	1 tablespoon	84	0.1	9.1	0.6	0	0.0	172	1
Italian, no oil, low calorie	1 tablespoon	8	0.1	0.0	1.8	0	0.0	161	1
Thousand Island	1 tablespoon	59	0.1	5.6	2.4	—	0.1	109	2
Thousand Island, low calorie	1 tablespoon	24	0.1	1.6	2.5	2	0.1	153	2
Salt, iodized	1 teaspoon	0	0.0	0.0	0.0	0	0.0	2343	15
Sauerkraut, canned	½ cup	16	0.9	0.2	3.2	0	0.4	788	27
Scallops, raw, large	1 each	13	2.5	0.1	0.4	5	0.0	24	4
Sesame seeds, dry, whole	1 teaspoon	17	0.5	1.5	0.7	0	0.4	0	29
Shallot, bulb, raw, chopped	½ cup	58	2.0	0.1	13.4	0	1.0	10	30
Sherbet, orange	½ cup	135	1.1	1.9	29.3	7	0.1	44	52
Shortening	1 tablespoon	94	0.0	10.6	0.0	—	—	—	—
Shrimp									
Fresh, peeled and deveined	½ pound	240	46.1	3.9	2.1	345	5.5	336	118
Canned, drained	½ cup	77	14.8	1.3	0.7	111	1.8	108	38
Soy sauce									
Regular	1 tablespoon	8	0.8	0.0	1.2	0	0.3	829	2
Reduced-sodium	1 tablespoon	8	0.8	0.0	1.2	0	0.3	484	2
Low-sodium	1 tablespoon	6	0.0	0.0	0.0	—	—	390	—
Soup, condensed, made with water									
Beef broth	1 cup	31	4.8	0.7	2.6	24	0.5	782	0
Chicken noodle	1 cup	75	4.0	2.4	9.3	7	0.7	1106	17
Chili, beef	1 cup	170	6.8	6.6	21.4	12	1.1	518	21
Cream of chicken	1 cup	117	2.9	7.3	9.0	10	0.6	986	34
Cream of mushroom	1 cup	129	2.3	9.0	9.0	2	0.5	1032	46
Cream of potato	1 cup	73	1.7	2.3	11.0	5	0.5	1000	20
Onion	1 cup	58	3.7	1.7	8.2	0	0.7	1053	27
Tomato	1 cup	85	2.0	1.9	16.6	0	1.7	871	12
Vegetable, beef	1 cup	82	3.0	1.9	13.1	2	1.0	810	17
Vegetable, vegetarian	1 cup	72	2.1	1.9	12.0	0	1.0	822	22
Spinach									
Fresh	1 cup	12	1.6	0.2	2.0	0	1.5	44	55
Cooked	½ cup	21	2.7	0.2	3.4	0	3.2	63	122
Canned, regular pack	½ cup	25	3.0	0.5	3.6	0	2.4	397	99
Squash, cooked									
Acorn	½ cup	57	1.1	0.1	14.9	0	1.0	4	45
Butternut	½ cup	41	0.8	0.1	10.7	0	0.6	4	42
Spaghetti	½ cup	22	0.5	0.2	5.0	0	0.3	14	16
Summer	½ cup	21	1.0	0.3	4.5	0	0.4	1	28
Strawberries, raw	1 cup	45	0.9	0.6	10.5	0	0.6	1	21

FOOD	APPROXIMATE MEASURE	FOOD ENERGY (CALORIES)	PROTEIN (GRAMS)	FAT (GRAMS)	CARBOHYDRATES (GRAMS)	CHOLESTEROL (MILLIGRAMS)	IRON (MILLIGRAMS)	SODIUM (MILLIGRAMS)	CALCIUM (MILLIGRAMS)
Sugar									
Granulated	1 tablespoon	48	0.0	0.0	12.4	0	0.0	0	0
Brown, packed	1 tablespoon	51	0.0	0.0	13.3	0	0.5	4	12
Powdered	1 tablespoon	29	0.0	0.0	7.5	0	0.0	0	0
Sunflower kernels	¼ cup	205	8.2	17.8	6.8	0	2.4	1	42
Sweet potatoes									
Whole, baked	½ cup	103	1.7	0.1	24.3	0	0.4	10	28
Mashed	½ cup	172	2.7	0.5	39.8	0	0.9	21	34
Syrup									
Corn, dark or light	1 tablespoon	60	0.0	0.0	15.4	0	0.8	14	9
Chocolate-flavored	1 tablespoon	49	0.6	0.2	11.0	—	0.3	13	3
Maple, reduced-calorie	1 tablespoon	6	0.0	0.0	2.0	0	—	4	—
Pancake	1 tablespoon	50	0.0	0.0	12.8	0	0.2	2	20
Taco shell	1 each	52	0.7	2.8	5.9	—	0.4	62	—
Tangerine									
Fresh	1 medium	38	0.5	0.1	9.6	0	0.1	1	12
Juice, unsweetened	½ cup	53	0.6	0.2	12.5	0	0.2	1	22
Tapioca, dry	1 tablespoon	32	0.1	0.0	7.8	0	0.0	0	1
Tofu									
Firm	4 ounces	94	9.0	6.5	1.5	—	1.0	8	113
Soft	4 ounces	65	6.0	4.0	2.0	—	1.4	2	193
Tomato									
Fresh	1 medium	27	1.2	0.3	6.1	0	0.6	11	10
Cooked	½ cup	30	1.3	0.3	6.8	0	0.7	13	10
Juice, regular	1 cup	41	1.8	0.1	10.3	0	1.4	881	22
Juice, no-salt-added	1 cup	41	1.8	0.1	10.3	0	1.4	24	22
Paste, regular	1 tablespoon	14	0.6	0.1	3.1	0	0.5	129	6
Paste, no-salt-added	1 tablespoon	14	0.6	0.1	3.1	0	0.5	11	6
Sauce, regular	½ cup	37	1.6	0.2	8.8	0	0.9	741	17
Sauce, no-salt-added	½ cup	42	1.2	0.0	9.7	—	—	27	—
Whole, canned, peeled	½ cup	25	1.2	0.2	5.1	—	0.6	155	38
Whole, canned, no-salt-added	½ cup	22	0.9	0.0	5.2	—	0.5	15	38
Tortilla									
Chips, plain	10 each	135	2.1	7.3	16.0	0	0.7	24	3
Corn, 6" diameter	1 each	67	2.1	1.1	12.8	0	1.4	53	42
Flour, 6" diameter	1 each	111	2.4	2.3	22.2	0	0.8	0	27
Turkey, skinned, boned, and roasted									
Dark meat	3 ounces	159	24.3	6.1	0.0	72	2.0	67	27
White meat	3 ounces	115	25.6	0.6	0.0	71	1.3	44	10
Turnip greens, cooked	½ cup	14	0.8	0.2	3.1	0	0.6	21	99
Turnips, cooked, cubed	½ cup	14	0.5	0.1	3.8	0	0.2	39	17
Veal									
Loin, broiled	3 ounces	199	22.4	11.3	0.0	86	2.7	68	9
Cutlet, pan-fried	3 ounces	155	28.2	3.9	0.0	111	0.8	69	—
Vegetable juice cocktail	1 cup	46	1.5	0.2	11.0	0	1.0	883	27
Venison									
Raw	4 ounces	143	23.8	4.5	0.0	74	1.7	102	11
Vinegar									
Apple cider	1 tablespoon	0	—	—	0.2	—	0.1	0	0
Distilled	1 tablespoon	2	0.0	0.0	0.8	0	0.0	0	0
Red wine	1 tablespoon	2	0.0	0.0	0.0	0	—	1	—
White wine	1 tablespoon	2	0.0	0.0	0.0	0	—	2	—
Tarragon	1 tablespoon	0	—	—	0.2	—	0.1	0	0

Dash (-) indicates insufficient data available

FOOD	APPROXIMATE MEASURE	FOOD ENERGY (CALORIES)	PROTEIN (GRAMS)	FAT (GRAMS)	CARBOHYDRATES (GRAMS)	CHOLESTEROL (MILLIGRAMS)	IRON (MILLIGRAMS)	SODIUM (MILLIGRAMS)	CALCIUM (MILLIGRAMS)
Water chestnuts, canned, sliced	½ cup	35	0.6	0.0	8.7	0	0.6	6	3
Watercress, fresh	½ cup	2	0.4	0.0	0.2	0	0.0	7	20
Watermelon, raw, diced	1 cup	51	1.0	0.7	11.5	0	0.3	3	13
Wheat germ	¼ cup	84	8.8	3.5	11.2	0	2.2	1	17
Whipped cream	1 tablespoon	26	0.2	2.8	0.2	10	0.0	3	5
Whipped topping, non-dairy, frozen	1 tablespoon	15	0.1	1.2	1.1	0	0.0	1	0
Wonton wrappers	1 each	6	0.2	0.1	0.9	5	0.1	12	1
Worcestershire sauce									
Regular	1 tablespoon	12	0.3	0.0	2.7	0	0.0	147	15
Low-sodium	1 tablespoon	12	0.0	0.0	3.0	0	—	57	—
Yeast, active, dry	1 package	20	2.6	0.1	2.7	0	1.1	4	3
Yogurt									
Plain, made from whole milk	1 cup	138	7.9	7.4	10.6	30	0.1	104	275
Plain, nonfat	1 cup	127	13.0	0.4	17.4	5	0.2	173	452
Plain, low-fat	1 cup	143	11.9	3.5	16.0	14	0.2	159	415
Fruit varieties, low-fat	1 cup	225	9.0	2.6	42.3	9	0.1	120	313
Frozen	½ cup	124	3.1	2.1	23.7	—	—	51	—
Zucchini									
Raw	½ cup	9	0.7	0.1	1.9	0	0.3	2	10
Cooked	½ cup	9	0.7	0.1	1.9	0	0.3	2	10

Sources of Data:

Adams, Catherine F. *NUTRITIVE VALUE OF AMERICAN FOODS.* U. S. Government
Printing Office, 1975.

Computrition, Inc., Chatsworth, California. Primarily comprised of *The Composition of Foods:
Raw, Processed, Prepared.* Handbooks - 8 series. United States Department of Agriculture,
Human Nutrition Information Service, 1976-1988.

Recipe Index

Subject Index